reinventing eden

the past, the present and the future of our fragile earth

First published in 2001 by
Quadrille Publishing Limited
Alhambra House
27-31 Charing Cross Road
London WC2H 0LS

Editorial Director Jane O'Shea
Art Director Mary Evans
Designer Jim Smith
Editor Nicki Marshall
Production Julie Hadingham

Cataloguing in Publication Data: a catalogue record for this book is available from the British Library.

ISBN 1 902757 87 4
Printed and bound by Mackays of Chatham, England.

Barbara Griggs

reinventing eden

the past, the present and the future of our fragile earth

Quadrille

contents

earth

air

water

light

the world of light

light and darkness

the healing power of light

solar power

foreword

Some four and a half billion years ago, our planet was a globe of dust and debris spinning around the sun. More than half a billion of those years went by before any kind of life appeared, another billion before Earth acquired its oxygen-rich atmosphere and its protective shield of ozone. As light and oxygen became available, the earliest single-celled organisms multiplied.

Single celled life continued unchecked while asteroid hits rocked the planet and climatic changes were dramatic. A great ice age halted progress for millions of years. But once the planet began to warm again, some 590,000,000 years ago, there was an explosion of life: multi-cellular organisms, soft-bodied worms, creatures with a protective shell or a skeletal scaffold for their forms and the first fish with backbones.

Almost as soon as life had got going, a series of mass extinctions, including another great ice age, wiped out 75% of these proliferating sea-born organisms. But progress was unstoppable now. The life forms that survived were resilient, adaptable, and in the slowly-warming planet there was another explosion of life. Many of these creatures moved from ocean to dry land. The first seed-bearing plants appeared, and then the first trees, the first insects, the first reptiles and mammals – 'cattle and creeping things and beasts of the earth'. The day of the dinosaurs came, and the Jurassic age, which saw the first birds take wing. And more than a hundred million years ago the first flowers blossomed.

As a species we are unique on earth, unique perhaps in the universe. But in important ways, we are no different from the untold billions of teeming life-forms with whom we share this planet. We need oxygen. We are 65–70% water and we need water all the time. We are nourished by the plants that form our earth's carpet of brilliant green, and by the animals, birds and fish that live off these plants. Above all we need light, the energy that drives all life on earth. These needs are so basic and so elementary that life stops if they are not met. Without food we can survive for a few weeks at most. Without water, two or three days is the limit. Without air we die within minutes. And without light we would not be here at all.

Early civilisations held these vital elements in the greatest respect, even awe, often worshipping them as deities. And when they were sick, they turned to them for healing – clay, water, air, sunshine. They knew what we have forgotten: what powerful medicine the elements can be. Over the last hundred years or so, as society became industrialised and populations soared, we have become extraordinarily careless about the quality of our life-support. We dump poisons into our streams, rivers and seas. We spray toxic chemicals into the air around us. We deluge the soil with pesticides. And we shut ourselves away from the living daylight in homes and classrooms, in cars and buses, and in offices, factories and shops insulated from fresh air, lit by a grossly distorted light and awash with electro-magnetic pollution.

How can we expect to stay healthy? Why should we be surprised that cancers, once comparatively rare, now kill one in four of us? That stress, fatigue and depression are epidemic? That millions of our children are drugged to damp down the hyperactivity that makes life impossible for parents and teachers? That the figures for asthma, eczema and hayfever – all symptoms of an immune system run ragged – are rocketing?

We are reaping as we have sown. There can be no real health for the human race until we have made sure that our most basic and elementary needs are being met: that, as far as possible, the water we drink, the food we eat and the air we breathe are pure and uncontaminated; and that our days contain as many hours as possible of natural light.

This book is a study and a celebration of light, air, earth and water, those extraordinary and wonderful elements, and of how they can affect our lives and wellbeing. It sets out strategies for countering the pollution omnipresent in our world and suggests ways, new and old, to enjoy pure air and water, quality food, and the sunshine we need so badly. It gives a clear account of air, water, sun and earth treatments for sickness or for enhancing your everyday life, together with practical advice on how to make each of them work for you. It looks at the ways in which – almost too late and painfully slowly – we are at last making steps to clean up some of the appalling manmade mess in our world.

When we talk of saving the planet, we are not just uttering the mantra of the environmentalist, we are expressing a most enlightened self-interest. As it has shown throughout its long history, the planet can look after itself. It will certainly survive the worst that we can throw at it, just as it has survived any number of the doomsday scenarios that are the stuff of latter-day Hollywood epics – ice ages, meteoric impacts, the eruption of giant volcanoes and the shifting and rending apart of whole continents. Life will survive too, in a billion different forms. It is the fate of *homo sapiens* we need to worry about. In poisoning our planet we have first poisoned ourselves. By cleaning up the planet and getting our environmental act together, we shall be the first to benefit.

> 'Society, like a house, does not start at ground level, but begins quite literally beneath the surface of our planet, within the soil itself. For out of the soil are we fashioned, and by the products of the soil is our earthly existence maintained. If we destroy our soil – and it is not indestructible – mankind will vanish from the earth as surely as has the dinosaurus.'
>
> E. B. Balfour *The Living Soil*

earth
the living soil

1 earth's green carpet

We think of the earth as a green planet, its land masses covered with trees, shrubs, grasses and flowering plants. But for most of its four-and-a-half billion years of history, there was not so much as a blade of grass on its bare and rocky surface. Not until the end of the enormous slice of prehistory known as the Palaeozoic – the 'time of old life' – some half a billion years ago, did the first plants appear on land.

Their ancestors were algae or seaweeds, rocking gently at the edges of the vast oceans, and sucking food, water and carbon dioxide directly into their cells from the water around them. Life in the ocean wave was easy for algae. But the bleak immensities of land offered two advantages: direct access to life-giving sunshine, and plenty of space – unlike the crowded competitive seas. And on some long-vanished riverbank or lakeside, life on land established a first beach-head.

The climate at this time was mainly warm and humid, with plentiful inland seas and lakes. At their edges, the ebb and flow of the tide supplied a proving ground for evolutionary skills. The earliest of all green land-plants, much like tiny mossy liverworts, never strayed much further. They settled at the water's edge and fed by putting out small creeping shoots and short roots. They survive today only in moist dark places like the shaded banks of streams. Millions of the tiny plants attempting the tough transition from water to land must have withered away for lack of moisture. The successful pioneers developed a protective waxy coating for their fronds to conserve precious moisture. Plants need carbon dioxide as well as water, so there were tiny openings called stomata in this coating, which sealed when the air became too dry. And unlike the algae and the mosses, whose reproductive system of spores depends on a supply of water, the early land-plants developed tiny, light wax-coated spores that could travel by air without drying out, as well as in the water.

With the earliest plants, such as *Cooksonia*, creepie-crawlies and soil arrived. Fossil traces of *Cooksonia* have survived in rocks more than 430 million years old. Visitors to a modern garden centre would turn up their noses at such an insignificant little plant – no leaves, flowers or roots: just a few branching stems tipped with spore-capsules. But *Cooksonia* had already solved one formidable evolutionary problem: how to grow upwards towards the life-giving sun. Its stems were made of long thick-walled cells that formed tubular structures, the ancestors of thick, tough tree-trunks. Water and nutrients could travel upwards through the stems, while sugars made by photosynthesis could travel downwards.

Gradually dense, tangled green masses of these early long-stemmed plants began forming around the edges of the planet's waters. As they competed for space and for light, three plants – club mosses, horsetails and ferns – led the field. All of them had developed stiffer stems that allowed for greater height, and thicker roots that provided buttressing stability. Soon dense forests carpeted much of the land, flourishing in the humid tropical climate of around 400 million years ago.

One tree, *Archiopteris*, soon outgrew the competition, dominating the earth's forests for over 15 million years. Two innovations gave this runaway advantage: leaves and an elaborate root system. With their millions of green chloroplasts, the 5cm-long leaves sprouting from its branches enormously increased its uptake of solar energy. They also solved another problem: how to get water from roots up to branch-tips. As the leaves transpired to lose moisture, capillary action drew water upwards from the roots. And *Archiopteris* developed an extensive underground root system which gave it both anchorage and access to ground waters.

For all its new-look leaves and roots, however, *Archiopteris* still propagated itself the old-fashioned way – by releasing spores. Fertilized on the ground, these spores were vulnerable to a growing army of hungry insects and amphibian creatures. Soon *Archiopteris* in turn was crowded out by a new generation of trees with a much more foolproof system of reproduction: primitive seed and pollen. Old-style spores swelled into seeds, housed in a hard protective covering with its own food supplies tucked inside. The new seed-bearing trees – evergreen conifers – soon dominated the dense forests on land. They are named after the thick, woody cones in which their fertilized seeds shelter for months on end, until they are released to germinate and take root.

Around this time all the great land masses started to drift together to form the super-continent Pangaea. This completely changed the world's climate, with deserts predominating. And about 250 million years ago, more than 90% of the planet's teeming life – fish, plants, trees, insects, reptiles – was wiped out by gases from a cataclysmic series of volcanic eruptions in Siberia, which buried more than 2 million square kilometres of land in lava and caused drastic climate change. Life struggled back, little by little reclaiming the ravaged planet. And as Pangaea slowly deconstructed itself again – North America and Eurasia sliding away from South America and Africa – the long reign of the great reptiles began, the dinosaurs became lords of the planet, the first small mammals appeared and the first feathered birds took wing.

It was the explosion of winged insect life – flies, beetles, butterflies, dragonflies – as well as the voracious eating habits of the dinosaurs that triggered the evolution of that marvel of creation, the flower, which is a faster way for plants to reproduce. Trees and small shrubby bushes already carried both pollen and seeds, and the pollen was rich food for these insects. The flowers that first appeared just over 250 million years ago were a delectable new lure for the pollinators, bribing them with a feast of sweet nectar, an irresistible fragrance, a special brilliance of colouring. Questing insects flitted from flower to flower, offloading pollen onto the receptive stigma. Close flower–insect relationships developed as a mutually profitable arrangement, which ensured that pollen was not wastefully deposited on the wrong flower, and in which plant and pollinator evolved side by side.

Flowers have transformed the world of nature for us. It is hard to imagine life today without roses and lilies, or the perfumed blue flowers of lavender, or the first tiny snowdrops of winter. Flowers stir our hearts and our spirits. But they do not feed us. It was the final evolutionary development of plants that has made our lives on earth possible: that of the plants that bear fruit, seed and nuts. Many of these survived catastrophe 65 million years ago, when another major series of volcanic eruptions in western India coincided with the impact of an enormous meteorite, about 10km in diameter, exploding into earth in what is now Yucatan in Mexico. The dinosaurs disappeared – but the flowering plants, the insects and the small early mammals survived.

Not long after this another newcomer joined the plants: grasses appeared, spread, formed meadows and savannah, plains and prairies. With the grasses came an explosion of mammals – all the grazing animals nourished by grass alone, which are the ancestors of today's cows, sheep and goats. And from grasses, too, would come the great grain crops: rice, wheat, oats and barley.

Eden was ready.

2 down to earth

Soil is literally the stuff of life. Without those precious centimetres of topsoil, there would be no plants, trees or grasses on our planet, no birds or insects, no animals, and definitely no humanity.

Half a billion years ago, when the first aquatic plants struggled to establish a foothold ashore, what they encountered was bare rock. The soil that formed above this inhospitable rock is the product of millions of years of creative coexistence by a teeming community of bacteria, fungi, tiny thread-like organisms called actinomycetes, algae, protozoa, nematodes, earthworms and a host of insects. This coexistence is, in many instances, so close that it earns the name symbiosis – when two different organisms form a close relationship, a sort of marriage of convenience, which serves the interests of both.

'Life evolved in the sea,' asserts biologist Lynn Margulis in her provocative work *The Symbiotic Planet*, 'but the argument is strong that only interliving – symbiogenesis – made habitation of the hostile new dry land possible for life. ...symbiogenesis developed the Earth's terra firma into occupiable real estate.'

The earliest of these useful partnerships, in all probability, was that of algae and fungi to form lichens. The alga embedded within the sheltering fungus contributes foods produced by its photosynthesising powers. The fungus provides support, water and minerals. The lichen, which is the sum of their joint existence, has been a key player in the evolution of soils: by clever chemical trickery, they can break down the minerals locked up in the rocks to which they cling and convert them into a soluble form that plants can absorb. When these plants in their turn die, their decaying remains provide a feast of organic matter for other inhabitants of the soil.

Turn over a trowelful of soil. Apart from a few tiny, struggling, just-visible insects and maybe a fat earthworm or two, it looks inert, dead stuff. But nothing could be further from the truth. It is actually teeming with life and activity – a micro-universe of predators and prey, in which tens of millions of micro-organisms live out their brief competitive lives and die, in turn, to become food for a new generation of soil-dwellers.

The fertile soil, which makes plant and animal life possible, is a world of the quick and the dead – the decomposers and the decomposed.

Humus – which has been described by one of its earliest students, S.A. Waksman, as 'the most important source of human wealth on this planet' – is the product of this decomposition, a mixture of plant and animal remains. Humus is wonderfully nourishing for plants – it supplies minerals, proteins, fats, carbohydrates, organic acids, alcohols and other organic compounds, as well as water, nitrogen and carbon dioxide, and other factors that improve plant growth and resistance. Humus helps soil hold together, retain water and combat the erosion that is destroying topsoils all around the world.

The study of the extraordinary ecosystem of the soil began in the nineteenth century and one of the earliest discoveries was that of the mycorrhizal fungi. These fungi live on the roots of plants, weaving a network of tiny threads around or actually inside the plant's own roots. At first it was assumed that they were no better than parasites. But it was soon realized that far from being a random parasitic infestation, this mycorrhizal association was found on a huge range of trees and plants around the world, including crops of the highest economic importance such as cereals, potatoes, hops, peas and beans, grapevines, tea, coffee, sugar-cane, coconut and rubber. Plants with no mycorrhizal association were soon being considered the exception rather than the rule. The parasitism theory was completely abandoned as studies began to show that the healthiest and sturdiest plants were those with the strongest and most active fungal association.

Today a huge amount of research is demonstrating the ways in which mycorrhizal fungi protect plants from disease and predators in a variety of intriguing ways. Mycorrhiza hoover up toxic chemicals in the soil: for instance, following the nuclear disaster at Chernobyl in the Ukraine, it was found that mycorrhizas had taken up large quantities of caesium from the soils around the plant. It is also clear that they are the key to well-nourished plants. 'Mycorrhizas, not roots, are the chief organs of nutrient uptake by land plants,' say Sally Smith and David Read in their authoritative work *Mycorrhizal Symbiosis*. Mycorrhizal fungi are not the only organisms in the soil working for healthy plants. Some bacteria wage chemical warfare on plant pathogens by producing antibiotics or hormones, others promote root and shoot growth, or encourage the establishment of mycorrhizal connections.

But it is the mycorrhizal association in particular that works for healthy plants resistant to pests and disease. 'The symbiosis has probably been a part of the lifestyle of all plants since they first arrived on land well over 400 million years ago,' points out soil ecologist Dr James Merryweather of the University of York, 'effecting the uptake of some less available nutrients such as phosphorus, and conferring some degree of protection from disease, pests and water stress.'

The study of mycorrhizal fungi languished until the late 1950s, when one or two teams of academic researchers started to work in more depth: thereafter it took off. The soil itself, in all its mysterious biodiversity, has attracted extraordinarily little scientific research over the last century considering its importance to our survival. But it is now at last the subject of a huge £6 million study. The Soil Biodiversity Programme, launched at the Edinburgh International Science Festival in 1999 and based at the Centre for Ecology and Hydrology in Cumbria, will link soil scientists in England, Scotland and the USA to answer the most urgent question in agriculture: does biodiversity make soil work? And if so, exactly how?

'Science has only identified a small proportion of the creatures that inhabit soil,' points out Richard Scott, Programme Manager. 'These soil communities are exposed to a wide range of impacts – soil erosion, intensive farming, the use of synthetic fertilizers and pesticides – and we have very little idea what this does to the whole complex ecosystem, and the way it functions. I think it's a fair assumption that by dumping pesticides in, you're interfering with biological processes – but to what effect? Which living things carry out which physical and chemical processes in the soil? Which species are particularly vital to soil fertility? How do microbes, nutrients and plants interact?'

Questions like these should be answered by detailed studies of 25 experimental plots at Sourhope Research Farm in the Cheviot Hills on the England/Scotland border. Each plot will receive one of five treatments – among them the addition of sewage slurry, lime, a powerful pesticide (chlorpyrifos) or a heavy metal. 'We'll be using powerful research tools not available to previous generations of researchers,' says Scott, 'molecular techniques among them: with the use of carbon isotopes to identify DNA, for instance, we can track microbial organisms all through the food chain.'

The Soil Biodiversity Programme will take soil science into the twenty-first century at one bound. It is also likely to provide scientific proof at last of what the proponents of sustainable agriculture have been saying for decades: that 'the mixed-up, crumbled, intoxicated and degraded agricultural/horticultural medium some folk care to call "soil"', in the words of Dr Merryweather, is unlikely to produce healthy crops.

When farmers drench their fields with powerful biocides, they are, paradoxically, damaging or destroying the best natural defence of their crops against both predators and disease: the living soil.

3 the sacred animals of Cleopatra

In the last year of his life Charles Darwin published a book that summed up a lifetime's fascinated study: *The Formation of Vegetable Mould Through the Action of Earthworms, with Observations on Their Habits.*

Darwin's study of the lowly earthworm had begun in his college days in the mid-1830s. Throughout his life he observed earthworms and their ways with a scientist's painstaking attention to detail: he watched, he weighed, he measured, he counted, he calculated and he noted it all down. On certain soils in England, he found, there might be as many as 53,000 earthworms to the acre, annually bringing up to the surface as much as 18 tons of dry earth in the form of their castings. These castings, the 'vegetable mould' of his title, form the fertile topsoil of our land. Every crumb of it, he noted, 'has passed many times through and will again pass many times through, the intestinal canals of worms.' 'It may be doubted,' concluded Darwin, 'whether there are many other animals which have played so important a part in the history of the world...'

Cleopatra, that wily queen, might have found this only faint praise. So high was her regard for earthworms and their role in the maintenance of Egypt's wonderfully fertile soil that she decreed sacred status for them, and drastic penalties for the fellahin (peasants) who removed or destroyed them.

Earthworms were among the earliest inhabitants of our earth, and come in myriad shapes, colours and sizes. Probably the most familiar is *Lumbricus terrestris*, the wriggling, pinkish one that every gardener has turned up in a spadeful of earth. The life of the earthworm is devoted to eating and digesting: it is little more than a streamlined digestive tube, encased in up to 400 rings of muscle which give it extraordinary strength. At night-time it comes up to the surface to feed on dead or dying vegetable matter, dragging most of it under the surface: in the three months of autumn, it will eat up almost all those fallen leaves. As it powers its sightless way through the soil, it aerates even the most compacted clay with the long tunnels it leaves behind, to a depth of 3m and more.

The same soil – bacteria, roots, mineral particles, vegetable or animal remains and all – is breakfast, lunch and dinner, sucked into a voracious mouth to start the long slow journey down through the worm, to end up as those little wormcasts of rich crumbly humus on the surface. Other animals eat to satisfy their own needs alone. That earthworm in your back garden literally eats for his country. Once inside the earthworm, this earthy meal journeys down the oesophagus to be bathed in the calcium-rich secretions of an unusual set of glands, before entering the crop as a moist and pliable mass. Passing on into the gizzard, it is ground up with the aid of the tiny stones or other hard mineral matter it may contain. Strong digestive juices, meanwhile, convert mineral nutrients into a water-soluble form, which plant roots can absorb and use. And out of the other end, deposited on the surface of the ground, comes perfect topsoil, rich in water-soluble plant food and in perfect pH balance.

The earthworm is the secret weapon of the organic farmer, who spreads a feast of compost for these welcome guests to distribute through his soil.

The scientists of the agrochemical industry, on the other hand, have ignored earthworms for decades. Some fertilizers or pesticides will banish earthworm populations, many more are actively lethal. And others concentrate in its body so that the earthworm, in turn, becomes lethal to birds who feast on it.

In the late 1960s, another threat to these useful creatures arrived in the UK in the unwelcome shape of Australian and New Zealand flatworms, illegal immigrants who probably hitched a ride attached to a plant or plant pot. The New Zealand flatworm is instantly recognizable: a chocolate-brown, ribbon-like creature with a cream edging, usually seen curled up in a flat coil in a patch of slime. Australian flatworms are less common. Both feast on our native earthworms and are much less vulnerable to common predators. In the mid-1990s there were alarming stories in the press about their rapid spread and the threat they posed to the true British earthworm.

Dr Hugh Jones, lecturer in zoology at the University of Manchester, England, is an authority on worms and he refuses to panic. 'The actual threat is hard to assess,' he says, 'and they were a source of great anxiety originally – a new pressure on a group of vital soil animals. ...In certain areas – small gardens, for instance – flatworms can wipe out whole earthworm populations. But I've seen a Scottish farm which has loads of flatworms, and there are still plenty of earthworms. Earthworms are quite resilient. And most predator–prey relationships usually end up striking some kind of balance. Long term, they're probably not a great threat.'

Happily for our planet, the earthworm has a fast-growing fanclub today. Millions of people are discovering that, with the help of half a kilo or so of worms, their rotting kitchen wastes can be recycled into sweet-smelling rich humus better than anything they can buy at the garden centre.

Wormeries are easy to look after and need little space, but their benefits – both to you and the environment – are huge.

More and more city councils around the world are discovering that among all the recycling options, earthworms can be one of the most effective and cheapest, recycling as marketable compost millions of tonnes of household wastes, paper and cardboard that would otherwise have gone to landfill. In the UK, Wiggly Wigglers supply millions of wormeries to companies, local authorities and individual customers: many local councils supply them either free or at cost to rate-payers. In Australia, over 4% of households use the Can o' Worms, built from recycled plastic. And the world over, self-styled Worm Workers pore over their bible, Mary Appelhof's *Worms Eat My Garbage*, first published in the States in 1982 and now available in over 60 countries.

4 sowers and reapers

For the first three million years or so of human history, when tribes or individuals lived their lives on the move, hunting was much the most important source of food. But even the most successful hunters couldn't always fill the pot. Gathering, too, made its contribution.

The forests, the undergrowth and the bushes were combed for anything edible: grubs, insects, birds' eggs, perhaps honey. As the seasons came and went there were berries to be harvested and nuts, roots, young leaves and fruits. And the gatherers learned that certain grassy plants had dense seeds – a chewy, sustaining mouthful.

Since a keen and observant eye was the most basic survival tool in those distant times, it cannot have been long before people began saving some of the seed, and pushing it into the ground to let it germinate. The first harvests must have been magical occasions. Imagine the excitement of glimpsing those first tender young shoots, the thrill of watching the first ears of wild wheat and barley ripen, and the triumph of reaping their first crops of grains.

Was it chiefly women who were responsible for these earliest harvests? The association of women with fecundity and harvest did, after all, become enshrined in religious belief. In almost every ancient civilization, the ideas of seeds, grains, fertility and fecundity were linked in one goddess figure. Later on, the Egyptians worshipped her as Isis, the Greeks as Demeter, the Romans as Ceres.

The cultivation of grains changed lifestyles almost immediately. It became an argument for staying put, for semi-permanent settlements – and as the amount of land cultivated in each settlement increased, grain crops freed their inhabitants from the daily need to hunt for food. Plenty bred leisure, and leisure gave rise to the earliest of the civilized arts – the building of houses. Leisure gave time for experimentation, too: as grains became the foundation of settled life, other plants began to be cultivated, and wild animals were caught and kept, and gradually domesticated. Pigs, sheep, goats and oxen were valued initially for their meat; soon they were equally prized for their wool, their milk and their hides, while the hooves and horns of cattle burnt down to provide splendid fertilizer.

It is no coincidence that the great civilizations of the ancient world grew up in the valleys and along the banks of mighty rivers – the Nile in northeast Africa, the Huang Ho in China, the Indus in present-day Pakistan, and the Tigris and Euphrates. The vast alluvial plains of the Tigris and the Euphrates were known as the Fertile Crescent, an enormous swathe of land which curved around from the Persian Gulf in the east to the shores of the Mediterranean in the west. To its north stood the mountain ranges of Toros, in Turkey; it was on the lower slopes and foothills of these mountains that the first crops of wild grasses were cultivated, perhaps 10,000 years ago. In parallel developments, millet and rice began to be cultivated in the Far East and maize in Central America.

By 4000–3000BC cities had sprung up, arts, architecture, crafts and trades were flourishing, and highly organized societies were developing in tight hierarchical patterns. Their wealth and luxury was made possible by the backbreaking toil of millions of peasants, labouring to construct the aqueducts and drainage canals of vast irrigation projects, as well as performing all the work involved in the actual raising of the crops. In northern Europe, where rainfall replaced floodwaters and irrigation canals, poor soil and uncertain water supplies made the life of the agricultural labourer just as demanding. And everywhere in the world, farmers struggled to overcome the four perennial plagues of cultivation – animal and insect predators, weeds, diseases and, most of all, the vagaries of the weather.

The huge labour forces in the Middle East were fed on grains and pulses; meat was only for the ruling classes. Although the older varieties of grain were often richer in protein than modern hybrid grains – the amaranth of the Aztecs was 16% protein, compared to the 10% of modern wheat – the protein gap still had to be filled. Pulses were the answer, since the combination of cereal and pulse supplies protein equal to meat. In his study *Man, Nature and History*, W.M.S. Russell notes some of the earliest records of these vital pulses: remains of peas have been found in a Swiss neolithic village of the fifth millennium BC; remains of kidney beans dating from 4000BC or earlier occur in caves in Mexico. Vital crops like kidney beans and soybeans – together with chickpeas, lentils, peas and other beans – travelled around the world.

Manuals on how to grow soybeans were among the earliest Chinese books from the second millennium BC.

Over thousands of years, tools designed to take some of the backache out of farming were developed. The first wooden ploughs were used in Egypt to draw a long rut across the soft and fertile fields. Once draught oxen had been enlisted into the farm workforce, heavier ploughs and other implements could be used. An unknown genius invented the indispensable wheel around 3000BC – the earliest were simply sections cut from tree-trunks – and wheeled wagons drawn by oxen took still more of the backache out of the labourer's life. And around the seventh century AD, another genius in the Middle East built the first windmill.

But for thousands of years, most of the work had to be done by hand with the help of rough tools made of wood and iron. Heavy soil had to be broken up with mattocks, drainage ditches made, fields cleared, hedges or fences built, seeds sown, crops harvested, the sheaves made and stacked, the grain threshed with flails – until finally it was ground into the flour which was now the world's daily bread.

Not until 1786 was the first threshing machine invented by a Scotsman. It worked by rubbing the corn between rollers and was at first powered by horses but later with a steam engine. Thousands of winter farming jobs disappeared and desperate workers rioted. But it was the first rumble of the mechanization of agriculture, which within a century would drive hundreds of thousands of men into the new industrial cities looking for factory work.

The first mechanized reaping machine was made in the USA in 1840. That same year saw the publication of a book that was to revolutionize agriculture just as completely: *Chemistry in its Applications to Agriculture and Physiology* was the work of a celebrated German chemist, Baron Justus von Liebig.

earth
poisoning the planet

5 the chemical fix

Since the earliest days of agriculture, farmers have been dumping various things on their fields to improve their crops. They gathered plant material and food wastes and composted them. They used animal remains – ground-up bones, hooves and horns, dried blood and the farmyard manure. The sea yielded fish meal and seaweed. The droppings of certain seafowl around the coastal areas of Peru were so rich in ammonia and phosphates that guano, as it was called, was one of the country's most profitable exports. And finally human excrement was applied to the soil either composted, or directly – as is still sometimes done in the Far East. Every farmer knew that his land must be supplied with organic material if it was to produce good crops.

In the mid-nineteenth century the German chemist Justus von Liebig took a long hard look at the whole question of soil fertility. He approached it as a chemical problem, and he soon threw out accepted notions about compost: '...the excrements of men and animals are supposed to contain an incomprehensible something which assists in the nutrition of plants, and increases their size...' Instead, he burned plants, studied their ashes and noticed that three mineral elements in particular were always present. This vital trio consists of nitrogen, phosphorus and potassium – the NPK of every agricultural textbook. These, he deduced, must come from the soil: this was what fertility was all about. And all three could be easily and abundantly supplied by inorganic salts, processed in the laboratory.

Liebig was the outstanding chemist of the day, at a time when life itself had been defined as a chemical function, and when chemistry was as exciting to the general public as dinosaurs are today. To prove his point, he made and marketed an artificial fertilizer based on the chemical composition of guano. It was not particularly successful, being too low in nitrogen, but the idea itself was dazzling.

In England, it caught the imagination of a young landowner called Lawes, who enjoyed dabbling in chemistry. On his country estate he made up various chemical mixes, applied them to experimental plots and compared the resulting crops. In 1843 he took on a professional chemist, Dr Gilbert, who had actually been assistant to the great Liebig. By means of a number of trial plots, they were able to prove that by adding Lawes' concoctions they could produce a marked increase in crop yields. Soon Lawes was manufacturing and marketing a range of artificial fertilizers.

His timing was excellent. At the beginning of the nineteenth century few farmers had to worry about manure supplies. Their own horses and draught animals, and the local coaching establishment, were reliable sources – and if they reared cattle, sheep or pigs to satisfy the voracious British appetite for meat, they had a profitable surplus. As the Industrial Age got into its stride, however, railways spread across the country, steam-driven farm tractors began to replace the heavy shire horses, and livery stables in town and country were soon closing down, one after another, as the motor car and the bus came into their own. The market for meat, meanwhile, was increasingly supplied by cheap imports, made possible by the new refrigerated ships. So the supply of manure fell disastrously.

Growing populations all over Europe were putting a strain, too, on soils that had been farmed for centuries. From England and Ireland, from Germany and Poland, from Sweden and Holland, rural families were emigrating to America because their land no longer gave a living.

There were other pressures on farmers, particularly in the UK. The Industrial Revolution sucked numbers of young men into cities, and wages rose. The abolition of the Corn Laws brought a flood of cheap imported food into the country, and although at first improvements in farming practice and soil management (together with a long series of golden summers) kept farmers reasonably prosperous, by the late nineteenth century they were struggling.

Gradually synthetic fertilizers began to dominate in the agricultural market. They often served a useful purpose for industry, too, allowing wastes and by-products to be profitably recycled. The gas industry produced sulphate of ammonia – to yield nitrogen – from the water used in washing coal-distilled gas; the steel industry offered its waste product basic slag, which contained useful amounts of phosphates, and the flue dusts from blast furnaces yielded potash.

Two world wars gave artificial fertilizers a secure future, since embattled countries had to rely on the food they could grow themselves. Wartime needs also spurred technological innovations, which soon made synthetic fertilizers both cheaper and more readily available. In the First World War, for instance, the Germans – cut off from supplies of imported South American nitrate salt – developed a new chemical technique, the Haber-Bosch process, for fixing the nitrogen essential to the manufacture of explosives. Once war was over, the explosives factories were turned over to fertilizer production.

After the Depression of the 1930s, which left many of the UK's bankrupt farms in terrible shape, only artificial fertilizers could have made possible the huge crop yields desperately needed by an island under siege. For the duration of the Second World War, the price of these artificial fertilizers was heavily subsidized by the government and their use urged on all farmers as a patriotic duty, backed up by frequent visits by 'the man from the War Ag'.

It was still assumed by most experts that fertilizers could never completely replace old-fashioned 'muck and magic'.

Experts felt that manure and composted organic wastes would always be needed to complement the new chemical agents. But by the end of the war chemical fertilizers had become a way of life on British farms, and not just because of those huge crops. They freed farmers from the tiresome need to rotate their crops, to let fields lie fallow for an entire season, and to devote scarce and expensive manpower to the preparation of compost.

What fertilizers could not do, however, was eliminate the billions of pests – weeds, insects, viruses and fungi – which prey on crops. Over the centuries, numbers of ingenious pesticides had been tried, including brimstone, sulphur, soap suds, tobacco juice, derris dust, infusions of elder or walnut leaves, tar, quicklime, copper sulphate, arsenic, even the acutely poisonous mercury. Chemical weedkillers, insecticides and fungicides had all been developed by the beginning of the twentieth century and the two world wars gave massive impetus to pesticide research.

The first organochlorine pesticide, dichloro-diphenyl-trichloro-ethane (DDT), was developed in Switzerland and rushed into production to protect Allied armies moving in mosquito-infested areas. DDT was astoundingly effective, appeared to be virtually non-toxic to human beings and annihilated mosquitoes and other bugs with effortless ease. It hung about for weeks, too – which was originally seen as a great bonus – and there was a post-war rush to develop other organochlorines, such as lindane.

Organophosphate compounds interested scientists as potential nerve gases long before their potential as pesticides was exploited. A third group, the phenoxyacetic herbicides, were first conceived as weapons of war: designed to destroy the enemy's food crops by aerial spraying or – as in Vietnam, in the form of the notorious Agent Orange – by defoliating the jungles which gave his armies cover.

More than any other pesticide, it was DDT that conferred almost magical status on the whole idea of chemical pest control. The untold millions of lives that DDT saved – especially when combined with the powerful new antimalarials developed for the US and British armies – were alone enough to silence most critics.

When the Second World War ended in 1945, millions of people stared famine in the face as cities, farms and factories lay everywhere in ruins, and huge armies of refugees and displaced people crowded into temporary camps. Within the United Nations (UN), formed in 1945, there were two technical divisions: the Food and Agriculture Organization (FAO), set up to help eradicate hunger by increased crop yields everywhere, and the World Health Organisation (WHO), devoted to reducing the global burden of disease.

The Freedom from Hunger campaign launched by the FAO included a fertilizer programme, which the industry was delighted to support. Demonstrations and trials were set up all over the world. The WHO, meanwhile, was equally busy sending the pesticide message around the globe. The hope was that insect-borne diseases such as malaria, which killed millions, might be controlled by carefully planned campaigns of intensive and regular spraying, combined with the vigorous use of antimalarials. As well as DDT, the antimalaria programme was drawing on a whole arsenal of pesticides: chlorinated hydrocarbons like benzene hexachloride (BHC), chlordane, lindane, dieldrin and aldrin. So successful was the WHO initiative that in 1955 its long-term objective became not control, but eradication. A flood of new wonder drugs bred a dream that disease might be conquered.

The increase of pesticides brought the hope that food pests and insect-borne diseases might be eliminated, if the industry were given free rein. Given such high hopes, those responsible for regulation were hardly likely to hamstring manufacturers by insisting on time-consuming and costly toxicity testing. 'Pesticide law,' explains John Wargo in his study *Our Children's Toxic Legacy*, 'was built on early enthusiasm for their immediate benefits and required the government to weigh benefits against risks when licensing new products.'

There were, it is true, occasional accidental poisonings and environmental mishaps. But no one would have thought of calling for a ban on pesticides any more than air disasters today provoke demands for a ban on flying.

Not until the early 1960s, with the publication of distinguished American genetic biologist Rachel Carson's *Silent Spring* (see also pages 33 and 54), did ordinary people wake up to the poisoning of their planet now apparent in the countryside and even in their own backyard.

intoxication

Michael Brown first heard the name 'Love Canal' at a public hearing in Niagara Falls, New York State, in 1977. A reporter for the local newspaper, he had gone along to cover the hearing, about a new toxic waste disposal site in a suburb of Niagara Falls. A woman present got up and burst into tears as she spoke of another local dump site – that of Love Canal – which she said was damaging her own neighbourhood.

Intrigued, Brown began investigating. Over months of painstaking research and door-to-door interviews, he learned that an entire neighbourhood was being devastated by factory wastes buried under the ground. Love Canal had been part of an ambitious early twentieth-century scheme to bring cheap power and jobs to Niagara Falls by linking the upper and lower reaches of the Niagara River. The scheme had come to nothing, but a stretch of canal 18m wide and 90m long remained: it became a useful local dump for the city, the US Army and the site's owners, Hooker Chemical Corporation, the biggest local industry.

For 30 years metal barrels full of toxic wastes were trucked in and dumped into the canal. Among the estimated 20,000 tonnes dumped were waste residues from Hooker's manufacture of pesticides and plasticizers, and material from the US Army's chemical warfare research. Finally, in 1953, Hooker filled the canal with a dirt covering, and sold the land to the Local Board of Education for a token dollar. By 1955, 400 pupils were attending an elementary school on the site, and houses and apartment buildings had sprung up around the school. There were endless complaints of appalling smells, of sinister leaks into basements and backyards – and of a whole slew of health problems. But since Hooker was a major local employer, nobody in city hall wanted to know.

Michael Brown was appalled by the Love Canal experience: 'I saw homes where dogs had lost their fur. I saw children with serious birth defects. I saw entire families in inexplicably poor health. When I walked on the Love Canal, I gasped for air as my lungs heaved in fits of wheezing. My eyes burned...' He began publishing a series of articles about the toxic dump in the *Niagara Gazette* – and the story was later taken up by the *New York Times.* Goaded by media coverage, the New York State Department of Health finally closed the school, and agreed to purchase at a fair price the 239 houses nearest the canal. The whole area was fenced off, and a clean-up promised.

Among the Love Canal residents was Lois Gibbs, whose child had attended the school. She began her own investigation, talking to other parents, and soon realized the huge scale of the disaster. With other angry residents she started a pressure group, the Love Canal Homeowners' Association, representing 500 families living outside the fence and theoretically 'safe'. The findings of a health study within this group were devastating: among them were massive increases in miscarriage, birth defects and urinary tract disorders. Only 4 normal babies were born from 22 pregnancies.

These findings were dismissed out of hand by the state authorities as 'useless housewifely data'. It took long months of organized public protest and media coverage before President Carter himself finally ordered the total evacuation of the area in October 1980. During these months Lois Gibbs became a nationally known campaigner just as well known as Erin Brockovitch later became, and even more effective.

Like journalist Michael Brown, Lois Gibbs was contacted by hundreds of householders across the USA made desperate by similar toxic waste problems. Between them they have exposed shaming instances of negligence, fraud, flouting of environmental law and city hall corruption, in which earth, water and air have been poisoned with deadly wastes, and the health and lives of millions put at risk. Love Canal is no isolated horror story: the US Environmental Protection Agency conservatively estimates that there may be 50,000 such dumps scattered across the USA. And the problem is worldwide.

Over the last 150 years over ten million new chemicals have been synthesized. Not all of them are actually 'new': certain algae produce chloroform and carbon tetrachloride, chlorine is one of the natural elements, dioxins – generated when wood burns – have turned up in sediments 8000 years old. And nobody does toxins better than Mother Nature: think of that lethal mushroom *Amanita*. Men have been tinkering with natural chemicals like these for hundreds of years: alchemy was applied chemistry with a philosophical agenda. But our modern synthetic chemical industry got going in earnest around the mid-nineteenth century, with the invention of celluloid. Rayon, or cellulose acetate – the foundation of today's garment industry – followed in 1900, Bakelite in 1909, cellophane in the 1930s, and then a flood of familiar names, among them nylon, polyester, PVC and Perspex. Computers, telephones, mineral water bottles, TV sets, sticky tape, Band-Aids, watches, food packaging – all these are the stuff of our western way of life.

Economic growth and the consumer boom alike rest on chemical foundations, and our modern world is unthinkable without these materials.

For years it was carelessly assumed by manufacturers and legislators that the by-products of the vast and fast-growing chemical industry could safely be dumped in the nearest river, landfill or any other convenient hole in the ground, where they would somehow or other disappear. Similarly, it was assumed that even persistent pesticides like DDT posed a threat only to their insect targets.

Even when the facts started to leak out, corporations terrified of huge clean-up bills and city halls reluctant to recognize their responsibility colluded to talk down the risks or deny their existence. Rachel Carson's book *Silent Spring*, published in 1962, ended this era of complacency (see also pages 30 and 54). It was also the start of a new public awareness: chemicals might seriously damage your health. Disasters like Seveso in Italy, in 1976 and Bhopal in India, in 1984, and a later series of scares about dioxins, have fostered a strongly negative public view of chemicals. Isn't it chemicals, too, which are tearing holes in the ozone layer?

One of the most damaging chemicals environmentally is friendly, versatile PVC, which turns up in anything from credit cards to disposable surgical instruments. PVC production is rocketing all over the world, but both its manufacture and its disposal present appalling problems. The European Union alone generates around 4 million tonnes of PVC waste – an amount expected almost to double within the next 20 years. But the stuff is virtually unrecyclable. Incineration of 1kg of PVC waste simply produces the same weight of waste in another, equally hazardous form, and dumping it in landfill can release yet another class of deadly chemicals called phthalates. Landfill fires are common and two by-products of the PVC in a blazing landfill would be furans and dioxins, yet more chemical vandals.

There are actually hundreds of different dioxins, many of them found in nature: but it is one in particular – tetrachlorodibenzodioxin (TCDD) – that alarms experts. Dioxins are formed as an unintentional by-product of many industrial processes that involve chlorine – such as chemical and pesticide manufacture, the bleaching of pulp or paper, and the incineration of wastes. TCDD has been classed by an agency of the World Health Organization (WHO) as a known human carcinogen. Damage to the immune system, reproductive problems and disruption of hormone systems are among other possible consequences of exposure to too much TCDD.

But of all the hundreds of thousands of chemicals, it is pesticides which worry people most. This is understandable. You have to be seriously unlucky to find yourself living on top of a waste dump.

But pesticides are omnipresent in all our lives, stored in our body fat, present in the air we breathe, much of the food we eat and the water we drink.

The most worrying of these pesticides belong to two chief groups, the organophosphates (OPs) and the organochlorines (OCs). The OPs are chemicals originally developed as nerve gases, with names like Imidan Abate and Counter. They are capable of causing a range of symptoms including 'flu-like symptoms, fatigue, memory loss, cramps, depression, and perhaps multiple sclerosis and motor neurone disease. From 1976 to 1992 the 50,000 sheep farmers of the UK were obliged by law to use OP sheep dips to eliminate parasite problems. Over a thousand of them claimed that the toxic dips have wrecked their health but their complaints met only with bland official reassurances until a £500,000 government-funded study officially recognized a connection between OP use and nerve damage.

The second lot of nasties, the OCs, do their damage in the central nervous system and the liver. Well-known OC pesticides include lindane, chlordane and heptachlor, dieldrin and aldrin. They also include a group of chemicals called polychlorinated biphenyls (PCBs), hundreds of thousands of tonnes of which were manufactured up to the late 1970s for use, among other things, as lubricants, plasticizers and brake fluids.

Most of these have been banned since the 1980s in western countries. But they are not known as persistent organic pollutants for nothing, since they can hang about in the environment, slowly accumulating all the way up the food chain, for decades. One race that is now paying a heavy price for our comfortable chemical way of life is the Inuit Eskimos of the Canadian Arctic. The seals, the fish and the whale meat they live on are loaded with heavy metals like mercury, and pesticides like PCBs and chlordane. One study showed that nearly half the women in Baffin in the Canadian Arctic take in levels of the pesticide chlordane above levels considered 'tolerable' by the WHO. High levels of mercury, cadmium and PCBs are also all found in large numbers of these women – so much so that many of them now hesitate to breastfeed their children.

The toll of death and injury due to pesticides is far higher in developing countries. According to statistics published by the WHO, as many as 25 million agricultural workers in the Third World may suffer at least one incident of pesticide poisoning a year. There are obvious reasons: the warning labels and instructions aren't translated into the local language, it is too hot and humid for protective suits, gloves or masks, and nobody bothers to spell out the dangers. Pesticides banned in the West often find their way onto the market in developing countries – from which, by the nicest of ironies, they are now coming home in the shape of high residues in imported foodstuffs.

Pesticides aren't just used by farmers. They are also sprayed in city streets and on country road verges, in municipal parks, on golf courses, along railway sidings. They turn up in clothes, carpets, wood finishes, wallpaper. They are present in flea collars for pets, in those sticky hanging insecticide strips, in headlice shampoos. If you're a customer of the local garden centre, you've probably sprayed them around your garden. And of course pesticide residues turn up in our food. That succulent lettuce you dump into your supermarket trolley has probably been treated with over 11 pesticides. The UK government officially advises that carrots should be topped, tailed and peeled because of the high levels of OP residues that may lurk in them, and dark chocolate may come with an extra helping of lindane.

Worldwide, around $30 billion' worth of pesticides are made and marketed annually, in the form of around 1000 different pesticides, based on combinations of around 600 active ingredients. Many of these active ingredients have never been properly tested for safety – either singly or in combination. And 99.9% of a pesticide formulation may consist of 'inert ingredients', which sound harmless – but the number of these 'inerts' almost doubled in the ten years up to 1997, many aren't even mentioned on the label, and fewer than a quarter have been examined for possible toxicity. Over 600 of them have been classed as hazardous by official agencies.

The technology for assessing pesticide risk has lagged decades behind the chemical know-how that invented them.

Although scientists can now detect the presence of almost homeopathic quantities of pesticide residues – parts per billion or trillion – there are other questions they can never answer. How much is actually dangerous? And for whom? Are combinations of two or more pesticides more toxic than the sum of the separate pesticides? Are the effects of pesticide ingestion cumulative? Can we become sensitized to individual pesticides? And can their effects linger on from one generation to the next, to produce the horrifying birth defects seen in the children of Vietnam veterans or Vietnamese families whose land was bombarded with tonnes of the herbicide 2,4,5-T or Agent Orange?

Some grim answers are beginning to emerge. 'Chemical Pollution Wiping out Males' screamed a headline in the British newspaper the

Mirror in March 2000. It was based on a report from Friends of the Earth that many chemicals – known as endocrine disrupters – disrupt sexual development in wildlife. Could they be having the same effect on us? As the report pointed out, sperm counts worldwide have dropped 50% over the last 50 years; rates of prostate cancer have doubled, and those of testicular cancer have tripled over the same half-century. Endometriosis – a once-rare, painful disorder causing womb cells to die – now affects five million US women. And while in 1960 a woman in the West had 1 in 20 chances of getting breast cancer, today that figure has soared to 1 in 8.

Asthma, eczema and hayfever are all allergic problems which are now becoming frighteningly common, especially among children. Professor Nicholas Ashford, of the Massachusetts Institute of Technology, believes that exposure to pesticides – particularly organophosphates – may be responsible, as well as being the cause of a condition he has called Multiple Chemical Sensitivity (MCS). This illness, he believes, can leave people sensitive even to common chemicals like tobacco, detergents and traffic fumes. 'I think pesticides are the most serious problem we have today in the industrialized countries,' says Professor Ashford. Today's teenagers constantly complain of fatigue, and Tired All The Time (TATT) takes more people to their doctors than any other health problem. Its most prostrating form – Chronic Fatigue Syndrome (ME) – wrecks lives.

Constant, debilitating fatigue seems a peculiarly modern disease.

The similarity between ME and the symptoms of OP poisoning reported by sheep-dipping farmers is striking. At a conference on environmental illness held at the Royal College of Physicians in June 1994, a Scottish doctor presented an interesting theory. He was sure that most people now carry enough pesticide residues in their body fat to cause debilitating fatigue if released into the bloodstream by sudden weight loss – as might happen following a viral illness such as 'flu.

Chemicals with a long life – such as the dioxins and OC or OP pesticides – are named Persistent Organic Pollutants (POPs). Efforts are being made internationally towards phase-out and replacement of

POPs. The moving force behind these efforts is the International POPs Elimination Network (IPEN), a global network of non-governmental organizations (NGOs) united in support of a ban.

IPEN is one of the thousands of grassroots activist movements that sprang up during the 1990s. The worldwide web has endowed such movements with unprecedented clout, linking concerned scientists and doctors with lay people, and allowing them to reach millions of people with a minimum of time and expense. Local campaigning groups can link with umbrella organizations, which in turn benefit from local feedback and reporting. The Pesticide Action Network (PAN) is one such. With a mission to replace the use of hazardous pesticides with ecologically sound alternatives, it links over 600 NGOs in 60 countries. Governments can shrug off individual letters of protest, but movements like PAN, IPEN or Friends of the Earth can no longer be dismissed as uninformed hysteria.

One way or another, it is hardly surprising that chemicals have come to be equated in the public mind with bad news about pollution and health. The number of students applying to study chemistry has been falling year on year at European and US universities. 'Chemistry and the chemical industry have tarnished images,' says James Clark, Professor of Industrial Chemistry at England's York University.

But you can't combat the problems of the technological age with the tools of the Stone Age. If chemistry got us into this mess, then perhaps chemistry can help get us out. And Professor Clark is one of a number of leading international chemists working to promote the much more attractive image of 'Green Chemistry'. He has now set up the Green Chemistry Network, under the auspices of the Royal Society of Chemistry, to reduce or eliminate the use or generation of hazardous substances in the design, manufacture and application of chemical products. The products of Green Chemistry should need neither treatment nor clean-up; the raw materials should be sustainable, natural products; and when they degrade, the end-product should be harmless.

In the green world of the environmentalist's vision, the new cleaned-up chemistry will have a vital part to play. And the successful chemical companies of the future, according to Clark, will be those who exploit its opportunities to their competitive advantage.

7 playing God

There are some issues which bring out the worst in everybody. In the UK, at the end of the twentieth century, an undignified squabble took place over genetically modified organisms (GMOs), which distorted the facts and clouded the issues so badly that the debate is still ongoing.

Who came out of this well? No one, frankly.

The newspapers whipped up unprecedented hysteria, no doubt with fond memories of the circulation-boosting BSE days. 'Frankenstein Foods' was the label the British newspaper the *Daily Mail* slapped on GMOs, running stories that blamed the new technology for everything from world hunger to meningitis.

The UK government handled it disastrously. Initially, they simply brushed aside all criticism or doubts, reiterating that the technology carried no dangers whatever, either to ourselves or to the environment: assurances that the public found no more convincing than pictures of a Conservative minister force-feeding hamburger to his little daughter to 'prove' that BSE was a media myth. When Labour's spin doctors made it clear to Prime Minister Tony Blair that he had massively underestimated public anger and unease, the subsequent U-turn and assurances of future precautions did little to recover the situation.

And finally, both the companies promoting GMOs and the environmental campaigners confronting them played fast and loose with the truth whenever it suited them. The campaigners were happy to let urban myths such as the tomato with the fish gene or the allergenic Brazil nut protein go on doing the rounds even after the tomato was shown never to have existed, while the nut proteins had been withdrawn long before they hit the market. Their crusading was greatly assisted by the attitude of Monsanto, the market leader in biotechnology, who had anticipated none of this – in the USA the introduction of GMOs was problem-free – and who committed one blunder after another in their responses, in the process turning Monsanto into the most hated name in global capitalism. Their way of doing business – seized upon joyfully by the press – included sending out private investigators to check up on their customers, suing farmers who broke their contract by saving seed, and setting up a 'snitch line' to encourage people to inform on their neighbours.

Other biotech firms have recorded their frustration with and disapproval of Monsanto for undermining public confidence, but it is too late. Europe has imposed fierce regulations on GMOs and there is a moratorium on their use in the UK, while even the USA is suffering a backlash: a market survey in early 2000 revealed that nervous US farmers were planning to plant 20% less GM corn than last year, while Worldwatch believe that the global acreage of all GM crops could actually fall by 25%. The whole industry has been tainted and it will be a long time, if ever, before it regains consumer trust. Because of the hysteria and polemics in which the whole debate has been mired, it has been conducted with little real access to the facts.

GMOs present us with some very exciting possibilities, which in theory could solve some of the planet's worst problems – of disease, of pollution and of hunger.

There is talk of plants that can be engineered specifically to absorb toxic metals like cadmium and nickel from contaminated soil; of plants adapted to flourish in drought-stricken areas; of plants enriched with nutrients to meet special local needs – the famous 'golden rice' with a high vitamin A content, for instance – or tailored to carry a vaccine against a common disease. (GM opponents would counter that plants with many of these qualities already exist, and that turning plants into vaccine-bearers is a highly dodgy form of mass medication.)

When the GMOs are new drugs designed to combat some of the world's medical problems, few people have any great anxieties. It is the GMOs set to replace traditional food crops that have called up such a storm of controversy and protest. And with good reason.

Will GMOs poison us or damage our health in some subtle way? Will they destroy the environment? Will they threaten the livelihood of small farmers everywhere? These are the burning questions being asked today. And the answers are not, so far, reassuring.

Could GMOs damage our health? This concern was highlighted in the ongoing controversy stirred up by biochemist Dr Arpad Pusztai when he went public on research he was conducting at the prestigious Rowett Research Institute in Aberdeen, Scotland. He had been running experiments which involved feeding rats either on potatoes that had been genetically modified to contain a lectin extracted from snowdrops that was lethal to insects, on potatoes that had simply had the lectin added, or on ordinary potatoes. He found that the rats fed on the GM potatoes had developmental changes in kidney, brain and spleen, and showed evidence of impaired immunity as well as changes in the lining of their guts. In a move which automatically isolated him from the scientific community, Dr Pusztai announced this sensational finding on television, while the research was still in progress, thus triggering a storm of angry controversy. Criticism rained in, he was suspended from his job – and later sacked – and his future as a scientific researcher is compromised, though he is fighting back with his own web-page.

The problem is that Dr Pusztai may have come across some genuinely useful information, but as critics from a Royal Society team announced, his study was not only poorly designed but far too small to use as a basis for generalization. He used only six rats – so only two ate the GM potatoes; potatoes are not a natural diet for rats in any case; and even non-GM raw potatoes contain some nasty toxins. Since two of the rats were fed potatoes in which the lectin had been physically added but showed no changes in their stomach lining, one might infer that it is the process of genetic manipulation itself that causes the problem. But how can you generalize on numbers like these?

This is one of the ways in which GM foods might 'poison' us: if the process produces basic changes in the food itself, of which we cannot guess the consequences. This is what Dr Pusztai's research pointed at, but we simply do not know enough. And where is the research being carried out?

The great promise of GMOs was that they would massively reduce the need for pesticides. The first, and still the majority of, GM crops being grown are of the Roundup Ready variety, tailored to be resistant to Monsanto's pesticide glyphosate. On non-GM crops glyphosate (Roundup) can only be used at certain phases in crop growth, which are not necessarily the best time for killing pests. The resistant crops can be sprayed just when the weeds are most vulnerable, and the weedkiller therefore most effective. The theory is that less weedkiller will be needed.

This is, once more, a highly contentious issue, but a university-based survey of 8200 field trials of the most widely grown GM crops – herbicide-tolerant soya beans – revealed that they yield 66.7% less and require two to five times more herbicides than non-GM varieties.

Other GMOs have pesticides engineered into the very tissue of plants. Again, in theory that means less pesticide residue in the end-product, since the plants will not need constant spraying; but at least you can wash most of the pesticide off vegetables that have been sprayed, whereas when tissue contains it – one GM potato in the USA is officially classed as a pesticide for this reason – there is no way of avoiding it. Action Aid campaigner Alex Wijeratna has been to numbers of shareholder meetings of the big four GM companies. 'Nowhere,' he says, 'have I heard of the need for less pesticide.'

Could GMOs destroy – or irrevocably damage – our environment? This is a question that most people find far more worrying than that of their toxicity for humans. It is a well-known horticultural truth that most successful weed populations come from 'exotic introductions' – and you don't get much more exotic than this. In the USA, farmers are already finding the previous year's GM cotton coming up again among their other crops, with nothing that can be done about it. If herbicide-resistant strains start breeding with the wild weeds, we could find super weeds springing up.

An interim report on UK government-sponsored field trials confirmed hybridization between adjacent plots of different herbicide-tolerant GM oilseed rape varieties: this resulted in the development of hybrids tolerant to multiple herbicides. In the end, the problem that the GMOs were invented to circumvent could worsen, as more and stronger weeds grow around GM farms.

It may already be too late. In May 2000 the UK government admitted that 5400 acres of British land had been sown with allegedly GM-free oilseed rape, which the seed company Aventis now admits was contaminated with GM rape. The contamination had occurred, Aventis executives revealed, even though the sister company producing the seed had used a 4km buffer zone between its crop and GM crops. If a 4km buffer zone isn't enough to contain GM crops, then any idea of preventing GM contamination of other crops, or of weeds, is clearly hopelessly unrealistic.

Perhaps the single most disturbing aspect of the GM revolution in agriculture is that it has concentrated so much power in the hands of just four global giants – Monsanto, Syngenta, Aventis and du Pont – who now control the entire global market, and who are certainly not in business for philanthropic reasons. Syngenta recently swallowed up two biotech companies – Novartis and Seneca – to form a new mammoth company with worldwide sales of $7 billion and a research team of 5000.

In the autumn of 2000, 364 scientists from 45 countries signed an Open Letter to all Governments on Genetically Modified Organisms. Its distinguished signatories included molecular biologists, geneticists and ecologists, as well as spokespeople for Third World countries. 'GM crops', said their letter, 'intensify corporate monopoly on food, which is driving family farmers to destitution, and preventing the essential shift to sustainable agriculture that can guarantee food security and health around the world.'

What conclusions can be drawn from this tangle of conflicting interests, controversy and virulent debate? The first is the saddening realization, yet again, that big business will always put profit first, and that cash comes before the planet as far as shareholders are concerned. But the second conclusion is that whatever marvellous benefits the technology may confer, at a basic human level it is deeply frightening.

Genetic modification is not just simply splicing one plant to another. It is reaching into the basic stuff of life itself and playing God.

It was a massive miscalculation on the parts of governments and biotech companies to have believed that we would adjust to genetic modification as easily as we accept a new drug or another wonder-fabric: this is a science which at some point might bring our own existence into question. Perhaps this sense, more than any other – of touching the unknown, of playing with forces that we do not fully understand – explains the amazing strength of public reaction.

8 the throwaway world

Have you ever wondered what happens to those bulging black bags of rubbish carted away by your local council every week? About 82% of it gets dropped into deep holes in the countryside – landfill, to give it its technical name – and the British are among the world's leaders in generating rubbish. We throw away 28 million tonnes of household and garden wastes annually – before we even start on industrial or commercial wastes.

Among the rubbish that goes hurtling into those huge holes are scraps of fruit and vegetables, dead leaves, old clothes, cans, glass and plastic containers, cardboard boxes, discarded mobile phones, a few million tonnes of disposable nappies, computers, clocks, shoes, TVs, radios, textiles, tennis rackets, golf balls, keys, empty spray cans, scrap metal, dead batteries, suitcases, unwanted toys, the contents of builders' skips – including whole built-in cupboards stripped out, yards of skirting or panelling, joists, shelves, and entire doors and their frames – rubber tyres, old cookers, refrigerators and all the other detritus of our unthinking, throwaway civilization.

The USA leads the world in this nonchalant trashing: the average American generates about 1.85kg of solid rubbish every day. But the rest of the western world certainly isn't far behind.

We're top-grade consumers – but we haven't learned, or we have completely forgotten, that the natural resources that supply our limitless consumer appetites are themselves limited.

In the Third World, or among the very poor of the West's richest cities, such waste is unimaginable. The contents of one of our big-city builders' skips would probably furnish homes for three or four shanty-town families. The food thrown away weekly by just one big supermarket would keep a small village fed for a day. And in places like Mexico City, scavenging around the city's dumps is a way of life for thousands of people, picking through the reeking piles for cardboard, glass, metal and plastic which have a resale or re-use value.

Thrift and economy were once seen as estimable traits, and their practice plain common sense. My mother used to save envelopes, slicing them open and stashing them in a drawer, so that when we needed paper for drawing, writing or games of battleships there was a supply at hand. Who saves scraps of paper today? When my own children went to school, they learned to write on one side of the page only, in the exercise books liberally doled out.

Yet the wasteful West is slowly – very slowly – mending its ways. The statistics are still awesome – but at least in some countries they are a staggering improvement on 10 or 20 years ago. The US monthly *Biocycle* carried out a first audit of America's garbage in 1989. It made dismal reading. Forty-one of the 50 US states estimated that 80% or more of their waste went to landfill, while recycling and composting was minimal – in only nine states did it exceed 10% – and the top recycling rate, claimed by the state of Washington, was 22%.

In 1998, when *Biocycle* repeated the exercise, the improvement was startling. The amount of the nation's garbage going to landfill had dropped to 61%; nearly 30% of the remainder was being recycled; and around two-thirds of US states had beaten Washington's 1989 record of 22% recycling. Other countries show similar rates of improvement. How has such a major change come about and what has made it possible?

Probably the most important factor has been a growing public perception of the need for change and a willingness to get personally involved. Sticking stuff in the trash can is a lot less effort than sorting it out and taking it to the kerb-side bin or the recycling centre – yet growing numbers of people do make the effort. And all the way down the chain of legislation, a stream of laws, rules and regulations come regularly spilling out, all aimed at reducing the amount of garbage dumped and encouraging its recycling in a variety of ingenious ways.

Most countries, for instance, now tax landfills and devote at least some of the profits to recycling research or projects. Landfill charges have gone up anyway in response to growing demand, so the dumping tab has become an increasingly heavy item in municipal budgets. In the late 1980s, for instance, the average US landfill tipping fee was around $10 a ton: by 1997, it was nearer $30.

Gone, too, are the days when garbage was simply trucked to the nearest landfill and dumped, no questions asked. The well-run, modern landfill operation is hedged around by regulations governing depth, lining, control of emissions, treatment of leachates, identification of truckloads brought in and so on.

Municipal authorities all over Europe now face a daunting piece of legislation, the Landfill Directive, which specifies that by 2020 only 35% of household waste can go to landfill – currently 85% goes into landfill. This means that since the UK rubbish mountain is actually growing at the rate of about 3% a year, by 2020 about 33 million tonnes of rubbish will have to be dealt with annually somehow other than by dumping it in landfills. Which leaves two alternatives: incineration or recycling.

Around 130 giant incinerators, with an annual capacity of 200,000 tonnes, would be needed to cope with that amount of rubbish: and none of us wants an incinerator on our doorstep.

The other option, recycling, is carried out by thousands of companies – large and small – around the world, based on the advice and research input from armies of advisory bodies, university science departments and government-funded research establishments, with an international communications network of specialized journals, and regular international conferences.

Despite all this expertise, however, recycling isn't an entirely satisfactory answer, either. Much of the rubbish specially sorted and separated by conscientious rate-payers ends up in landfill anyway, as there simply isn't a recycling market for it. The going price for waste paper can fluctuate wildly according to supply: if the price falls too low, it may end dumped in landfills or be shipped to countries as distant as Indonesia: hardly the true spirit of recycling.

The ideal way to cut the garbage mountain, of course, would be not to create it in the first place, and governments could be a lot more creative in their use of taxes as disincentive. I'd love to see a tax on those plastic bags that every single supermarket, shop and market barrow hands out free – often with very small purchases.

Making a charge to householders for refuse collection – Pay As You Throw – is already happening in some US cities. Householders pay for refuse collection through local taxes anyway.

A dustbin tax would send a very powerful message about the problems of waste.

Most large companies already pay contractors to remove much of their waste, particularly paper. This is an expense that can be shifted to the other side of the balance sheet, as Wastebusters points out. This UK company was set up by Lesley Millett in 1991 as an environmental consultancy, specializing in the office sector. It targets the huge amounts of waste generated by even quite small offices: not just paper, but glass, cans, toner cartridges and staggering amounts of perfectly good furniture.

Lesley Millett is guardedly optimistic about the recycling future. 'I think most people do have a conscience about it,' she says. 'There are very few people who simply don't care at all. The Rio Summit changed a lot of things. And local councils are getting more involved – more and more of our business is coming from the public sector.'

Municipal councils are the first stop for our waste, and recycling practices can vary not just from one country to another but between one borough and its neighbour. Copenhagen in Denmark is a shining example of what can be done. The city fathers have adopted a programme aimed at a 58% recycling rate for the city's household, commercial and industrial waste; 24% to be incinerated – mostly in plants that convert waste to energy; and a mere 18% going to landfill. Today only three landfill sites are being used, where once there were 30. And more than 50% of the city's commercial, industrial and demolition waste is recycled.

Contrast this with the UK national average of a shameful 9.4% recycling rate – against the national target of 25% by the year 2000 set ten years previously. And many councils are nowhere near this: in some the recycling figure is as low as 1.4%.

Cans, bottles, metal scrap, textiles and paper are relatively easy to recycle. Plastics are a tougher nut to crack – and some forms, like PVC, are too hazardous even to recycle. But the inventive technology that got us into this mess is also helping to get us out of it, too, and a number of ingenious ways of sorting and treating plastic waste are already in operation, as well as ways to extract specific plastics.

The real waste in waste, however, is the organic stuff – everything which was once food that you and I chuck into the bin without a second thought, and which ends up as compact mash in the garbage trucks before going to landfill. This waste is densely packed with nutrients absorbed from the soil, but we dump it into landfill and then buy extra vitamins and minerals because our food is impoverished.

In any rationally run economy, organic waste would be scrupulously composted before being returned to the soil.

Even the green wastes – the dead leaves gathered up in city streets, the trimmings from parks and gardens – can have fertilizer value. But most municipal councils don't attempt to separate and compost such wastes. At least one UK council – St Edmundsbury in Suffolk – has shown that it can be done, and was actually nominated a Beacon Council for its recycling record, thanks to an energetic Recycling Officer, Sandra Pell. With the help of the brown bins supplied to almost every household in the borough, many tonnes of household waste – as well as green wastes from parks and gardens – is now recovered annually, turned into high-quality compost and sold through garden centres or directly from the council.

Waste is the child of wealth: poor countries are often more enlightened. Libya has built waste-recycling plants in the suburbs of five major cities – Tripoli, Beida, Benghazi, Musurata and Derna, according to a report from the Pan-African News Agency. Household wastes are separated from metal, plastic and other non-biodegradable wastes at the plants, and processed in big fermentation tanks into organic fertilizer. One tonne of household waste produces 21kg of fertilizer at a cost of $30.

There is no reason why this shouldn't be done worldwide. In the early 1950s, as Peter Tompkins and Christopher Bird recount in their classic *Secrets of the Soil* (see also page 60), the famous biodynamic scientist Ehrenfried Pfeiffer developed a powerful mix of bacteria for the digestion of garbage. He persuaded the city of Oakland in California, USA, to try out his bugs – and within a year all the city's garbage was being trucked to a small processing plant and loaded onto conveyor belts where paper, metal, glass and other foreign bodies were extracted by hand.

The remaining wastes were ground into a mush and sprayed with water spiked with Pfeiffer's bacteria. Within two to four days the piles were literally steaming, as bacterial activity heated them up to over 150°C. Within three weeks, sweet-smelling black compost was ready for selling. The results were extraordinary: '...vegetables grown with the converted garbage were found to weigh 25% more than those grown with conventional fertilizers, and have around three times as much vitamin A. Grain showed a consistently higher protein content...' Other trials showed that Pfeiffer's compost could restore even sterile sand to fertility. It comes as no surprise to learn that the influence of the agrochemical industry closed down Pfeiffer's plant within two years. But Pfeiffer's bugs could be the solution to a more urgent question: the human wastes flushed away down billions of toilets.

These 'wastes' are organic matter crammed with potential nutrition for hungry soils – not just the NPK of chemical fertilizers but other nutrients, too, vitamins, minerals and trace elements among them. The amounts generated are staggering. According to data from the US Department of Agriculture in the late 1980s, quoted by Tompkins and Bird, the population of the USA alone produces 6000kg of excrement every single second; and US livestock – in that same second – another 125,000kg. You can see what water companies all over the hygienic, toilet-flushing western world are up against. When they run household effluents – drinking water, washing-up water, flushed water and all – through their elaborate treatment systems, what they're left with is recycled water and mountains of what are sometimes known, in the delicate parlance of the wastewater treatment engineer, as bio-solids.

What is to be done with these huge mountains of – well, shit? In the past, they were just dumped into the nearest lake, river or sea, a practice forbidden by the European Union since 1998. Or they were dumped in landfills – but as we have seen, that's an increasingly expensive option. There's a third and logical option – use the stuff for fertilizer. Unfortunately, in western sanitation systems, humanure (as J.C. Jenkins has termed it in *The Humanure Handbook*) shares the sewers with stuff that nobody in their right mind would want to dump on land being used for growing food – toxic pollutants, motor oil and quantities of heavy metals. And the pathogens present in the humanure itself may include salmonella and the Hepatitis C virus, which can survive even advanced treatment.

When the British press revealed late in 1999 that farmers were spreading sewage sludge that hadn't been treated on their land – more than 100,000 tonnes of it in 1998 – shock waves rippled through the entire nation. In Sweden they won't allow even treated sewage on arable land.

The solution already exists: the no-water or compost-toilet, from which wastes can be transferred straight to the compost heap for treatment. 'The very latest no-water loos do offer an advance in gentility, you might say,' says Peter Harper, of the biology section at the Centre for Alternative Technology in Wales, 'and some day I suppose you might envisage a complete collection scheme with service contracts. But we're a long way from that – and before it could happen, you'd have to reinvent the whole plumbing system of major cities.'

But the problem of what to do with sewage sludge is, sooner or later, going to compel us to reappraise the composting option. And to recognize, as J.C. Jenkins puts it, that 'humanure is a natural substance produced by a process vital to life (human digestion) originating from the earth in the form of food, and valuable as an organic refuse material that can be returned to earth in order to produce more food for humans.'

earth
a sustainable future

9 the law of return

What's on the menu for baby's lunch? Creamed chicken and rice, strained carrots, puréed apple, all in those handy little jars. But there may be hidden extras not stated in the long list of ingredients: traces of the antibiotics and growth-promoting hormones with which the chicken will have been intensively reared, and of the cocktail of toxic chemicals applied to the fruit and vegetables at every stage of growth, storage and transport to the processing plant.

Ten years ago, most people believed the bland assurances of public health authorities that these residues, although sometimes found to exceed regulatory levels, were no real cause for concern. But the 1990s, with their succession of food scares – especially the BSE crisis and the furore over genetically modified foods – have turned us all into sceptics. Is there really a safe level for toxic chemicals in our food? Is it safe even at the maximum level of 0.01mg per kg proposed in new European Union (EU) safety regulations for babyfoods?

A study published in 1993 by the US National Research Council and National Academy of Sciences found that babies were far more at risk than adults from pesticide residues, and that cancer and damaged immune and nervous systems were likely to result from regular exposure. Organophosphates were a particular concern, since they could cross the blood–brain barrier of babies and small children to cause brain damage. Are they one explanation for today's epidemic of hyperactive or dull, retarded children?

More and more mothers aren't waiting to find out. The organic babyfood market developed from nowhere in the early 1990s to become the fastest-growing section of the organic food business today. In Germany, processed babyfoods are well on the way to becoming 100% organic, with Hipp, the biggest company, going worldwide. Organix in the UK started out in 1992 with a modest five items, including garden vegetables, apple and cherry, and carrot purée. Today there are over 50 items in the range of little gourmet dishes, and their UK market share is already 5%.

Conventional babyfood companies like Boots and Gerber have been compelled to fall into line. In Germany, Nestlé snapped up Alete organic babyfoods. In the USA, one of the most popular organic brands – Earthbest – is now a division of Heinz.

Research shows that mothers of young children are the real force driving today's organic boom.

'For a substantial portion of the next generation,' said a buyer from the UK supermarket Tesco, who conducted the research, 'choosing organic products will be a way of life. They will have known nothing else.'

It's a far cry from the days when belief in the superiority of food grown without agrochemicals labelled you a crank and a visionary. One of the earliest and most forceful of these 'cranks' was Albert Howard, whose book *An Agricultural Testament*, published in 1940, became the rallying call for England's organic revolution.

At the invitation of Lord Curzon, Viceroy of India, Howard had taken up the direction of an agricultural research station at Pusa in Bengal in 1904, to develop new disease-free strains of wheat, tobacco, gram and linseed for India. He came to the post free of any notion that western ideas and methods must be superior. And since he had decided to begin by growing the crops himself, he followed the methods of local farmers, who, by tilling and manuring their land according to centuries-old tradition, seemed able to produce disease-free crops without deluging them in insecticides.

He was startled by the results. Crops grown on this naturally fertilized soil not only flourished and remained almost pest-free, they also enhanced the health and resistance of the humans and animals fed with them. His own oxen never developed foot-and-mouth disease although it was rife at that time.

The obvious way to produce disease-free crops was thus to bring the soil up to 'the highest natural level of fertility'. Nobody had done this more successfully than the peasant farmers of China, who over 4000 years had cultivated their fields and kept them fertile by the application of compost carefully prepared from animal, human and vegetable wastes. Diseased plants, animals and people, concluded Howard, were ' ...the punishment meted out by Mother Earth for adopting methods of agriculture which are not in accordance with Nature's law of faithful return to the soil of all available animal, vegetable and human wastes.'

After eight years of experimentation, Howard perfected a system of composting known as the Indore Process. By the end of the 1930s it was being put into practice, with outstanding success, in sugar-cane fields in South Africa and coconut estates in Malaya, on cotton farms in India and tea plantations in Ceylon. Howard was by no means the only proponent of what was coming to be called organic farming, but it was his enthusiasm, his lectures and magazine articles, and his book which took the organic message around the world.

In the USA, J.I. Rodale, owner of the Rodale Press in Emmaus, Pennsylvania, came across Howard's work and found that it exactly agreed with his own notions of what he called 'scientific farming'. He launched a magazine called *Organic Farming and Gardening*, arranged for Howard's book to be published in the USA, and in his own book *Pay Dirt*, published in 1945, expressed his misgivings about the agrochemical revolution and the fertility of American soil. Later on, he and his son Robert set up the Rodale Research Center to promote scientific studies in organics. The name Rodale has been at the forefront of the organic revolution ever since.

Howard's best-known disciple in England was Lady Eve Balfour, who had been farming at Haughley in Suffolk since the end of the First World War. She had begun putting Howard's work into practice at Haughley in 1938. In her seminal book *The Living Soil*, published in 1943, she described the teeming micro-organisms which gave soil its fertility, and which were completely ignored by the agricultural chemist. She had expected to reach a handful of sympathetic and like-minded readers. To her astonishment, the book had to be reprinted within three months, went into a total of nine editions, was translated into Swedish, Spanish and German, and brought in demands for more information from all over the world. In response, the Soil Association came into being, officially launched in November 1946 in London.

Agribusiness shrugged off the criticisms of the organic lobby, dismissing them as homespun cranks opposed to scientific progress. It was not so easy to dismiss the views of Rachel Carson, whose 1962 best-seller *Silent Spring* (see also pages 30 and 33) exposed not only the devastating toll of pesticides on wildlife and human health, but also the fast-rising problem of pest resistance.

The emerging eco-consciousness inspired by *Silent Spring* gained ground rapidly, and the organic cause put up healthy shoots. The idea of an international body linking these organic movements grew out of talks between Bob Rodale and Roland Chevriot, President of France's Nature et Progres. It bore fruit with the launch at Versailles in November 1972 of the International Federation of Organic Agriculture Movements (IFOAM), with five founder members including Rodale Press and the Soil Association.

Quietly and insistently, support for the organic ideal grew. Through international scientific conferences held every two years from 1977 onwards, IFOAM has brought together organic thinkers from all over the world. Its policy of regionalization has fostered strong growth first in Africa, then in the former communist countries of Eastern Europe and in Latin America, where – especially in Mexico – organic agriculture has linked hands with the Fair Trade movement. By 1999 IFOAM could claim nearly 800 members worldwide.

Among IFOAM's most important accomplishments has been the setting of standards for organic produce which have served as the basis for regional or, increasingly, international standards, now adopted by the EU.

There is now huge demand for organic foods, and supermarkets – once reluctant to bother with this niche market – are struggling to keep pace. In 1996 the British supermarket giant Sainsbury stocked 42 organic lines. In 2000, the number was up to 650 and sales of their organic produce were running at £3.2 million a week. Waitrose was running a close second, and Iceland, the frozen-food supermarket, stunned the industry in September 2000 by announcing plans to switch its entire own-brand vegetable range to organic – a move which would consume 40% of the world's total organic vegetable supplies.

Sales in the UK have been growing by 40% a year since 1995; they were expected to reach £550 million in 2000 and over £1 billion by 2002. An estimated 1 in 4 British people now regularly eats organic food. '2000 will be remembered as the year organic became mainstream,' commented a spokesman for Tesco supermarkets, currently bidding for leadership in the organic field. This group will increase its range of organic products to over 750, presented in special packaging – and, for starters, it slashed 12% off all its organic prices in autumn 2000.

Royal patronage has given huge impetus to the British organic movement: HRH Prince Charles is a highly active patron of the Soil Association and more than one sceptic has been converted by the hospitality of his Highgrove estate in Gloucestershire, with its 100% organic home farm. After senior Tesco staff paid visits during 2000, the supermarket announced plans to fund the first-ever research base for organic agriculture at a British university, donating £450,000 over five years to Newcastle University.

Today, the biggest problem in organic agriculture is how to meet soaring demand – a problem that could not have been anticipated 20 years ago.

10 the greening of agriculture

At the start of the twenty-first century, intensive farming is in trouble. The honeymoon is over. The old arguments that only agrochemical farming could feed the world are falling on deaf – or sceptical – ears.

The rapid rise in demand for organically grown food is all the more impressive since it owes little, in most countries, to official government support. In the UK, for example, conventional farming receives government and EU subsidies to the tune of some £3 billion a year. Despite this, hundreds of desperate farmers face acute poverty if not bankruptcy, caught in a vicious downward spiral of plummeting prices and the soaring costs of agrochemicals. Organic farming is one way out which rising numbers would love to take: but only a miserly £10 million or so is made available annually to help with the cost of conversion.

In an article for *Audubon* magazine in March–April 1999, agronomist Joel Bourne pointed out that of 30,000 research projects supported by the US Department of Agriculture in 1995 and 1996, only 34 focused on organic production. In his Reith Lecture for May 2000, HRH Prince Charles argued that if even a fraction of the money currently being invested in developing genetically modified crops was applied to understanding and improving traditional systems of agriculture, the results would be 'remarkable'.

Agrochemical farming has huge hidden costs.

A study carried out at the Centre for Environment and Society at the University of Essex, published in 1999, came up with a devastating balance sheet of the financial costs of farming in the UK. The total of £2.3 billion, ultimately paid by higher prices or taxes, includes figures for soil erosion, loss of biodiversity and the cost of treating food poisoning; £214 million for cleaning up water supplies polluted by pesticides and nitrates draining off farm land; and £25 million for the cost of nature conservation. It doesn't include the cost of damage to the health of agricultural workers caused by pesticides, nor less quantifiable costs such as ruined landscapes and vanishing wildflower meadows. If the report's authors had included the cost to the British taxpayer of BSE, their total would have soared by another £4 billion.

Agrochemicals – as the organic lobby always argued – can wear out soils in the long run, leaving them hopelessly impoverished. In May 2000 the International Food Policy Research Institute published a study showing that almost 40% of the world's farmland is seriously degraded due to problems such as erosion and nutrient depletion. Even the once-unarguable defence of agrochemical farming – that it produced significantly higher yields – is less unassailable than it once was. Organic farmers who have been in business for many years, and whose soils are richly fertile following season after season of nurture, are beginning to match the yields of their non-organic neighbours. In a study comparing conventional and organic farming systems which has been running over 13 years at the Rodale Research Center in Pennsylvania, USA, researchers found that yields of organic corn and soybeans have consistently equalled those of conventionally grown crops and have actually been higher in dry years. Another US study, published in *Nature* in 1998, showed that over ten years the difference in yields between industrial and organically farmed maize was only 1%.

Even this 1% advantage may sometimes be illusory. An experiment conducted by the Swedish Biodynamic Institute at the University of Uppsala compared conventionally grown crops of potatoes with those grown biodynamically (see below). The conventionally grown potatoes yielded 38.2 tonnes per hectare when they were lifted in October, but 30% of the crop was lost in grading and storing. The biodynamically grown crop initially weighed less, at 34.2 tonnes, but only 12.5% of this was lost in storage and grading. Nor was there a difference in weight alone: the biodynamically grown potatoes were richer in both protein and vitamin C.

Biodynamic farming has a low profile in the UK, although it is much more widely known on the Continent. Its accreditation symbol, the Demeter trademark, is recognized throughout the world. This system of agriculture originated in a series of lectures given to about a hundred East German farmers by Rudolf Steiner in 1924.

Steiner is better known as the founder of Anthroposophy – a Greek word meaning wisdom of man – which extends scientific research and discovery beyond the parameters of natural material laws. He was an imaginative and original thinker – a scientist as well as a philosopher and clairvoyant. In the Steiner view, earth is a living organism, in which human beings, animals, plants and minerals are interrelated and interdependent, and all subject to the rhythms and influence of the entire cosmos. When these principles are applied to agriculture, Steiner taught, balance and healing will return to the earth, and richly nutritious food for man and beast will be the result.

The ideal biodynamic farm is self-contained, with just enough animals to provide manure for fertility and these animals in turn being fed from the farm.

Like organic thinkers such as Albert Howard and Eve Balfour (see also pages 52–54), Steiner taught the key importance of compost. But in his lectures, Steiner also revealed details of certain preparations that should be made and applied to increase fertility and growth. It says much for the faith that this extraordinary man inspired that dozens of farmers carried out his instructions to the letter.

Even today, some biodynamic farmers are a little shy of revealing how these preparations should be made. Each autumn they bury cows' horns stuffed with manure in the ground 60cm deep and leave them there until Easter. In spring more cows' horns, filled with finely ground quartz powder, are buried in the earth until summer. These two preparations, referred to as 'horn manure' and 'horn silica' respectively, are applied as field sprays. Small quantities are diluted in rainwater and stirred rhythmically for one hour to release the active energies, and they are then sprayed onto the soil (horn manure) or onto growing plants (horn silica). These two preparations, working as polarities, serve to balance and harmonize the assimilation of plant nutrients from the soil and the light and warmth from the cosmos.

A further group of preparations known as the 'biodynamic compost preparations' are made from well-known medicinal plants which undergo an unusual fermentation process, many of them within animal organ sheaths, during the time spent beneath the soil. These preparations are inserted into compost piles to regulate and enhance humus-forming and nutrient-stabilizing processes. 'I know perfectly well that all of this may seem utterly mad,' concluded Steiner with a smile. 'I only ask you to remember how many things have seemed utterly mad which have been introduced a few years later.'

There was more to stretch the credulity of later practitioners. A young German woman called Maria Thun was intrigued by the attention that peasant farmers paid to the phases of the moon. For more than half a century she experimented with planting at different points not only in the lunar cycle, but according to the orbit of the moon through the signs of the zodiac. Willy Schilthuis, who was President of the Dutch Biodynamic Association for 25 years, has described her work. The tests, she says, '...clearly showed that each of the 12 signs of the zodiac has a special relationship with one of the four life forces, which are manifest in the "elements" earth, water, light/air and heat. All four forces can be seen to have an effect on the life body for the growth and development of the plant. ...the earth element has a particular effect on root formation, the water element on the formation of the leaves, the light/air element on the flowers, and the heat element on the formation of fruit and seed.' Lunar calendars drawn up in accordance with Maria Thun's findings are now published regularly for the use of biodynamic farmers.

Hitler's Germany banned biodynamic farming, but after the war it was re-established in Europe. In 1954 the Demeter Association was formed and the Demeter logo adopted. The movement has spread: today there is a Biodynamic Association in over 26 countries. Steiner's colleague Ehrenfried Pfeiffer took it to the USA in the early 1940s.

Among the converts to the biodynamic methods are a number of France's leading viticulturists. Two women are producing some of the finest wines in Burgundy at vineyards where pesticides or conventional fertilizers are no longer used: Domaine Leflaive, in Puligny-Montrachet, and Domaine Leroy, with holdings in Corton-Charlemagne and Richebourg. And nowhere has the influence of biodynamic farming been more profound than in Australia and New Zealand: in Victoria alone over 600,000 hectares are farmed biodynamically.

The Australian success story began with one man, Alex Podolinsky, who grew up in pre-war Germany where he absorbed some of Steiner's ideas. He arrived in Australia, where a friend loaned him a small rundown farm. With no cows to provide manure, Podolinsky applied one of Steiner's preparations, transformed the dying fields into rich living soil – and launched the biodynamic revolution that is changing the face of Australian farming. Peter Tompkins and Christopher Bird tell the amazing story in their book *Secrets of the Soil* (see also page 49). The turning point came with a prime-time programme on ABC television in 1985. 'Opening with a haunting scene of Podolinsky on his tractor spraying [the preparation] on a moonlit pasture, with an owl hooting in the background,' say Tompkins and Bird, 'it went on to show Alex professionally stuffing and burying cow horns, communing with his herd of cattle in a rich and fertile landscape to which not a speck of chemical of any sort had been added in over 25 years.' The station received over 6000 letters from farmers wanting to know more.

Farmers contemplating rich, fertile soils, high yields and a non-existent bill for agrochemicals can easily swallow a lunar calendar and a cow horn or two. As one horticulturist told the UK newspaper *The Guardian*, 'I have to admit we were a little sceptical at first about all these techniques. But if the moon can push great oceans around, I suppose we shouldn't be too sceptical about what else it can do.'

Like biodynamic agriculture, permaculture grew out of one man's musing on the way nature does things.

While Steiner's inspiration was visionary in its sweep, however, the views of Bill Mollison, the Tasmanian who, together with David Holmgren, was responsible for inventing permaculture, seem like nothing so much as common sense.

Take, for example, today's battery chicken farm, as Patrick Whitefield does in his excellent book, *Permaculture in a Nutshell.* Intensively reared battery chickens are housed in a big specially built shed and fed mainly with grain grown with the help of a lot of energy – farm machinery, fertilizer and pesticides. The battery house needs more energy – for water supplies, and for ventilation to stop the indoor temperature from rocketing because of the body heat of all those birds. The industry is highly polluting, too, it takes quite a lot of labour, the chickens are wretched, and the end-product – eggs – are of low quality.

Permaculture does it differently. The open-air chicken run is planted with trees and bushes producing seeds or fruits which hens eat when they fall. A water-butt collects rainwater from the roof of the chicken shed – where the birds sleep at night – to supply most of their drinking needs. Near the chicken run may be a wheat field, a vegetable garden or an orchard in which the chickens can be allowed to forage at certain times: they will eat up insects, grain left over from harvesting, odd weeds – and leave some organic manure behind. Up against the sunny side of the chicken shed is a greenhouse: at night-time the chickens' body heat helps to keep it warm, while the carbon dioxide they breathe out helps plant growth. The chickens are happier, too.

A far cry from hippy dreams of self-sustaining communes, permaculture is irresistibly practical. Its adherents claim that it is more environmentally friendly than any other organic system, because it doesn't demand intensive use of machinery and focuses on supplying local needs rather than those of the international markets. 'The aim,' says Bill Mollison, 'is to create systems that are ecologically sound and economically viable, which provide for their own needs, do not exploit or pollute, and are therefore sustainable in the long term.' Permaculture is very joined-up thinking.

A good permaculture designer bears three principles in mind when s/he starts to plan. First, every element in the plan should serve more than one function: the chicken shed heating the greenhouse, for instance. Secondly, each need is served by more than just one element of the design: the chickens feed from the trees and bushes as well as from weeds, grubs, grains and insects where they forage. Thirdly, the system is interconnected, just as nature is, with all sorts of benefits constantly arising from this interconnectedness.

The La-akea Permaculture Gardens in Hawaii – where students come to study from all over the world – showcase these principles. They were designed on the site of an old guava orchard with soils wrecked by years of herbicide application. Don May and his staff set about improving the soil by mulching and composting. Sited on a slight incline, the farm is powered by solar energy and water is supplied by rainwater collected in tanks. Two greenhouses grow edible crops – including carrots, ginger, pumpkins, eggplant and pak choi. Inside the greenhouses, plants are arranged in the permaculture 'keyhole' pattern, with beds raying out from a central access area.

Fertilizer for the plants in the greenhouse is provided by geese, ducks and chickens. Beyond the greenhouse is what looks like natural wooded land. In fact, the fruit trees, shrubs and plants are carefully plotted for their 'companion' values: tall trees provide shade or windbreaks, other plants have deep roots to bring up nutrients, and beans fix nitrogen in the soil – as well as making excellent mulch. Fishponds, finally, supply fish for the community table, nourishing 'fishy' water for the plants – and a treat for the ducks and geese.

A more modest enterprise has been that of the School Gardens programme in Zimbabwe. Most of the country's schools are set in arid surroundings, and there is no money to pay for air-conditioning to help children concentrate when the temperature soars. But some of these schools now have a permaculture garden attached, consisting of a small forest area, ponds and vegetable plots tended by the children. The trees provide cool, green shade in which classes can be taught; the vegetable plots provide food for malnourished children and outdoor exercise; the gardens give the children a chance to learn about life and nature. Depending on political problems, it is hoped that the scheme will run throughout Zimbabwe's schools by 2010.

Both La-akea and the Zimbabwe schools illustrate another basic permaculture principle: that the 'yield' of any farming or gardening enterprise can't be counted in bushels or kilos alone. It also embraces factors like recreational value, job satisfaction, the chance to commune with nature and the opportunity to work with others.

Judged by such standards, modern chemical farming fails miserably. Originally an enterprise that produced food for communities, agriculture today, says Mollison, simply produces 'commodities for the international money market'. As he says, 'Agriculture is the most destructive activity on the face of the earth. It is responsible for poisoning sixty percent of our water supplies and for ruining most of our landscapes.'

11 biodiversity

In my country childhood we walked through meadows thick with cowslips and gathered bunches of primroses and violets. On the verges of wheat and cornfields there would be swathes of cornflowers; the fields themselves would be sprinkled with red poppies. My father taught us to recognize the song of the skylark and on warm summer nights we would go to the woods to hear the nightingales sing.

Today cowslips are disappearing from our countryside so fast that survivors are actually being counted, poppies are vanishing, cornflowers are officially a rare species. And when did you last hear a skylark? These losses have crept up on us slowly over the last 40 years or so. But it was the recent realization that the ordinary sparrow – that tough and cheerful little urban survivor – had vanished from central London and other big English cities that finally brought home to many people what was going on.

In the language of modern biologists, this is loss of biodiversity – the wonderful variety of life. There is nothing new about the extinction of species. In the millions of years of Earth life, there have been half a dozen mass extinctions, in which millions of species were wiped out by natural catastrophes. In the worst, 250 million years ago, up to 95% of all species perished. The most recent – caused by long years of volcanic activity in India as well as a giant meteorite plunging into the Bay of Mexico 65 million years ago – blotted out 85% of species. (Fortunately, that included the dinosaurs, with whom human coexistence would always have been problematic.)

In the eyes of many biologists, we are now in the middle of another extinction – but this one is almost certainly man-made.

It was Harvard's famous entomologist Edward Wilson who originally coined the word biodiversity. But it passed into the language in 1992 when, on 5 June in Rio de Janeiro, Brazil, more than 150 nations signed up to the Convention on Biological Diversity. Perhaps 99 out of 100 people couldn't begin to tell you what Rio was all about. The Convention itself has been bitterly criticized – for not going far enough, for being too vague, for generating more paper than action, for lacking teeth. Nevertheless, it was a huge step forward. Rio spelt out to the world a few simple hard-hitting truths. Humankind is a plunderer and a wrecker. We have already destroyed huge areas of the planet. We are exhausting its resources. We are devastating its ecosystems. We are destabilizing its weather systems. And since this is the only planet we have, it is high time we mended our ways – for the sake of ourselves and our children. Yet as this book goes to press, the USA and Australia have still to ratify the Convention.

Why does biodiversity matter? What difference will it make to our lives if a few species of South American butterfly disappear, if the Philippine eagle and the Chinese river dolphin are on the brink of extinction?

Biodiversity, in short, offers survival. The importance of the skylarks, for instance, goes far beyond the purely aesthetic. Skylarks are disappearing because of the intensive monoculture which turns countryside into prairie and douses soil with pesticides. When coppices and hedges are uprooted, and fruit- and seed-bearing trees and bushes torn down to make way for crops, bird numbers decline because their natural food supplies are disappearing. But birds also feast on crop pests, and when the birds disappear pest populations can explode, to the point where they can begin to become pesticide resistant.

Those broad-spectrum weedkillers, meanwhile, are wiping out old favourites like foxgloves and cornflowers, cowslips and clovers. But with the flowers go the bumblebees who live off their nectar, and bumblebees are pollinators of many important commercial crops such as tomatoes, cranberries and blueberries. Until Dutch tomato-growers set up bumblebee colonies in their greenhouses, the job had to be done by humans wielding electric vibrators, at a cost of £13,000 per hectare.

One of the many ways in which human blundering can devastate biodiversity is by the casual introduction of exotic plants, fish, animals or insects into habitats thousands of kilometres from their native homes. Africa's Lake Victoria spells out a cautionary tale. It was once home to over 350 species of small native fish, providing the livelihood of local fishermen and their villages. Since fat and profitable perch and tilapia have been introduced, native species have reduced by more than 80% and the villagers are going hungry, although perch and tilapia are hugely profitable exports. But without the activity of the local fish, whole areas of the lake are losing oxygen and exploding into 'blooms' of algae – which may soon threaten the perch and tilapia fishing.

Loss of biodiversity threatens our food supplies in other ways – a lesson which might have been learned in the nineteenth century, when famine slaughtered millions of Irish peasants dependent on a single food crop, the potato. As Edward Wilson pointed out in the special Earth Day 2000 edition of *Time* magazine, 'Throughout history, people have cultivated or gathered 7000 plant species for food. Today only 20 species provide 90% of the world's food and three – maize, wheat and rice – supply more than half.'

Even within these few food-crop species, variety is in dangerous decline. A century ago, according to a report by Rob Edwards in *New Scientist* (17 August 1996), American farmers could take their pick from nearly 700 varieties of beans, over 400 varieties of tomatoes, around 500 varieties of lettuce. The vast majority have disappeared. In 1991, a report from the US Academy of Sciences revealed that the country's main crops depended on just nine varieties.

In over 80 countries, according to the UN Food and Agriculture Organization in a 1996 report, a wide range of locally grown varieties were being replaced by a few profitable export crops. In many of these poor Third World countries, the local varieties were usually well adapted to local conditions, even if yields were low. The imported alternatives and a move towards a monoculture of cash crops produced gratifyingly large crops initially – but soon ceased to be profitable as the price of the imported pesticides they called for rose, adding to the burden of Third World debt.

In her Reith Lecture in the spring of 2000, the Indian environmental activist Vandana Shiva spoke of the despair among the farmers of

Warangal, in Andhra Pradesh, where numbers of them have resorted to suicide. Traditionally they grew rice and millet, until seed companies lured them into buying cotton seeds. Now they have to buy new seeds every year and spending on pesticides has gone up 2000% in three years.

Varieties of commercial crops developed for huge yields often lack the natural resistance of older wild strains. One wild maize from Argentina makes chemicals in its leaves that are lethal to the European corn-borer – a pest that does damage worth about $350 million to US crops every year. Cross-breeding with this wild cousin could save maize farmers these ruinous losses. 'Tens of thousands of species of the world's still surviving flora,' points out Edward Wilson, 'can be bred or provide genes to increase production in deserts, saline flats and other marginal habitats.' As climates shift dramatically around the world, we're going to need these resilient and adaptable species.

We may need to call on these wild gene pools for other important reasons. Allergies and sensitivities to certain foods afflict more and more people – over 35 million in the USA according to the National Institute of Health. Wheat is one of the commonest problem foods, and since wheat is omnipresent in western diets, mealtimes and social life can be a nightmare for these sufferers and their families. But clinical trials conducted in Chicago for the International Food Allergy Association show that 70% even of those severely allergic to wheat could tolerate kamut, an ancient Egyptian cousin of durum wheat now being grown in the USA. Amaranth, the staple food of the Incas and Aztecs, and spelt, the grain of the Roman armies, are other old grains which have been given the Lazarus treatment by the US healthfood industry. All three grains, incidentally, are richer in both protein and mineral content than our modern durum wheats, and sales are climbing in healthfood stores and supermarkets.

In medical terms alone, biodiversity has been priceless to the human race.

In rain forests especially, in a climate that never knows a winter let-up, plants and insects have engaged for millennia in an all-out chemical arms race. Some of our most valuable medicines have come out of this chemical warfare: quinine, cocaine, ipecacuanha, and more recently taxol, the first successful treatment for breast and ovarian cancers.

As the huge clean-up bill for hazardous chemicals such as dioxins becomes apparent, the green chemists of the twenty-first century will be looking more and more to natural products as source material for fabrics, dyes, resins, oils, plastics and building materials of all kinds.

Hemp is just one example of the versatile crops to which they will turn. It is an undemanding crop and can be made into almost anything from canvas and paper to cosmetics and composite flooring. Ralph Lauren and Calvin Klein have endowed hemp cloth with eco-chic by using it for jeans and shirts. The only thing now standing in the path of its rise is the fact that it belongs to the same species – *Cannabis sativa* – as gentle, mind-bending pot. Fans point out that you'd need to smoke 50–100 cigarettes made of the commercial variety to get anything like a high, but its cultivation is still banned in many countries. Bamboos and palms are two other versatile plant families that provide food, shelter, clothing, furniture and tools for billions of people around the world.

Over and beyond the survival of any particular plant, insect or animal, our future may depend more than we imagine on earth's various ecosystems. There is a growing realization that through this web of diverse life, the earth provides a number of essential services – soil renewal and excess erosion prevention, air purification and water filtration, climate regulation and food provision. Any attempt to put a cash value on these services comes up with dizzying rows of noughts.

Beyond all these purely selfish motives for looking after our planet, what right do the wealthy nations of the world have to vandalize the environment of people too poor and too powerless to protest? If loggers moved in on the Bois de Boulogne in the middle of Paris, the whole of the western world would be up in arms. When it happens to some remote people in the South American Andes, some lovely island in the Pacific, or the last unspoiled wildernesses of the Arctic, the protest is muffled. But perhaps conservation – like charity – will always begin at home.

12 biomass: energy that won't cost the earth

What do seaweed, sawdust, rice husks and chicken shit have in common? Answer: they can all be converted into energy for heating homes, powering factories and running cars. They are biomass: sources of bio-energy. And biomass is one of the most plentiful sources of renewable energy for our modern world.

There's nothing new about biomass as fuel. The first human beings to light a fire and char their wild boar on it were exploiting biomass energy. Good King Wenceslas braved the snow to help bring biomass energy to one poor peasant's home. And forests are dwindling all over the world cut down to provide firewood for warmth or cooking.

Renewable is the last word you'd think of applying to this use of wood, and you'd be right – but modern biomass concepts take the idea one step back. Instead of chopping down forests, biomass makes use of waste material: from plants or trees from which the useful parts have already been harvested. When such wastes are simply burned to dispose of them, all that energy goes up in polluting smoke – and more carbon dioxide is emitted. But when they're processed to produce energy, they are said to be 'carbon-neutral' – any carbon dioxide emitted in the conversion process is no more than the plant or tree originally absorbed.

The solar energy originally stored in them by photosynthesis can be released in a number of ways – by burning, by gasification, by liquefaction or by microbial conversion, in which bacteria ferment biomass to produce a gas (usually methane) or a liquid.

The litter from battery poultry farms is an ideal waste for biomass purposes, although it took an imaginative British businessman, Simon Fraser, to spot the potential. When oil prices collapsed in the mid-1980s, due to the oil crisis, he was already running Fibropower, one of the first commercial biomass businesses in the country, supplying energy to a distillery from forest wastes, and he began looking for a cheaper source.

The British poultry-rearing business produces over 1.5 million tonnes of wood shavings, straw and chicken shit annually – a valuable fertilizer, but many times more than can actually be used on the land. Disposing of it has been a worldwide environmental headache for years, overloading soils and waterways with nutrients, and emitting massive amounts of two greenhouse gases, methane and nitrous oxide. Not any more for those within reach of the three Fibropower plants, as the company actually pays to take it off farmers' hands. The newest plant – the £69 million power station at Thetford in Kent – is the biggest biomass plant in Europe, handling up to 450,000 tonnes a year. The litter is trucked into the plant in covered lorries and burned in furnaces at very high temperatures to generate steam, which drives a turbine linked to an electricity generator.

There are no waste products from this process. The ash from the furnaces is sold as a nitrate-free fertilizer, rich in phosphate and potash. The exhaust steam is recycled back into the boiler. The emissions are mainly steam, with very low amounts of greenhouse gases – well within European Union limits. The power fed into the local electricity grid, and sold to its customers by the local electricity company, is enough to supply 22,000 homes. It has been calculated that the carbon dioxide emissions it saves by replacing a conventional coal-fired plant is the equivalent of taking 400,000 cars a year off the roads.

Fibropower is also working with partners in Italy, Holland, Belgium and the USA – where poultry farms concentrated in Minnesota and Maryland produce over 20 million tonnes of litter a year.

Practical Australians see biomass as a neat solution to waste-disposal problems. Their huge sugar-cane plantations generate about 10 million tonnes of bagasse (crushed sugar-cane fibres) a year, and other large-scale wastes include macadamia nut shells and timber residues from sawmills. In Brazil, more than a third of cars run on ethanol produced from sugar-cane bagasse.

If there's one thing that is plentiful in India it is cattle dung. In 1982 the Indian government launched a National Project on Biogas Development, aimed at supplying clean and cheap energy to rural areas. Over two million small household plants have now been set up, using farm and household wastes as well as manure, and saving millions of tonnes of precious wood from trees annually.

Pig-farming in Denmark produces huge quantities of manure. Thousands of tonnes of it are now being processed by digester systems set up as co-operatives. Manure from farms within an 11km radius is collected and fed into the digesters: the gas is piped to a nearby town, and the processed manure returned to farmers as fertilizer. The Danish system exemplifies the first rule of a successful biomass operation: local production. If you have to expend too much energy transporting the material to the processing plant, you'll get a carbon overdraft again.

The imaginative Development Officers at Hereford and Worcester County Council in the UK set up an excellent example of the way biomass can work. Following the 1992 Earth Summit in Rio de Janeiro, they decided that a planned new primary school should not just be fuelled by locally produced biomass energy: it should also make a contribution to local employment. Weobley primary school today has a 350kW wood-fired boiler, which meets most of its heating needs as well as those of a nearby secondary school. The fuel is wood thinnings supplied by a local co-operative of more than 300 farmers and agricultural contractors, and the waste produced by the combustion and exhaust-gas cleaning process is used to fertilize the school garden.

Another key word in the biomass glossary is efficiency: your cheerful log fire captures only about 8% of the wood's energy to warm you: the rest goes straight up the chimney.

In Austria – where almost 20% of households use wood for heating – wood boilers using wood logs, chips or pellets have been developed which can use up to 93% of the solar energy stored in the wood.

An excellent example of the Growing Energy Business – as it is aptly styled – is the Arbre electricity generating power station commissioned at Eggborough in Yorkshire, England, in the summer of 2000. Drawing its fuel from high-yielding varieties of willow and poplar, grown in dense plantations and harvested every three years, the plant is set to produce 10MW of electricity, of which 8MW will be exported to the local grid – enough to supply 18,000 homes.

Biomass can meet the energy needs of isolated rural communities, and Shell Renewables are experimenting with small-scale biomass projects. Successfully managed, a biomass plantation could supply a village of up to 500 families with all their electricity needs, with a surplus for developing small local industries. Even landfill and incineration, properly handled, can yield an amount of biomass energy.

And if there isn't a reliable local supply of biomass material, grow your own. Energy crops, as they are called, make all kinds of sense. Useful energy plants, including many trees, can often be planted on marginal land too poor for food crops, such as old colliery sites or sand and gravel workings. They don't need pricey synthetic fertilizers and pesticides: instead, they can be safely fertilized with sewage sludge, which is too dangerous to be used on food crops. Some species can be used for soil regeneration; others can be intercropped with food plants – and will actually help to boost yield, like the leucaena trees planted in fields of corn in Kenya and Nigeria, whose fruits yield a kerosene-like oil.

The best biomass crops supply more than just energy. The kelor tree (*Moringa oleifera*) is one of the world's fastest-growing trees, reaching up to 4m from seed in its first year of growth. Theareafter it can be cut back to 1m or less annually, yielding valuable biomass material, while continuing to produce both flowers and fruit. The leaves, which are rich in vitamins A and C, plus iron and calcium, are widely eaten as a vegetable in Indonesia. In India they curry the fruits. The crushed seeds are widely used to purify muddy river water: trials at an Indonesian university showed that a single crushed seed could kill 90% of coliform bacteria in a litre of water within 20 minutes. The seeds also yield a fine oil much favoured by watchmakers. And the kelor tree grows just as happily in the humid tropics as in bone-dry grasslands.

What more could you ask of an energy crop? And what miracle of GM technology could ever rival the resourcefulness of nature?

earth therapy

13 the green pharmacy

Herbal medicine has a long history. When a 60,000-year-old Neanderthal burial site was excavated at Shanidar in north Iraq, grains of various flower pollens were found thickly clustered around the bones of the buried man. The pollens were analysed and found to belong to eight different genera of flowering plants, all of them still common in the surrounding fields and woods. And of those eight, seven are still used for medicine today by the people of that area.

Species of one, the little shrubby plant *ephedra*, have been used continuously in the Far East for thousands of years as a medicine for bronchial asthma. In 1887 a Japanese chemist took *ephedra* apart and isolated an alkaloid which he called ephedrine. By the 1930s it was being marketed as a useful drug for asthma, and a central nervous system stimulant. It is still prescribed as a nasal decongestant today and, together with other powerful constituents identified in the plant, it has served as the model for half a dozen useful modern drugs.

You could match this story over and over again: bark from the quinine tree for malaria, ipecacuanha for amoebic dysentery, senna the laxative, liquorice for peptic ulcers, white willow for pain relief and *digitalis* (foxglove) for heart conditions are just a handful of the huge treasury of healing plants that people have been drawing on since the dawn of our history, and which, newly 'discovered' by medical science, have become a major part of the modern pharmacy.

For hundreds of thousands of years, doctors and lay people relied on plants for the vast majority of their medicines. When printing was invented, herbals were among the most popular of the earliest printed books, and they were written largely for doctors: informative technical works about the drugs that were their stock-in-trade. But as medicine in Renaissance times grew into a highly specialized profession, highly paid physicians who had devoted 12 or 14 years to their training became anxious to distance themselves from the lower grades of medical practitioners, such as the apothecaries – the high-street chemists of their day. Gradually, they learned to despise the homegrown herbs country people used.

Doctors might have remained more faithful to the botanic medicine of their ancestors if herbs had yielded cures for any of the great epidemics which rampaged through Europe periodically. Plague, in the form of the Black Death, killed an estimated 1 in 3 of all Europeans within months in 1348 and continued to make regular visitations for centuries more. In 1492 another epidemic – supposedly brought by the returning fleet of Christopher Columbus – first appeared in the red-light district of Naples, and spread like wildfire through Europe. It was syphilis, the AIDS of its day. As with AIDS, there was no known cure, and wives and babies in the womb might be infected before the husband even knew he had the disease.

There were herbal treatments for syphilis: guaiac and sarsaparilla were both plant drugs from the New World, and many people claimed they were effective when administered as part of a tedious six-week regime of confinement to a warm room and austere diet. But few people were prepared to sit the treatment out. The alternative – mercury – was a highly toxic mineral drug, with appalling side-effects. But with the health of children and dynasties at stake, mercury soon became the treatment of choice.

Mercury was followed by other minerals – the equally toxic antimony, for instance, reputed to have saved the life of Louis XIV as a young man when he fell desperately ill with a fever. And over the following centuries, the new 'chemical' medicines, prepared in laboratories, gradually assumed the place of honour in any doctor's drug repertory.

By the nineteenth century, doctors who still used plants to any important extent, in England as in the USA, were a minority: medicine, lamented one of them, was become 'entirely chymical'.

Little or no research was carried out into medicinal plants, and although there were still herbalists in England, they were few in number and beneath the contempt of the medical 'regulars'. By the early twentieth century herbal medicine seemed doomed in the Anglo-Saxon world. With the discovery of Prontosil, the first of the sulphonamide drugs, in Germany in the 1930s, the terror went out of acute bacterial infections such as pneumonia, meningitis and septicaemia.

With penicillin in 1940, the age of the medical 'magic bullet' seemed to have arrived.

The next decades saw a series of astounding advances: the development of cortisone and the steroid drugs – a seeming instant cure for arthritis and other inflammatory diseases; new antibiotics, including the streptomycin which defeated tuberculosis (TB); the first tranquillizers. It was hardly surprising that Dr Morris Fishbein, editor of the powerful *Journal of the American Medical Association*, should dismiss herbal medicines as no more than 'veritable vegetable soups'.

The rise of the big pharmaceutical companies from the 1930s onwards apparently sealed the fate of this antiquated therapy. These companies spend enormous sums of money on developing new drugs which they can patent. Winners like the tranquillizers Valium and Prozac, and the anti-ulcer drugs like Zantac and Tagamet, made dizzying profits for the firms developing them.

But you can't patent a natural product – so who in the West was putting any money into researching herbs? The answer, it turned out, was a number of German companies, prosperous manufacturers of herbal medicines in a country where doctors still prescribed them. Their products were of pharmaceutical quality, developed following stringent clinical trials – something which most herbal manufacturers elsewhere were too poor to fund. Moreover, unlike conventional herbal remedies, these new 'phytopharmaceuticals' were standardized by clever chemical manipulation, in which specific levels of what were deemed to be the active ingredients could be guaranteed. This answered one of the great objections to herbal medicine raised by doctors: the impossibility of calculating exact dosages. What pleases patients as well as doctors is that the toll of side-effects from these plant drugs is strikingly lower than with synthetics.

One of the early successes of the new phytomedicines was *ginkgo biloba*. Developed as a treatment for failing memory and the early signs of dementia, it was phenomenally successful at a time when there was no conventional drug treatment for these problems: in 1988, German doctors wrote 5.4 million prescriptions for it – more than for any other drug. *Hypericum* (St John's Wort) outsells Prozac as a treatment for depression worldwide today. Hawthorn for the heart, garlic for the circulation, and valerian for anxiety and insomnia are other huge successes of the German phytomedicine industry.

But even without this seal of commercial success, herbal medicine is making an extraordinary comeback in the West (in eastern countries like China and India it has never been eclipsed). Herbal remedies are enjoying unprecedented sales: in the USA, for 1998 the figure was over $730 million. *Echinacea* to boost resistance to infection, feverfew to relieve migraine, cranberry for urinary tract infections, saw palmetto for prostate problems, and milk thistle for liver problems are some of the herbal remedies that chemists now sell as enthusiastically as do healthfood shops. And herbalists – once tiny isolated communities in Australia, the USA and the UK – are growing in numbers and confidence, with a choice of excellent training schools offering degree courses in herbal medicine.

Even pharmaceutical companies are now turning back to explore these once-despised plants. *Buddleia* may contain compounds which speed wound-healing, bluebells yield a cure for TB, stinging nettles provide pain relief for osteoarthritis. And trials have begun of a common-or-garden herb, sage, as a treatment for the memory loss characteristic of Alzheimer's disease. This is even more interesting when you hear that, just over 400 years ago, a famous English herbalist, John Gerard, recommended sage warmly to his readers: it is, he wrote, 'singularly good for the head and brain, it quickeneth the senses and memory...'

14 the therapeutic earth

It is easy to understand why primitive people worshipped the earth as a Mother-Goddess. Was She not their great provider – of food for themselves and their animals, of shelter, of building materials, clothing, cooking pots and tools? And when they were sick or injured, the earth became their medicine, too – earth, clay, mud, even sand have all been used as therapy in the past, and clay and mud are still in widespread and effective use today.

Baths of sand have a long history: over 2000 years ago the Greek Herodotus warmly recommended them for asthma, respiratory infections, gout and paralysis. Modern naturopaths add sciatica, general weakness and every form of joint problem, including arthritis, lumbago and rheumatism. Sand baths are taken on hot days: a shallow pit the length of the sick person is hollowed out in the sand and left to warm up. Then the patient is laid in it, covered with more warm sand and left for two hours or so, their heads well protected from the sun and their faces sponged with cold water from time to time.

During the centuries when seamen were often devastated by scurvy, there are accounts of dying sailors being carried ashore, buried up to their necks in fresh earth and making astonishing recoveries. This would not have surprised Native Americans, for whom burying the sick up to their necks in earth for some hours was a commonly practised therapy, and who believed that the healing power of earth was even greater than that of plants. In nineteenth-century Germany, two famous naturopaths – Adolf Just and Emanuel Felke – both used earth baths to great effect, treatments still carried out today in some German sanitaria.

Adolf Just (1838–1936) believed that sleeping in direct contact with the earth was especially curative: 'the entire body is aroused from its lethargy to a new manifestation of vital energy, so that it can now effectively remove old morbid matter... and receive a sensation of new health, new life and new unthought-of vigour and strength.'

Supposedly, both sand and earth draw on the earth's own special magnetism for their curative powers.

Add water and earth turns into mud. But there is mud, and mud – and the mud moistened by the waters of certain mineral springs can have as profoundly healing powers as the springs themselves. At spas throughout Europe, mud baths and mud packs are standard treatments, recommended for skin and joint diseases because of their ability to draw out toxins and remineralize the body.

Mud from the Dead Sea in the Middle East, which is fed by a number of mineral springs, is particularly rich in calcium and magnesium, minerals present in molecules small enough to be absorbed through the skin, plus other minerals that have well-documented anti-inflammatory and antiseptic effects, making both the mud from the sea bottom and the water itself powerful healers for diseases like psoriasis.

Neydharting Moor in Austria is the source of a mud so ancient that the Celts and Romans may have used it. Around 300 medicinal herbs, lipids, minerals and enzymes are among the constituents of a mud so richly healing that its products are used in many European hospitals. Therapists working with it have seen astonishing improvements in skin diseases such as acne, eczema and psoriasis, and in painful cases of rheumatism and arthritis. Treatment combines local applications of the mud with drinks of the mud mixed with water: a regime said to be deeply detoxifying and energizing.

Of all the forms of earth therapy, clay is the most ancient.

A mineral-rich ash spewed out from the hot heart of the earth in volcanic eruptions, clay sifted back down to the soil to settle in moistened layers or veins later sealed in by rock. Subsequent movement of the rocks brought these veins closer to the surface. In technical terms, it is a colloidal hydrated aluminium silicate. It dries as a fine grit-free powder, which can be green, red or white in colour.

The Chinese treated summer diarrhoea and cholera with clay – kaolin is actually named after a mountain in China where it was first extracted. Clay was mentioned in the earliest western *Materia Medica*, that of Dioscorides, surgeon to the Roman armies in the first century AD. An observant dentist, Weston Price, who spent years early in the twentieth century travelling the world and studying the health of primitive tribes, observed people continents apart using clay in the same way: in the high South American Andes, in Central Africa and among the aboriginal people of Australia. It was their custom, he noted, to dip food before it was eaten in water containing a little of the dissolved clay, 'to prevent sickness of the stomach'. In the 1920s the son of a mining engineer working in Mexico noticed that the native Yucatan Indians used to slap a dressing of moist clay from a particular spot on wounds, bruises, cuts or insect bites.

And Europe preserved its long traditions of healing with clay. Father Sebastian Kneipp (see also Water, page 195) noted the use of clay in folk-medicine and began trying it out on his patients late in the nineteenth century. He wrote of its healing powers with enthusiasm: 'Clay takes away inflammation, draws putrid and dead matter to the surface and absorbs them, and in that way purifies abscesses or ulcers. It has also been shown to be an excellent treatment for head- or back-ache, inflammations, swellings, toxic conditions and sprains...'

In the Balkan Wars of 1910, the use of clay helped to reduce the predicted mortality from a cholera outbreak from 60% to 3%. At the tuberculosis (TB) sanatorium in Davos, Switzerland, in the 1930s, patients were given hot clay packs over the thorax – and credited with near-miraculous cures.

In 1961 a New York physician, Dr Frederic Damrau, who had come across stories like these in medical literature, decided to conduct his own trial of clay. He picked 35 cases of acute diarrhoea from among his patients: in 18 of them, it was caused by a viral infection, in 8 food allergy, in 4 spastic colitis, in 3 mucous colitis, and in the remaining 2, food poisoning. The regime prescribed for most of them was two tablespoonfuls of powdered bentonite clay in distilled water three times a day. The results, published in the *Medical Annals of the District of Columbia* (vol. 30, no. 6, June 1961) were astounding.

Clay brought relief to 34 out of the 35 in an average of under four days. Those problems due to a viral infection cleared up especially rapidly, some within 24 hours. No side-effects were noted.

How does clay bring about such rapid and effective cures? The answer seems to be the fantastic clean-up job it performs along the length of the digestive tract, mopping up toxins, viruses, bacteria, even the gases of excess intestinal fermentation, to carry them safely out of the body.

In our polluted age, clay's detoxifying powers deserve to be more widely recognized.

Due to its high mineral content, clay is also strongly alkaline and thus able to neutralize acidic body wastes – a common cause of fatigue.

An American mineralogist at the Massachusetts Institute of Technology, Dr Robert T. Martin, after long studies of bentonite clay, claims that it owes this unique cleansing ability to its large and varied mineral content, which gives it a powerful negative electrical attraction for positively charged particles. Most diseases are accompanied by congestion – an uneliminated accumulation of normal body wastes, on which viruses and bacteria can thrive. Most of these toxins, viruses and bacteria are positively charged. Clay particles are shaped like cards, with the faces negatively and the edges positively charged, so that they have vastly more negative than positive pulling power. That shape also gives them an enormous surface area – 800 square metres for a single gram of clay – allowing them to pick up, or absorb, many times their own weight in positively charged particles.

This extraordinary property of clay was tested with cultures of different bacteria by a Massachusetts bacteriologist, Dr Howard Lind. The bacterial cultures, in high concentration, were added to a liquid suspension of bentonite clay. It took 90 minutes for the clay to mop up 91–100% of *Escherichia coli* – a gram-negative bacterium responsible for a rising toll of food poisoning cases today. The clay was only a third as effective against *Staphylococcus aureus*, a gram-positive organism, removing about 33%. In lower concentrations, even *S. aureus* was 100% removed by clay.

So powerful is clay's ability to absorb wastes that even when applied externally, in the form of poultices, deep-seated toxins are gently drawn out through the skin, as in the case of the Davos TB patients.

But its detoxifying powers may not be the whole of the clay story, according to French clay expert Raymond Dextreit, who has been using it to treat patients for more than 40 years. 'Clay does not merely cure a case of constipation or diarrhoea, which is already an achievement,' says Dextreit, 'but it acts upon every organ, upon the whole body. The same teaspoonful of clay can clear up an obstinate abscess – and a case of persistent anaemia. The abscess we can understand – but the anaemia?' The mere presence of clay in the body, Dextreit believes, brings with it a powerful charge of vitality and energy which helps the body repair its deficiencies and heal itself. How else to account for the many miracles he has seen clay perform?

Clay therapy

Clay is available in several forms. If you need it in quantity – to poultice limbs, for instance – the cheapest kind is broken green clay. Clay is also available in the form of a more refined powder, in white as well as green, which is best for internal use. The French clay specialists, Argiletz, also supply a ready-mixed paste in a tube, a useful addition to the family medicine chest. If you do not buy a ready-mixed paste, the clay powder needs to be prepared before use. Put the quantity needed in a china or glass (not metal) bowl, and add enough water to cover it. Do not stir: allow to stand until all the water is absorbed – about one hour – and the clay has become a pliable paste. To warm it: stand the bowl in a container filled with hot (not boiling) water.

Insect bites or stings Apply a thick layer of clay paste and leave until the pain has subsided to draw out the toxin. This even works for jellyfish stings.

Ear ache Apply a thick layer of clay paste behind the ear, cover with gauze and leave for 30 minutes. Repeat until the pain ceases.

Bruises Apply a thick layer of clay paste and leave on for several hours.

Splinters Apply a thick layer of ready-mixed clay paste, bandage lightly and leave for two hours: if the splinter cannot be removed with tweezers, repeat the clay treatment.

Burns or sunburn If blistered, sprinkle with powdered green clay. Otherwise, apply a thick layer of clay paste to the inflamed area.

Verrucas For a single verruca, apply a thick paste of clay, cover with gauze, tape into place and leave overnight. Two or three applications will probably be enough. For more serious infestations, combine 15 drops of thuja tincture (from homoeopathic chemists), 20 drops of lemon essential oil and the contents of a garlic capsule in a little water, and use this to make up a paste with fine green clay. Apply to verrucas with a cotton bud and leave on overnight. The mix should be kept in the refrigerator.

Hangover or jet lag Stir one teaspoon of fine green clay powder into a glass of water (using a wooden spoon) and drink. Repeat the dose after two hours or so if you still feel under the weather. You may prefer to let the mixture stand until some of the clay has settled to the bottom.

Diarrhoea Prepare as for a hangover, using one teaspoon of white or green clay. Repeat every two hours for three to four doses or until symptoms subside.

Acne Apply a mask of green clay paste to the affected areas three times a week, leave on until dry and rinse off. Dutch naturopath Marijke Vogel suggests the following facial wash: dissolve one teaspoon of powdered white clay in half a glass of skimmed milk, add two drops of rosemary (not recommended during pregnancy), camomile or lavender essential oil: shake this mixture. Wipe over your face morning and evening, leave to dry and then rinse off. The mix can be kept in the refrigerator for up to three days.

Caution Clay should not be taken internally if you have just eaten a meal, if you are suffering from constipation or any other form of intestinal blockage, if you suffer from high blood pressure, if you are on prescribed medication or if you are following a course of chemotherapy. Clay which has been used for external treatment should be disposed of in your garbage, not flushed away. (For clay suppliers, see Resources.)

the good earth action plan

1. Buy organic food as often as possible. If you can't find it in a shop, supermarket or farmer's market near you, buy it on-line (see Resources).

2. Lobby your MP to urge that the government give more support for organic farming and sustainable agriculture.

3. If you have a garden, plant trees. If you do not have a garden, find out whether there is a tree-planting scheme near you that you could join.

4. Grow at least some of your own food. If you have a garden or patio you can grow fruit, vegetables and herbs. For ideas on how to make the most of the space at your disposal, study one of the many permaculture books available (see Resources).

5. Compost all your household wastes. If you only have a small garden or patio, the easiest way to do this is with the help of earthworms. They'll do all the work for you and present you with rich compost – far better than anything you could buy in a garden centre (see Resources). If you live in an apartment with no space for a compost heap, find out if your local council collect household wastes for turning into compost.

6. Buy a couple of string or cotton bags and use them for your shopping. If you do use plastic bags, take them back for re-use – or collect them and give them to local market-traders. For the big supermarket shop, ask for boxes and recycle them later, or use the Bag for Life that most of them now supply.

7. Recycle as much as possible, especially cans, which are the most costly material to manufacture in earth terms. Your local council should provide recycling facilities – if they don't, find out why not and lobby them until they do. Buy products made from recycled materials – toilet paper and kitchen paper are obvious choices. And since bleaching dioxins are some of the deadliest pollutants around – choose unbleached products.

8. Avoid buying food presented in too much packaging: meat does not need to be wrapped in individual plastic boxes, and vegetables that are presented in plastic containers have often been flown in from other countries at a huge and wasteful cost in energy.

9. Household cleaners contribute plenty of toxic chemicals to the environment, but there are eco-conscious alternatives available. A couple of good books (see Resources) will remind you of the old-fashioned non-polluting ways to clean your house using simple products like salt, vinegar and bicarbonate of soda.

10. If you work in an office that doesn't have a recycling policy for its wastes, campaign for them to set one up.

11. If there is a baby in the family, use washable nappies rather than disposables, which are non-recyclable and so end up in wasteful landfill or polluting incineration. You'll find that washable nappies are cheaper, too.

12. Buy as little plastic as possible: cane, wood, glass, china and clay are readily recycled and degrade naturally. Plastic is a problem, both in manufacturing and recycling.

13. Re-learn an unfashionable new skill: thrift. Don't replace gadgets just because there's a newer, more up-to-the-minute version available. Re-use as much as possible: containers, both sides of sheets of paper, etc.

14. Join Friends of the Earth or a similar organization (see Resources).

> 'Wild Air, world-mothering air, nestling me everywhere...
> this needful, never-spent and nursing element
> my more than meat and drink, my meal at every wink.
> This air which by life's law my lung must draw and draw...'
>
> Gerard Manley Hopkins

1 the first breath

The young earth was a barren and inhospitable planet. Four billion years ago the seas crashed endlessly on naked rocky strands; volcanoes glared and roared, rumbling in the depths of the oceans and frequently spewing their molten rock upon the desolate shores. There was no oxygen in the atmosphere, which was thick and murky with volcanic dust. But there was plenty of methane, ammonia and carbon dioxide – 'greenhouse' gases that between them trapped enough of the sun's radiant warmth in the atmosphere to save the young planet from freezing to death.

And somewhere, deep in the waters of the earth, life drew its first breath.

Life was a tiny single-celled bacterium, a few thousandths of a millimetre in size. Some of these anoxic micro-organisms lived around hot springs – the scorching vents of fumaroles pouring out acid water and sulphurous fumes into the oceans. Others flourished in surface waters, secreting a coat of slime to shield them from ultraviolet radiation. In a world without oxygen, they made a living in a variety of ingenious chemical ways, lunching off sulphur, nitrogen and carbon dioxide. For hundreds of millions of years they were the masters of the planet.

Then a new race of micro-organisms, the cyanobacteria (or blue-green algae), arrived on the scene. The newcomers evolved a much easier and more efficient way to make a living. They used light energy to combine carbon dioxide with water to produce sugars and oxygen. There was plenty of carbon dioxide, water was all around them, and there was limitless light. This is photosynthesis, the technology on which all green plants still depend for food and energy. Its originators, the cyanobacteria, could successfully replicate themselves and so multiplied throughout the oceans of earth. And photosynthesis had an interesting – and new – by-product: oxygen.

The earlier settlers survived in hidden worlds where oxygen could not reach them. They live on today in their anoxic strongholds: in the depths of the oceans, in marshes, bogs and wetlands – and in the hospitable guts of animals like ourselves. The cyanobacteria exploited a new environment of surface waters and shallows, and for nearly half a billion years they breathed out their infinitesimal puffs of oxygen. Gradually, oxygen began to build up in the atmosphere.

During all those millions of years, the cyanobacteria too were changing. In their secure world of plenty, they began to evolve. Groups of cells combined to form larger, more complex cells: families of bacteria throwing in their lot together inside a single sheltering membrane. As in a modern commune, resources were pooled and specialist skills put to work. The new improved organisms contained the green-pigmented chloroplasts that plants still use today to capture the energy of sunshine. They contained mitochondria, tiny power stations where this energy could be released. And they contained a nucleus, where sophisticated genetic software could be stored. Replication simply by splitting became yesterday's technique. Sexual reproduction took over.

Diversification became the order of the day, heralding the rich and complex tapestry of the living world as we know it.

As the percentage of free oxygen in the air rose, evolution made another giant stride forward. A new race of cyanobacteria evolved respiration techniques. They began using oxygen to break down organic matter for food and energy – a faster and more efficient process than photosynthesis. These were the first 'animal' cells. 'At first,' suggests James Lovelock in his book *The Ages of Gaia*, 'these new organisms may have existed peacefully with the photosynthesizers, merely eating their debris and dead bodies. But before long there would be consumers, organisms that had learned to eat fresh food and that grazed the photosynthesizers as they grew.'

The move from single cells to multi-celled organisms more than 550 million years ago triggered an explosion of new life-forms in the oceans and a huge diversity of shelled creatures of all shapes and sizes.

The peacefully grazing cow and the green grass of its meadow are both descended from those ancient families of cyanobacteria, and one could not exist without the other. The producers and the consumers of oxygen have lived in balance ever since.

2 the nose job

When God created man, as it is related in the Book of Genesis, 'He breathed into his nostrils the breath of life.' Our nostrils are wonderfully well adapted for this work of taking in oxygen. Shielded by bone and cartilage, they open into twin sections, lined near the entrance with tiny stiff hairs – a first line of defence against intruding dust or pollen.

Inside the nose, the cavities at the back are lined with membrane that secretes bactericidal mucus. This membrane is rich in blood vessels, which help warm the incoming breath, and it is covered with thousands of tiny, waving, hair-like cilia. Like flies caught on fly-paper, bugs are trapped and die on the sticky mucus, to be wafted to the back of the throat by the cilia and spat out or swallowed. It takes an ingenious bug to get right up your nose.

The nose does an excellent air-conditioning job, too. Even the driest, most freezing winter air is successfully warmed and moistened before it reaches the lungs. Rises in air temperature inside the nose from below freezing point to 25°C have been recorded, while the driest air reaches the lungs laden with moisture.

Breathe through the mouth, unlike Adam, and the air that whooshes into your unprotected lungs will be loaded with impurities and bacteria.

Our noses have another vital duty to perform. Thousands of years ago, they kept us out of a lot of trouble. Primitive man could smell approaching predators, anger or hostility in people, meat too putrid to eat, threatening changes in weather. In hunting, eating, drinking and sexual encounters early man was led by his nose.

Neurologist Oliver Sacks tells the story of a man who, in his early twenties, high on drugs, experienced a heightened sense of smell. The young man found that he could recognize all his friends, every street and every shop by their individual scents alone: as Sacks says, 'He could find his way round New York, infallibly, by smell.' His ancient 'smell-brain' had been briefly activated to something like the level of our remote hunter-gatherer ancestors.

In primitive man the sense of smell was an efficient early warning system: he could literally smell danger. In sophisticated modern man this sense of smell is blunted.

But the millions of tiny odour receptors in the roof of the nasal cavity can still tune in to up to 10,000 different odour molecules coming in on the breath. Our brain registers and 'reads' them individually. And since these scents may include leaking gas, food that is off and the smoke of a house fire, as well as perfume and flowers, the modern man's sense of smell can still be a lifesaver.

3 the great outdoors

We are outdoor animals. Fresh air is vital to our health and we cannot enjoy true well-being if we are often deprived of it. This truth was obvious to physicians in ancient Greece. According to Plutarch, almost all the asclepia – the health temples of Greece – were to be found on high ground, near the sea, near medicinal springs, or in pine forests where the aroma is healing for delicate lungs.

This respect for pure fresh air, cleanliness and natural hygiene was not unique to the Greeks; it was equally common to the civilization of the Indus valley of ancient India, the Cretans and the Assyrians. But by medieval times the idea that fresh air had any connection with health had faded. The wonderful battlemented castles were actually reeking slums, their wastes draining into subterranean cesspits, which spread a foul stench throughout the building.

For centuries physicians believed that fresh air was a hazard from which the old, the young and the sick must be carefully shielded.

Sickrooms were hermetically sealed and often heated to fever point. Night air was thought particularly deadly: the well-to-do slept with their windows closed, the curtains of their four-posters drawn, while in peasant houses the bed was often in a cupboard off the living room.

Such prejudices survived well into the nineteenth century. When Florence Nightingale tackled the horrors of Scutari hospital during the Crimean War – and went on to revolutionize the design of military hospitals – one of her fiercest battles was for fresh air. Outraged doctors told her the men would die of pneumonia, as she forced open the windows in foetid wards. The men survived – and the death rates from pneumonia fell. 'The very first canon of nursing,' she wrote, 'is to keep the air inside as fresh as the air outside, by night as well as by day... cleanliness and fresh air do not so much give life as they are life itself to the patient.' What would she have thought of our big modern hospitals – hermetically sealed, air-conditioned and heated?

Why is fresh air so vital for us and so therapeutic? Human history provides the answer. Our ancestors evolved as outdoor creatures, nourished by the air they breathed, and exposed to extremes of heat or cold as billions of people still are today. Our skin, our respiratory system and the complex mechanisms that keep our internal temperature constant are all part of our evolutionary response to this environment.

The out-breath is one of the body's excretory routes: out goes excess carbon dioxide, together with a cargo of cellular wastes, including lactic and uric acid. At night-time when the body devotes its energy to repair and detoxing, the production of these wastes is accelerated, and there is plenty of rubbish to be disposed of. Just go into a bedroom where someone has slept with the windows closed all night. The air will be stuffy and slightly offensive. If the sleeper reeled home late from a night on the town, it may be so foul that you wrinkle your nose with disgust. Even if you live on a busy street, the night air will still be fresher than indoors.

Dr T.R. Allinson, the English Edwardian doctor who taught his patients in the East End of London to eat wholemeal bread and take plenty of exercise, was adamant: 'Persons who sleep in unventilated bedrooms must not expect that freshness of a morning, that liveliness, that feeling of buoyancy and that go in them and relish for food that a person enjoys who keeps his bedroom window open at night.'

Our skin has been programmed over millions of years to function in fresh air, in any but the most extreme cold.

A living, breathing tissue, constantly renewing itself, skin wraps us up against the outside world. It is our cooling system in hot weather, our personal central heating in the cold. It protects us from the dangerous ultraviolet rays of the sun, while lapping up the sun's life and energy to trigger dozens of essential biological processes throughout the body. And it is, finally, an organ of excretion: it has been estimated that our body sloughs off ten billion dead cells from its outermost layer every day, cells which have absorbed wastes excreted through the skin. In a lifetime we may shed up to 20kg of this.

Fresh air enhances the performance of every one of these life-sustaining processes, stimulating the muscles in the cell walls of the millions of blood capillaries in our skin, to speed circulation both locally and throughout the system. The colder the air, the more striking this effect, which is why a brisk walk on a freezing winter day will warm you more effectively than crouching over a fire indoors.

Frequent exposure to cold, far from weakening us and lowering our vitality, is actually very invigorating. The colder the air we breathe, the more the flow of blood is speeded up in the membranes lining the nose, throat and air passages as they battle to warm the incoming air. This increased flow keeps the membrane super-healthy and efficient, enhancing our resistance and boosting our vitality. Sailors on long voyages and travellers in the Antarctic are usually immune to colds. So were soldiers in the trenches of the First World War. 'When I lived in Paris before the war,' wrote one French soldier, 'I never passed a winter without coughs and colds and rheumatics. Here in the trenches I never have a thing the matter with me and we're all like that.'

The colds that start as soon as winter sets in are seldom caused by falling temperatures: it's those closed windows that do it. An eminent physiologist, Sir Leonard Hill, explained why nearly a century ago, 'Careful observations have proved that in badly ventilated rooms in which the air was warm and stagnant, the mucous membranes of the nose become swollen, congested and covered with thick secretion. A probe pushed into the swollen membrane formed a pit, showing how boggy it was... a favourable condition for the growth of bacteria.' It is this swelling and congestion of the membrane in nose and sinus passages, Sir Leonard surmised, which largely cause the feelings of stuffiness in the head and headache felt in crowded, overheated places.

But fresh air is in short supply for modern western man. Central heating was once a luxury: today it is standard. We are urged to save fuel and keep warm by insulating our houses against even the tiniest draught. And the good work is completed with double glazing: windows that can never be flung open to the winds.

Many of us spend our days working in enclosed environments. Commuters may spend no more than half an hour of a weekday in fresh air, as they move from home to car, train or bus, to office, and the same routine in reverse at the end of the day. And in homes and offices alike, as we shall see in later chapters, the air is contaminated by emissions from the thousands of synthetic chemicals used in building and insulating materials, furniture, flooring, carpeting, paints, glues, varnishes, finishes and cleaning material. Even the clothes we wear conspire to rob our bodies of fresh air: non-porous synthetics made into sweaters and shirts, nylon underwear for women, shoes in man-made fabrics that cannot breathe.

City streets are another formidable threat to our health. In a World Health Organization study recently carried out in France, Austria and Switzerland, researchers focused on exposure to particulate pollution – tiny invisible flecks of matter easily breathed into the lungs, coming mainly from diesel vehicle exhausts. Their findings were frightening. Up to 50% of particulate pollution in cities came from traffic, causing the premature death from heart or respiratory disease of 21,000 adults a year in the three countries studied – more than double the number of adults killed by traffic accidents. It also caused respiratory problems in 500,000 people, 300,000 extra cases of bronchitis in children and sent 15,000 people to hospital with heart disease. Its total financial cost was Euro 27 billion (£17.5 billion) a year.

If you think you're safe inside your own car, think again. Unless it is fitted with a sophisticated air filtering system, levels of pollution inside may be up to 100 times higher than outside. Cars suck in fumes just where they are most concentrated. In a family car driven on a motorway, particulate pollution reached 100,000 parts per cubic cm – double the amount a pedestrian breathes. This trebled in the wake of a lorry.

Coal-fire smoke and reeking factory chimneys no longer darken our city skies, but today's pollution smog of ozone, nitrogen dioxide and particulates makes city life almost as hazardous.

air

the world we live in

4 negative and positive

Why do the pleasure gardens of princes and potentates always feature splendid fountains at play? Why are people and animals edgy when a thunderstorm is brewing – and why does the air feel so fresh after the thunderstorm has 'cleared' it? Why do people with weak lungs feel happier in clean mountain air? Why is seaside air so bracing? Why is a shower so much more refreshing than a bath?

The answer to all of these questions is ions – tiny, electrically charged particles in the air we breathe. Too many positively charged ions and we could be in trouble. Plenty of negatively charged ions and life can be brighter and better. American scientist Benjamin Franklin first demonstrated the existence of atmospheric electricity in the mid-eighteenth century. Just a century ago, scientists discovered that this atmospheric electricity was conveyed by charged particles of gas in the air. These minute, invisible molecules called ions are generated by the action of natural phenomena such as radioactive gases, lightning, cosmic rays, ultraviolet rays, air flow friction and solar activity.

In clean, unpolluted country air or out at sea, ions both positive and negative abound, and their normal balance is in a ratio of five positive to four negative – a balance comfortable for plants, animals and people. In other places, and at certain times, either positive or negative ions may build up to spectacularly high levels.

Water crashing onto rocks or falling from a height generates billions of negative ions – Niagara Falls in North America are said to be the world's biggest ionizer. The shower in your bathroom – a mini-waterfall – produces an exhilarating negative-ion boost. Negative ions also stream off the leaves of plants: the needles of pine trees are an especially prolific source. Positive ions are generated by friction – the friction between air masses, or layers of wind, or colliding weather fronts, or between air and earth, or between the air and dust or sand particles. Warm winds blowing over arid or desert areas lose their negative ions to sand and dust particles; when the air is humid, more negative ions are lost when they latch onto the droplets of moisture. This is one reason why most people are uncomfortable in humid weather.

'Witches' winds', such as the French Mistral, the Sharav of Israel or the Santa Ana of California, are loaded with positive ions and can trigger anxiety, malaise or even suicidal depression. Hours before an electrical storm arrives, the air is already loaded with positive ions – causing animals to become restless, and triggering asthma attacks in susceptible individuals.

The influence of the waxing or waning of the moon on plant germination and growth (see Earth, page 59) – long dismissed as the grossest superstition – can now be explained in terms of ion-generated biological activity. The moon at full – when it is closest to the earth – is responsible for a major build-up of positive ions in the air. And the dire influence of the full moon on mental health and well-being is enshrined in folklore.

> The importance of ions to life and well-being has always been recognized – long before their existence was even known.

When St Bernard reformed the Benedictine order in the twelfth century he ordered that new monasteries should be built near running waters – a fact reflected in their very names: Clairvaux, Riveaulx, Fountains Abbey. Hot, dusty Mediterranean cities abound with fountains in important squares or at street corners. Mountain air and pine forests, both rich in negative ions, have long been the sites of health resorts.

Although the ratio of ordinary, uncharged particles of air to ions may be of the order of trillions of billions to one, even this infinitesimal ion content in the air we breathe appears to be essential to life. In Russian experiments, small animals died within days of being left in a de-ionized atmosphere, so scientists have concluded that ions may be essential to oxygen uptake in living creatures. Ions, like T-shirts, come in three sizes: small, medium and large. Large and medium ions are effective cleansers of air, combining with particles of dust, sand, smoke or pollen and carrying them down to earth. But small ions are special: they have a wide range of biological activity, too.

Sales of small, cheap ionizers enjoyed a first boom in the 1950s, when unscrupulous American manufacturers marketed them as cure-alls. But most of the machines on offer were badly designed with a high failure rate, and eventually the US Food and Drug Administration banned their sale as medical devices – a ban still in force today. In the USA and Canada they may only be marketed as 'air cleaners'. Later models contained tritium, but since this is a radioactive isotope, they were banned in turn as unsafe.

There was another boom in the late 1970s as part of a new public love affair with 'alternative' lifestyles. By this time, most of the post-tritium ionizers on the market were producing plenty of the large and medium negative ions but none of the small biologically active ones, so although they sucked up environmental dust, pollen and other irritating particles (before spewing them out as black sticky dust onto neighbouring walls) – and thus benefited asthmatics and hayfever victims – they did not deliver on most of their promises.

Fortunately, thanks to research carried out over 33 years by Joshua Shaw of the Australian company Bionic Products, ionizers that consistently produce the small biologically active negative ions are now available. This has made serious clinical research acceptable to the medical world, and a first major trial of ionizer usefulness for asthmatics is now under way at a Melbourne university.

Further reputable research is badly needed: until very recently, most of it has been scattered and uncoordinated, and much of it so poorly designed as to carry little scientific clout. But to anyone with an unbiased mind there is certainly enough good research, coupled with serious observation by doctors and scientists, to make the subject of ions one of pressing public concern because of its health implications.

Among the most striking biological effects of high positive-ion counts is the behaviour of blood. Numbers of surgeons will not operate when 'witches' winds' are blowing. They have noted that at the time of the full moon, severe bleeding and post-operative blood clots are both much more common. One Florida surgeon kept careful records of 1000 patients operated on, and found that 82% of all serious bleeding took place around the time of the full moon.

Serotonin is a brain chemical associated with sleep, the efficiency of our immune systems and how we deal with stress. Positive-ion exposure can result in raised levels of serotonin in the brain and states of anxiety, hyperactivity, insomnia, migraine, irritability – even suicidal depression. It has been speculated that high levels of serotonin may interfere with learning and memory. In a study published in 1984 in the *Journal of Abnormal Child Psychology*, 40 normal and 33 learning-disabled fourth-grade children were divided into groups, half of whom were exposed to negative-ion treatment. All the children breathing negatively ionized air performed better at tasks involving memory, but the improvement was much greater for the learning-disabled children, who improved by 23.6%, and greater still for the mildly retarded, at 54.8%.

The charge in ions is absorbed by tiny nerve-endings in the nose so, as you might expect, both positive and negative ions have a dramatic impact on respiratory problems. Dr Albert Krueger of the University of California, one of the pioneer researchers in the ion field, exposed tissue from human airways to negative ions. He found that the beat of the tiny, hair-like cilia was speeded up from 900 to 1200 beats a minute and mucus output was increased. Positive ions, particularly when combined with cigarette smoke, had the opposite effect. Asthmatics and hayfever victims are thus obvious candidates for negative ion therapy. At two hospitals in Philadelphia, Dr Igho Kornblueh and associates sat hundreds of patients with hayfever, bronchial asthma or other breathing problems in front of negative-ionizing machines: 63% experienced total or partial relief.

Doses of positive ions may make us more vulnerable to airborne infections. When researchers introduced fungi, bacteria and viruses into the noses of small experimental animals kept in air high in positive ions, death rates following infection were high: negative ions reversed this trend. Negative ionizers can act as efficient bactericides by combining with germs in the air to render them harmless. Anecdotal accounts of negative-ion effects often mention lower rates of respiratory infections, colds and 'flu.

At Philadelphia's Northeastern Hospital, where he worked, Dr Kornblueh also tried out the effect of negative ions on patients in pain. Relief was dramatic. Over a six-month period in 1958–9, 138 patients in severe pain following burns or major surgery were treated with regular doses of negative ions. As a control, another 49 were given painkilling drugs. In well over half the patients in the study treated with negative ions, pain was eliminated or dramatically eased. Only 22.5% of the control group improved as quickly as those treated with negative ions, or to the same degree.

What happens to human beings when they are compelled to live or work in air depleted of these lifesaving negative ions, or else high in positive ions?

We are all guinea pigs, and the answers are not reassuring. Much of the 90% of our time which is spent indoors may find us inside homes, vehicles or workplaces where in ion terms the air is not fit to breathe. As will be discussed in later chapters, synthetic building and furnishing materials, air conditioning systems and electronic equipment all combine to produce an atmosphere detrimental to health. These elements exude high levels of electromagnetic radiation or volatile organic compounds (VOCs – see chapter 6), which ensure an atmosphere either ion-depleted or high in positive ions.

At Surrey University in the south of England, Dr Lesley Hawkins has researched this problem. In office buildings with metal-ducted ventilation systems – almost universal in new buildings – he found that total ion levels rarely exceeded an average of 700 positive and 200 negative. In buildings with high levels of static or particulate contamination – both very common – negative ion levels often fell to zero, though levels of positive ions sometimes soared to as high as 10,000 parts per cubic cm. When negative ionizers were installed in some offices, workers reported fewer headaches, greater well-being: they found the air fresher and less stuffy.

Emerge from that gleaming, high-rise office block to take your lunch break strolling through the streets and you may not be much better off, unless there's a park within easy reach. City air, heavily polluted by traffic, is likely to be almost as high in positive ions. Like brand-new office blocks, motor vehicles can become Faraday cages in which high levels of positive ions gradually build up, thanks to car heaters and fresh-air vent systems. As more and more drivers take to their cars after hours spent in ion-unfriendly buildings, is this one explanation for 'road rage'? Even synthetic clothing can be a hazard. Synthetic fabrics can generate a positive charge when rubbed – which is why they cling or even give off sparks when rubbed. As a result they may attract any negative ions around, thus robbing their wearers of them.

If negative ions influence the uptake of oxygen by the cells in our bodies, as scientific research suggests, may not Chronic Fatigue Syndrome (ME) be at least partly due to work among electronic equipment in new office buildings? May not negative-ion-depleted air be one explanation for the growing numbers of schoolchildren who find it hard to learn and hard to behave as they sit wearing their nice new synthetic uniforms in their modern computer-equipped classrooms? And might not hospital rates of cross-infection – notoriously high and increasingly resistant to antibiotics – be far lower if hospitals themselves, with their sealed windows, air conditioning and ubiquitous electronic gadgetry, were not swarming with positive ions?

Is it not high time that standards for ion levels were routinely imposed on all public buildings, including offices, shops, factories, hospitals, government buildings and schools? Ask your company to get an ionizer, or buy one yourself – and after the management see the effects, they should offer you your money back.

5 our wired world

If electromagnetic (EM) fields were visible light, it has been said, we should all spend every second of every day of our lives bathed in all-pervading high-intensity light, high in radiation.

The thought is not a comfortable one, but it is an accurate analogy. EM fields are no new experience for humanity. Earth, with its spinning core of molten iron, generates an enormous magnetic field known as the magnetosphere, which envelops the entire planet. For millions of years human beings have lived with this constant, natural, background radiation. However, this geomagnetic field is generated by direct current (DC) in contrast to the alternating current (AC) fields produced by man-made power generation.

The twentieth century exposed the human race to levels of radiation at least a million times higher than this – and, some argue, hundreds of millions of times higher. Today the entire planet is awash with the EM fields generated by electronic items we take for granted: domestic appliances, hundreds of pieces of computer gadgetry, mobile phones and their masts, power lines and substations, and radio and TV transmitters.

This radiation is of two forms: ionizing radiation and non-ionizing radiation. Ionizing radiation consists of very short, very powerful wavelengths of energy – such as X-rays and nuclear radiation. It took a long time before the perils of X-rays became apparent: I am old enough to have stood with my feet inside an X-ray machine in a shoe shop, wiggling my toes while I gazed fascinated at the skeletal image of my feet. It took much too long before the perils of nuclear radiation were discovered: thousands of servicemen paid with their health or their lives. The effects of non-ionizing radiation have only recently begun to be assessed. We do not know whether, or to what degree, these longer, less powerful wavelengths, which power so much that we take for granted today from domestic gadgets to mobile phones, may affect our health, although there is growing evidence that they do.

The global market in electronics has boomed with relatively little research into any harmful effects it might be having on our health, and with any regulation, taking only heating effects into account. Belatedly, the World Health Organization announced in 1996 a wide-ranging International EMF (electromagnetic field) Research Project, due to deliver its findings in the year 2005. In the USA the National Institute of Health and the National Cancer Institute have announced more research, and much more is coming from medical and science laboratories around the world.

The evidence is patchy. Much of it is dismissed as not statistically significant or only 'weakly' significant. Some of it is contradictory. But looked at in total, it is very far from reassuring.

The association between childhood leukaemia and power lines has been the most distressing and contentious research.

In the mid-1970s Nancy Wertheimer, an epidemiologist from Denver, Colorado, in the USA, began an investigation into the causes of this devastating form of cancer – known in those days as the Christmas Disease since so few children struck down survived beyond the first Christmas. With a colleague, physicist Ed Leeper, she examined the homes of 344 child leukaemia victims and compared them with the homes of healthy controls. They found that a two- to threefold increase in cancer risk occurred in homes closest to electrical transformers.

There have since been reports of 'clusters' of cancer cases and other disorders near power lines, nuclear power stations and radar facilities. Blake Leavitt, an American science journalist details these clusters in her book *Electromagnetic Fields.* In Vernon, New Jersey, the US Center for Disease Control identified an unusually high number of babies born with Down's Syndrome and other genetic abnormalities: Vernon has a number of microwave satellite link-up stations. Another cluster of leukaemia and other cancers was reported in Birmingham, England, among residents living near a 230m-high BBC radio and TV tower mounted with transmitters. And in Hawaii a twofold increase in the incidence of childhood leukaemia was reported among children living close to a US Navy communications facility.

Leukaemia is one of the most frequently reported effects of long-term exposure to radiation. In a 15-year study, Dr Stanislas Szmigielski, a Warsaw epidemiologist, found that among Polish military personnel those most exposed to radio-frequency and microwave radiation had up to eight times the expected rate of leukaemia and lymphoma.

A recent study from Canada gives an even bleaker warning. A team of researchers at the Toronto Hospital for Sick Children gave 88 children with leukaemia and 133 controls Positron meters to wear for two days to measure their exposure to EM fields. The leukaemia risk for the children with the highest rate of exposure was 4.5 times higher than for those with the lowest.

At the end of a six-year research programme on power-line health effects, the US National Institute of Environmental Health Sciences conceded that they had found a fairly consistent pattern – a small increase in leukaemia risk among children exposed at home or workers exposed on the job, although the evidence was 'weak'.

At Bristol University in the UK, Professor Denis Henshaw has shown that the electric (as opposed to magnetic) field from power lines can charge airborne carcinogens around the lines, which makes them stick more easily to the lungs when breathed in. A colleague, Dr Alan Preece, studied cancer distribution near power lines and found a 29% increased risk of lung cancer in those living 400–500m downwind of 400,000-volt lines. The National Grid Company are furiously trying to downplay the findings. If replicated, the evidence indicates that some 3000 lung cancer cases a year could be due to such exposure. This would trigger class action litigation and require National Grid to bury all lines near residences, and no more homes will be built near power lines.

In later work, Wertheimer and Leeper found an increase of up to 50% of miscarriage rates in women who slept on electrically heated waterbeds, under electric blankets or in rooms with ceiling-cable heat: the miscarriage rate, predictably, rose dramatically during the winter months. Short-term memory loss, suicides, depression, migraine, brain tumours, learning disorders and hyperactivity, cot deaths, high blood pressure, stress, Parkinson's disease, breast cancer and weakened immunity are other conditions which have been strongly linked with exposure to EM fields.

If rising levels of EM pollution were indeed responsible for some of the most disturbing medical conditions, you would expect that there would be a consistent increase in incidences of them. Isn't that what is going on?

From the beginning of the 1990s the EM pollution count has been sent spiralling upwards, thanks to the mobile phone. Count the number of mobile-phone shops next time you saunter down your local high street, note the number of mobile phones in use, take a look at the balance sheets of the global telecommunications giants. The stupendous financial clout of this burgeoning branch of electro-technology is unmistakable. By the end of the twentieth century 300 million people worldwide were already mobile-phone owners. It is a technology running far out of control, with attempts to regulate it or even understand its potential for damage lagging pitifully far behind.

Mobile phones work by bouncing signals from one transmitter mast to the next, and hundreds of thousands of these transmitter masts have already been erected. Many are near schools, hospitals and domestic housing, exposing the young and the sick as well as the rest of us to long-term, low-level electromagnetic pollution. In June 1999 international health experts met at the House of Commons in London to call for a ban on sitings within 200m of schools and homes. But the industry has been far ahead of the game. Concerned consumers in the USA, waking up to discover new masts (or cellular towers, as they are known there) sprouting within a few metres of their front doors, found that the 1996 Telecommunications Act, rushed through Congress, removed the power from local authorities to ban the towers.

Mobile-phone users themselves have been alarmed by dozens of reports of adverse effects for which their handy new toy may be responsible. Roger Coghill, a British scientist specializing in biomagnetic research at his independent laboratory, has argued for tighter regulation of the electronics industry, and writing in the UK newspaper the *Daily Mail* in July 1998, he summed up the bad news.

According to Coghill, researchers had found that signals similar to those from mobile phones could disrupt parts of the brain involved in memory and learning. They also found that the use of mobiles could lower levels of vital brain hormones, and frequent users of mobile phones had significantly lower levels of the crucial hormone melatonin, which regulates body function in hundreds of different ways, and may help protect us against cancer and ageing. According to an Australian study, higher levels of mobile-phone usage were linked with higher rates of brain cancer. Mobile phones, concluded Coghill, should carry a government health warning – along with all the other electric gadgets we find indispensable.

Some consumers are beginning to react against this technology, which they sense may turn out to be desperately dangerous. And as with pesticides and food additives, the BSE crisis and the genetically modified (GM) food controversy (see Earth, chapter 7), they are no longer prepared to accept without question official assurances that all is well. In the UK, medical editor Simon Best, assisted by Alasdair Philips, Director of Powerwatch, produces a quarterly news report, *Electromagnetic Hazard & Therapy*, which updates the public on research, developments and debate.

Evidence is now emerging that researchers may have been looking in the wrong place for answers to safety questions. When safety levels for EM exposure were first set by regulatory bodies such as the British National Radiological Protection Board in the 1950s, they were based on levels that did not cause a rise in body temperature of 1°C. The possibility of a biological effect other than that of raising temperature was ignored.

It has long been known that human brain waves have specific electrical frequencies, the slowest delta waves being associated with deep sleep and the faster beta waves linked with conscious thought. Minute pulses of electrical energy activate the human nervous system and the beating of our hearts. Human beings also generate an EM field, and have their own natural frequency. They also appear to be highly sensitive to minute fluctuations in the earth's own magnetic field in its regular 24-hour cycle. Our circadian rhythms – the internal 'clock' which governs our patterns of waking and sleeping, and such other cyclical variations as temperature and hormone levels – are cued by this cycle as well as by light.

UK biophysicist Gerard Hyland at the University of Warwick suggests that the human body is itself a highly sensitive electronic instrument with its own microwave activity. If microwave sources such as mobile phones happened to match one of these key human microwave patterns, the result could be quite dangerous. Moreover, while the frequencies found in nature are often random and fluctuating, man-made radio waves are regular and coherent, with a consistent pulsing effect.

It is these well-researched hypotheses – as well as mounting evidence of biological damage from mobile phone use – that has set regulators and governments initiating new research. They are aware that the more deadly effects on health may take years to appear. It happened with asbestos: strictly controlled since 1970, yet the death rate is not expected to peak until about 2020. It happened with smoking: tobacco companies in the USA were facing ruin late in 1999 as the US Surgeon-General threatened to sue them to recover the costs to government of the crippling tobacco-linked damage to health. It happened with X-rays: how many cancers are still developing due to over-exposure? And it may be happening with BSE: experts agree that we still do not know whether hundreds or thousands of people are at risk of new variant Creutzfeldt-Jakob Disease (vCJD).

Mobile-phone companies may be gung-ho about denying any risk to users, but quietly they are already investing millions in producing new models that reduce the radiation into the heads of users, or in non-pulsed systems that represent a lower potential risk. And scenting a huge market opportunity, a new minor industry – that of shielding devices for mobile phones – has sprung into being.

The consumers of the twenty-first century are asking more and more questions about the safety of electro-technology. The research that answers these questions is already coming up with exciting findings about the way living systems work. When we know more about the ways in which radiation can harm us, we shall know more about how it can be used for healing, too. Cancers and other diseases could well be treated even more effectively once we have more thorough research on the effects of short- and long-term exposure to radiation.

6 sick building syndrome

Do you suffer from homesickness? Thousands – maybe even millions – of people do, without ever realizing it. Home is where you feel safe. Yet your home may be contributing to your migraines, irritability, fatigue or asthma. Do you work in an office? Do you suffer constantly from headaches, a stuffy nose, dry skin, aching eyes and the unconquerable post-lunch lethargy? The modern office is not a people-friendly place. Our living and working environments have hidden hazards and can actually be making us ill. How is this possible?

Today's home and office are environments invisibly polluted with thousands of synthetic chemicals – and the cleaner, more modern and efficient they are, the more polluted they are likely to be.

The US Environmental Protection Agency accepts officially that the indoor air of homes is likely to be more polluted than air outside.

Where do all these chemicals come from? Synthetic materials used in building and insulation, fibreboard, plywood, flooring, paints, resins, varnishes and finishes are all sources of noxious chemical emissions. Modern furnishings may make a further contribution – synthetic or semi-synthetic carpets and fabrics, plastics, fibreglass and the photocopier. All of these may give off emissions known as Volatile Organic Compounds (VOCs).

Many VOCs are known to be potentially harmful to human health. Benzene, given off by paints, glues, cleaning products and synthetic fabrics, can cause headaches, eye and skin irritation, and fatigue. Ammonia from cleaning supplies can cause eye and skin irritation, headaches and sinus problems. Formaldehyde from new carpeting, wall coverings and plywood has been linked with drowsiness, respiratory problems, memory loss, depression and throat cancer. Trichloroethylene (TCE) from dry-cleaning materials, paints, glues and varnishes has been implicated in headaches and irritation of the eyes, skin and respiratory tract. In 1975 the US National Institute of Cancer Research stated that it could also cause liver cancer.

Cleaning agents make a powerful contribution to the level of VOCs.

The lemony scent of washing-up liquid, the pine-like whiff of the spray-on furniture polish, the fragrance in bathroom cleaners, washing powders, fabric softeners – all redolent of cleanliness and fresh air – contribute more VOCs. And perfumes, deodorants, bath oils, cosmetics and aftershave further compound the brew. There are hundreds more in the fast-growing ranks of products designed not so much to disguise the chemical reek of cleaning products as to produce smells supposedly desirable in themselves. Each of these synthetic perfumes may contain dozens of VOCs such as xylenes, ketones, terpenes and aldehydes, which can be toxic in high doses.

The average British householder buys 36 aerosol cans every year – but alarming research, presented at an international conference on indoor air pollution at Edinburgh in Scotland in the summer of 1999, suggests that the products may be harming those exposed to them. In a survey of 14,000 pregnant women, epidemiologists at Bristol University's Institute of Child Health found that women who used such aerosols on most days suffered 25% more headaches and 19% more postnatal depression than women who used them no more than once a week. And in babies under six months, who were frequently exposed to such aerosols, there were 30% more ear infections and 22% more cases of diarrhoea.

Very few of the hundreds of chemicals these products may contain, mainly to make them fragrant, have actually been tested – and some that have are suspected carcinogens. According to a report published in the *British Journal of Dermatology*, as many as 1 in 100 people may be allergic to some of them with reactions that include eczema and dermatitis. In studies carried out at the Anderson Toxicology Laboratory in Vermont, USA, mice exposed to airfresheners and colognes suffered irritation of the eyes and lungs, asthma-like breathing difficulties and symptoms of neurotoxicity, such as loss of balance.

Aerosols diffuse molecules of these chemicals into the surrounding atmosphere in the form of airborne droplets, which enter our lungs to be absorbed into the blood and travel right around our bodies. Other smells reach us as vapour-born particles, which bind with the olfactory receptors of which the nose houses many millions: in doing so, they trigger nervous impulses sent to the brain, which dispatch neurochemicals in response to every part of the body. And it has been suggested that some synthetic chemicals may be absorbed into our bodies through our skins, because one effect they may have is to lower the surface tension of the skin and make it more permeable.

Offices have special hazards of their own, including emissions of TCE from photocopiers, as well as ozone, which can cause runny eyes, sore throats and breathing difficulties even at quite low levels. All these and many more VOCs contribute to the noxious chemical smog in which office workers are condemned to spend their days – and the workers themselves make their own distinctive contribution in the form of VOCs from shampoos, deodorants, dry-cleaning fluid emissions, body odours, scent and aftershave.

Air-conditioning systems make sure that VOCs get well and truly broadcast. They also create an unnatural environment, often too cold or too hot, and the recirculated air easily spreads germs and bacteria around the office. Even the most sophisticated air-conditioning system can never match the great outdoors: air moving on the skin and countless small variations in temperature stimulate and enliven our entire organisms through our skin. A day spent in air-conditioned surroundings can leave you feeling drained and lethargic.

Research commissioned by a mineral water company showed that the atmosphere in some offices was as arid as the Sahara Desert. A healthy humidity level for air is 40–60%, but some offices were as low as 23%. At this level, workers become increasingly dehydrated, leaving them vulnerable to stress, infection and skin or eye problems. Hermetically sealed offices with less-than-optimal air-conditioning systems and plenty of electric equipment are the culprits.

Preliminary results from a survey commissioned by the British Health and Safety Executive in 1999 found that at least 1 in 5 workers among the 4000 studied claimed to suffer 'extreme stress at work'. Long hours, lack of job security, noise levels and bullying management were all blamed, but most of those who complained suffered from physical or mental health problems as well. No doubt Sick Building Syndrome (SBS) is a major factor in these.

Safety limits have been suggested for individual VOCs, but these do not take into account the impact of combinations of tens or hundreds that are quite normal. In experiments in the mid-1980s, Danish researchers exposed people known to suffer from SBS to a cocktail of 22 VOCs emitted by building materials. They complained of lapses in concentration and irritated eyes and airways. Each of the VOCs was at a concentration well below accepted safety levels.

Researchers from Bell Communications Research in New Jersey, USA, have pinpointed two more worries connected with VOCs. They found that the ozone emitted by photocopiers or coming in from outside can combine with VOCs to generate trillions of hydroxyl radicals, a particularly vicious form of the reactive atoms known as free radicals, which can cause molecular havoc throughout the human organism. Their activity is being firmly linked with cancer, heart problems and ageing. These free radicals also react with other VOCs to generate a second, more deadly generation of VOCs – formaldehyde, ketones, and acetic and nitric acids. Add to that the electromagnetic smog from all the electronic clutter (see chapter 5), and a total dearth of happy-making negative ions (see chapter 4), and it is no wonder that so many office workers have health problems.

One way or another, we may be absorbing substantial doses of these VOCs. And that's where the problems start. Some of them may be eliminated unchanged in breath or urine, some may be stored out of harm's way in fatty tissue, but most have to be detoxified by one of the systems of enzymes in the liver.

These systems have evolved over millions of years to cope with foreign intruders, and in most people, most of the time, they cope with synthetic chemicals as well as those found in nature. But in those particularly sensitive to such chemicals, one or another enzyme system may be weak or inoperative. In a study of chemically sensitive patients, just one enzymatic system looked at – out of many hundreds – was found to be deficient in 99% of the subjects.

So it is hardly surprising that the staggering rise in the number of these synthetic chemicals (the American Chemical Society registered its ten millionth in the late 1990s) is beginning to overwhelm the defences of the most vulnerable – babies and children. And it is no coincidence that asthma and eczema are both diseases of affluence, more common in wealthy West Germany than in polluted East Germany, or that in Australia – country of clean living and the Great Outdoors – almost 1 in 4 children is now asthmatic.

Recent studies suggest that over-clean and germ-free homes, far from protecting our children, may actually put them at risk of asthma and other allergic diseases.

In very clean homes, a child's immune system fails to reach full strength because they aren't practised at coping with germs. In the ongoing 'Children of the Nineties' study being carried out at the Institute of Child Health at Bristol University in the UK (which is following 14,000 children born in 1992), children who washed their hands more than five times a day and bathed twice a day had a 1 in 4 chance of developing asthma; children who bathed every other day had a 1 in 7 chance. Since bathrooms are favourite targets for 'fragrant' cleaners and airfresheners, and shampoos, bubble bath and soap are often high in these dubious chemicals, pollution may be as much to blame for higher asthma rates as an obsession with cleanliness.

This kind of chemical sensitivity was first recognized by a brilliant American allergy specialist, Theron Randolph, in the early 1960s. One of his disciples, a paediatric allergist named Doris Rapp, went on to make the connection between chemical sensitivities and hyperactivity in children, which is a huge and growing problem in western societies today. Forty years on, many mainstream allergy specialists are grudgingly accepting the notion of chemical sensitivity. Yet the possibility that your home, school or workplace can not only make you physically ill but also give rise to such mental problems as depression, irritability and hyperactive behaviour still has a long way to go before it is generally recognized.

At least one schools board has had the imagination to accept that such chemical sensitivities may be linked with hyperactivity and learning difficulties. The open-minded and progressive Waterloo School Counties Board in Ontario, Canada, set up a first experimental environmentally controlled classroom in the mid-1980s. Others have followed and now there are six in the state of Ontario. The eco-classrooms were built of natural materials with sealed concrete floors, wooden furniture, metal window blinds and efficient air-filtration and purification systems. Windows were made to be opened, lighting was by natural daylight (as far as possible), blackboards were replaced by white magnetic boards and odourless markers, art supplies were carefully vetted, students and teachers were asked to avoid the use of scented personal products, and pure, non-chlorinated drinking water in glass containers was always available.

The results were dramatic. A group of students who had previously had to be taught at home were able to attend school; behaviour and activity levels improved out of all recognition; and students who began being taught in the eco-classroom often recovered to the point where they could be taught in normal classrooms again.

Short of downshifting to life on a country commune, what can you do about your own home or place of work? The first and most obvious answer in an office is to make sure that the management is carrying out legal obligations to protect the health and safety of its employees. Under EU Health and Safety Regulations, for instance, your employer is obliged to have your work-station assessed in terms of your personal needs. Adjustable chairs, suitable lighting and a flicker-free screen are among points covered by the regulations.

In the home, use unscented products and try to find organic cleaning materials that limit the emissions of VOCs and will biodegrade. Open the windows so that fresh air can circulate freely, and rely less on chemical reproductions of nature. Keep flowers or plants around the house to increase the oxygen available and even help to rid the environment of VOCs.

The discovery that certain plants can mop up VOCs is one more useful by-product of space-race research.

In the late 1970s one of the US National Aeronautics and Space Administration (NASA's) chief scientists, Bill Wolverton, was faced with a build-up of VOCs in the air-conditioned, closed-system Skylab spacecraft. If plants could recycle oxygen, he speculated, maybe they could recycle pollutants, too? In experiments, he found that more than 50 plants – some of them garden favourites such as spider plant and mother-in-law's tongue – can soak up VOCs and convert them into food for themselves or the micro-organisms growing around their roots. In 1989 he used philodendrons and golden pothos (*Scindapsus aureus*) to clean up almost all the VOCs in NASA's Biohome, a tightly sealed room acting as a mock-up of a space-station. When the plants were taken out, the people inside began to complain of typical SBS symptoms – breathing problems, stuffy noses, streaming eyes and sore throats.

Since retirement, Bill Wolverton has devoted his time to this eminently useful research. Among the most efficient of these air-conditioning plants, he has found, are the beautiful – and hungry – peace lily, which flourishes on a diet of acetone, methanol, ethanol, benzene, TCE, ethyl acetate, formaldehyde and toluene. Rubber plants and poinsettias eat up more formaldehyde – one of the nastiest VOCs; *Dracaena marginata* and golden pothos dine on benzene, and the areca palm disposes of toluene.

It is by no means certain that plants in the wide open spaces of a modern block will do the same efficient clean-up job they performed in the sealed and controlled environments of the NASA experiments. What is certain is that people are happier when there are plants around.

Plants are a living reminder that there is a fresh green world out there to which we are most intimately connected, and in which for millions of years we have lived, moved and had our being. In a study of lengths of stays in hospital, it was found that patients who could gaze at a green landscape of trees, fields or gardens did far better than patients staring out at a brick, stone and concrete world.

Green is the colour of our natural habitat.

7 fear of flying

In the bright dawn of commercial aviation, the image of air travel was one of unrelieved glamour. Air hostesses were picked for their looks and advertisements showed suave men of the world accompanying chic and stylish women up the steps to the plane, wearing expressions of delighted anticipation.

That first careless rapture is gone for good. Even those travelling in the luxury seats up front seldom look forward to the journey, while the euphemistically renamed World Travellers behind them re-check their watches and yearn for touch-down. Does flying have to be so awful – especially over long distances? And can anything be done about it?

There are a number of problems about air travel which are unlikely to go away. You may not be aware of them, but on a long-haul flight you are likely to become increasingly aware of their effect on you.

The first is that of air quality. Your aeroplane is a closed artificial environment, more so than even the stuffiest office, ventilated by air drawn in through the engines and piped into the front of the cabin to be expelled at the rear. In the early years of commercial air travel, passengers enjoyed 100% fresh air, completely renewed every three minutes. Then came the fuel crisis of the early 1970s, and airlines began pressuring manufacturers for planes with ventilation systems which were less costly to run in energy terms.

In today's plane the flight deck still enjoys 100% fresh air, but the rest of us probably have to get by with a mix of 50% fresh air renewed every ten minutes and 50% filtered and recirculated.

Since the ventilation units on many aircraft can be adjusted in flight, there is no guarantee that even this miserly percentage of fresh air may not be turned down to 45% or even 40% while you sleep, to make a further significant cut in the fuel bill.

All this means that the air will contain a little less oxygen. It also means that any viruses or bacteria, as well as Volatile Organic Compounds (VOCs – see chapter 6) have a much higher chance of escaping filtration and circulating around the cabin, to your detriment. In a study often quoted by critics of aircraft conditioning, a Boeing 737 was grounded in Alaska for three hours. Three days later, 72% of the passengers had come down with a strain of 'flu identical to that from which a lone passenger on the flight was suffering at the time.

A number of countries, including Australia, insist that incoming aircraft are thoroughly sprayed with pesticides before landing. This, it is hoped, will be lethal to any unwanted pests that may have hitched a ride. It won't do anything for your health, either.

In the bad old days when in-flight smoking was allowed, poor ventilation was a lot more noticeable, and passengers were much more likely to complain. Now, they may simply wonder why they feel so stuffy and second-rate, and put it down to fatigue or lack of sleep. You can't do much about this during the flight, but going straight from a poorly ventilated plane to an air-conditioned office or hotel room for the night will make matters worse. Take time to stretch your legs and fill your lungs with good fresh air just before and after a flight.

The second problem is the air pressure inside the cabin, which is set to the equivalent of 2600m above sea level: about four-fifths of the air pressure at ground level. This is a compromise between the prohibitive cost of building aircraft strong and heavy enough to have normal ground-level pressure in the cabin, and the need to get passengers to their destination without undue risk to their health. But one result of this lower air pressure will be that you are getting slightly less oxygen than you are used to. We don't just breathe oxygen: it also fuels countless complex processes in our bodies, including the transmission of messages from our brains. So if you feel more tired or less alert than usual, blame it on the cabin pressure. You can't do much about this one either, but try not to carry out demanding intellectual work in-flight.

People may swell like a balloon during a flight: any gas trapped in closed or semi-closed cavities of the body will expand or contract as the plane climbs or descends. Most people don't notice any discomfort arising from this; the chief exceptions are people with sinus problems who may experience real pain and people with dodgy digestions who swallow too many fizzy drinks in flight. On long flights everyone should avoid fizzy drinks – from champagne to water.

The most common problems affect people with ear or upper respiratory tract infections who may experience severe pain in their ears or, in extreme cases, a burst eardrum when pressure on the tympanic membrane builds up inside the middle ear. In children and babies the middle ear cavity is much smaller, so pressure can be greater and the pain severe: this is why babies and small children often cry during descent. Swallowing, yawning, moving the lower jaw from side to side or chewing on sweets or gum may help. If they don't, try the Valsalva Manoeuvre: inhale, keep your mouth closed, close both nostrils with thumb and forefinger, and exhale quite vigorously; you should feel a pop in your ears as pressure is released. Because of the risk of burst eardrums, children with bad respiratory or ear infections should not travel – however inconvenient it may be to delay your journey.

Air sucked into the plane from the high atmosphere is bone dry. Humidity inside an aircraft, accordingly, may be as low as 1% compared to the 50% or 60% we're used to in homes and offices. This desert-dry air will dehydrate you: it may also dry and shrink the mucous membranes inside your air passages, which are your first line of defence against viral and bacterial infection. Your skin will also feel exceptionally dry, and if you wear contact lenses they could start to feel really uncomfortable. Drink plenty of water and say no to tea and coffee, which will dehydrate you further.

When you sit still for more than three hours, the blood is no longer being pumped back up to your heart by the use of calf and thigh muscles, so blood will pool in your feet and ankles, making them swell. A recent UK survey, which has horrified the travel industry as well as doctors, has shown that up to 1 in 10 passengers on long-haul flights may be at risk from 'economy-class syndrome'. Women who are pregnant or on the pill should consult their doctor before flying, as should anyone with a history of blood disorders. For everyone it is a good idea to do heel, toe and ankle exercises while you are seated, to take little walks around the plane and on stopovers to go for a really brisk walk around the terminal.

Hyperventilation is the commonest health problem among air travellers and is usually caused by fear, anxiety or stress, according to Farrol Kahn, director of the Aviation Health Institute. In his comprehensive study *Why Flying Endangers Your Health*, Kahn points out that early symptoms will be '...breathlessness followed by numbness, tingling of the face and limbs, and if it is not controlled, it can lead to muscle spasms, blurred vision, and unconsciousness.' The condition, according to Kahn, can also produce sweating, hallucinations, sleep disturbances and muscle cramps. As we shall see in chapter 11, hyperventilation can be remedied by taking in more carbon dioxide, so close the sick-bag thoughtfully provided by the airline around your nose and mouth, breathe into it, and then inhale.

Perhaps the worst of all problems confronting the long-haul air traveller is jet lag, which can wreck the first days of a holiday or significantly impair vital business, performing or negotiating skills, which may be on call within hours of landing.

Fly right around the globe and by the time you're back to where you started, you will have crossed 24 time zones, clocking up an hour's difference from your own local time with every zone.

Since all your body's rhythms are set by your own internal clock – which has never heard of time zones – long-distance travel is like switching straight to the night shift rota at the end of the day shift, and then back again before you've had time to adjust.

This enforced resetting of all your bodily systems to a different time schedule can be acutely debilitating. Kahn quotes a US study in which fit and healthy young soldiers were flown from Texas to West Germany, and carefully monitored over the next few days. Both physical strength and the ability to think straight were seriously affected, and even five days later not everybody was back to normal.

A health-writer friend, Jan Fairfax, has evolved her own strategy for coping with the rigours of long-distance travel and jet lag. 'For a couple of days beforehand, I try to think myself forward into a new time zone

– go to bed earlier, get up earlier. For the flight I wear loose and comfortable clothing – a cotton tracksuit is ideal. My in-flight bag contains a head pillow, then I can use the one they hand out on the plane for the small of my back. I use good light-excluding goggles, too. About 10–20 minutes before I want to go to sleep, I take 1–3mg of melatonin. I also pack two small bottles of essential oils – lavender to make me sleepy, which I inhale at night-time, and rosemary to wake me up in the morning. For a trip to Japan I borrowed a set of light-visors, which shine bright light into your eyes. I was wide awake and felt no jet lag on the trip, while my companions were zonked for four to five days.'

Getting a decent night's sleep – as opposed to a few hours' restless catnapping in your cramped seat – is half the jet-lag battle. And melatonin is the body's own natural sleep-inducer. In countries such as the UK, where its over-the-counter sale is illegal due mainly to safety concerns, doctors can prescribe it. Synthetic sleeping pills are a poor second best, since they tend to inhibit the deep rapid-eye-movement phase of sleep, which is the most refreshing, and you wake up feeling dazed, stale and tired. Herbal sedatives don't have this disadvantage: experiment beforehand to find one that works for you. Hops, passionflower and valerian are among the most effective: valerian also helps calm the jitters which so often keep air travellers awake. Pharmacies as well as healthfood shops sell a wide range of herbal sleeping remedies in which these three usually feature.

Aromatherapist Daniele Ryman has evolved a jet-lag pack featuring blends of essential oils for a wake-you-up or put-you-to-sleep bath on arrival at your hotel. Or you can improvise with tiny bottles of clary sage or lavender as sleep-inducers, and rosemary, geranium or pine as morning revivers. Put ten drops of one of these oils in your bath.

Eat and drink lightly on your flight, as even robust digestive systems can be affected by the stress of travel. Have a glass of good wine with dinner – but skip the post-prandial brandy. And take camomile or lime-flower tea bags for a calming herbal infusion instead of coffee.

8 climate change

Something alarming is happening to our planet.

The global temperature is climbing slowly but steadily, producing changes of climate, disturbed patterns of growth and breeding, and freak weather conditions all around the world. Record temperatures were registered in the 1980s and 1990s: July 1998 was the hottest month ever recorded in the UK.

In northern Europe, spring comes earlier every year. Farmers are battling pests normally killed off by winter frosts. Winters are warmer and wetter. And whatever happened to our regular white Christmas? Encouraged by warmer waters, fierce tropical fish are invading the Mediterranean. Searing heatwaves in Greece and Turkey are too much even for sun-loving tourists. Drought is hitting southern Spain harder and lasting longer – five years in the early 1990s. In parts of the southern Sahara, deserts are on the move, turning once-fertile lands into dust bowls and whipping up storms that send billions of tonnes of red sand eddying around the world, to fall as far away as Miami and Brazil: coral reefs are among the casualties. Tropical pests are already spreading into more temperate zones: malaria could return to North America or Europe.

Alaska's spruce forests are being eaten up by bud worms and bark beetles, flourishing in earlier springs and longer, warmer summers. Warmer winters and drier tundra are contributing to the disappearance of the grizzly bears, the caribou, the wolves and the foxes, on which the Inuit depend for food and clothing. And in the Arctic, polar bears, whales, seals and walruses are dying as their icy habitats retreat northwards.

The polar ice cap itself appears to be melting – in the last 20 years an area the size of France has already gone and the remaining ice is one-third thinner. Nowhere in the world have temperatures risen faster than they have at the poles – an average of 1.5°C in just three decades.

As patterns of climate destabilize around the world, freak weather and devastating natural catastrophes become more frequent. The 1990s saw a threefold rise in disasters. In 1998 alone there were killer ice storms in Canada, drought and raging forest fires in Indonesia, floods in the Sudan, Mexico and China, where the flooding Yangtze river killed 4000, and Hurricane Mitch devastated the Honduras, killing 10,000 and wrecking the national banana-based economy.

Natural catastrophes, particularly in southeastern Asia, are often triggered by El Niño, a surge of warm water from west to east of the Pacific which periodically disrupts weather patterns for thousands of kilometres around, giving rise to drought and forest fires, tornadoes, typhoons and hurricanes. The solid evidence of a connection with global warming isn't yet delivered, but the facts are extraordinarily suggestive. In the past five centuries there have only been nine really strong El Niños. None has come after less than a 20-year interval – except for the last two, in 1982–3 and 1997–8. And El Niño of 1997–8 was by far the most destructive ever recorded.

A new term has entered the language – environmental refugees, people driven from their homes by flood, quakes, deforestation...

By 1999 they numbered around 25 million. This is global warming in action. If it continues, it's a doomsday scenario for human life.

As the Arctic ice melts, rising sea levels could submerge Amsterdam with its canals and pretty gabled houses, low-lying parts of London, all of Manhattan, and countless cities and small towns along thousands of kilometres of the world's coastlines. Climate change could also have the opposite effect, according to some well-researched projections. Northern Europe is around 5°C warmer than the northeastern US and Canada in the same latitude. This is because the Gulf Stream brings warm waters north from the tropics and releases their heat into the cold northern atmosphere to keep our winters mild. Rising temperatures and extra freshwater flow into the Arctic from melting ice could disrupt this coastal central-heating system to lower northern Europe's temperatures drastically: we might find ourselves facing a new Ice Age, with winter-time temperatures dropping 10°C and more.

There are sceptics who still insist that these fluctuations in weather are no more than a normal blip in global patterns of wind and ocean currents, of the kind that has repeatedly plunged the earth in and out of Ice Ages. But international scientific consensus has now firmly fingered the true culprit: huge amounts of carbon dioxide being pumped into the atmosphere, most of it by human activity. A heavy gas, carbon dioxide traps the sun's radiance as it is bounced back from the earth's surface, to warm us up in the celebrated greenhouse effect.

For billions of years, this carbon dioxide was captured by vegetation and locked away inside the earth's crust. Slowly it was transformed into gas, coal and oil. Mining and burning of these fossil fuels began in earnest during the nineteenth century to power the Industrial Revolution. Carbon dioxide levels in the atmosphere have been rising ever since: by the 1990s they were 30% higher than in 1850. Millions of hectares of razed or burning forests have also contributed, by the loss of their collective absorption of carbon dioxide. And the internal combustion engine sends billions more tonnes of carbon dioxide into the stratosphere, with no sign of these emissions levelling out, let alone falling. Other greenhouse gases are methane, farted out by over a billion cattle, and the infamous chlorofluocarbon (CFC) gases, used in aerosols and refrigerators and phased out by the Montreal Treaty of 1987.

Not even politicians with powerful big-business lobbies could resist the urgency of the crisis: in 1997 160 nations met in Kyoto to agree goals for reducing fossil-fuel emissions. Their response was dismally inadequate. The United Nations' Intergovernmental Panel on Climate Change had called in 1990 for immediate cuts of 30% below current levels. At Kyoto a cut of just 5.2% was agreed reluctantly, to be achieved over more than a decade. By Christmas 1999 the US Congress had not even agreed to this modest proposal. The USA alone sends 1.6 billion tonnes of carbon dioxide into the atmosphere annually.

But the mere fact of governments agreeing on any action at all has had one hugely significant effect: it has transformed public awareness. When even governments admitted there was a problem, it was no longer possible to denounce environmentalists as scare-mongers and doom-merchants. If Friends of the Earth had been right all along, perhaps it was time to start listening. And as this realization has sunk in, so too have much more optimistic and comforting truths.

Solutions to the environmental crisis proposed in the 1960s focused on a hair-shirt future in a low-energy world: give up your car, toss away your dishwasher and TV, switch off the central heating for good. Renewable energy sources? Maybe, but long after our lifetimes.

The space race has been criticized as a gigantic waste of resources that should have been devoted to problems nearer home. In actual fact, half the technological problems of developing cheap energy from renewable sources have been cracked by space-travel research, and the solutions to other problems have been at least suggested.

At the start of a new millennium it is already clear that, within decades, cheap energy from solar, wind, wave, biomass or hydrogen will be a reality in a cleaner world, supplying all our energy needs and more – and two of the oil giants, BP and Shell, are putting more money and resources into developing them than anyone else. The European Union is deeply committed to the development of these alternatives – to which it gave a push in May 1999 with its Campaign for Take-Off, announcing a series of goals for Europe. Most northern European countries are developing the technology of renewable energy, which will eventually bring the prices down. Even now, as green energy becomes available on their local grid, millions of consumers around the planet are cheerfully opting to pay more than they would for power from fossil-fuel sources. They are all the more willing to do so since they are beginning to see the results of global warming at home. Typhoons, tornadoes, hurricanes, drought, raging forest fires, ice storms and killer heatwaves: the USA saw it all in the 1990s. And in the autumn of 2000 the UK had its own taste of extreme weather – in the shape of tornadoes, hurricanes and floods.

Developed countries already have much of the technology needed to speed up the switch to renewable energy. Given serious commitment on the part of governments in the form of public investment, taxes on pollution and tax breaks, growth could be phenomenal. But inertia, fear of electoral unpopularity, the power of fossil-fuel lobbies and sheer myopia are stalling progress, while in the oil and other industries dinosaurs still fight in defence of the status quo.

Yet big business is slowly getting the message that the economic price tag on global warming might well be far higher than the costs of a shift away from fossil fuel. No industry is more alive to this possibility than the insurance industry, as it reels from a decade of catastrophes. As Jeremy Leggett, former Science Director of Greenpeace, was quoted as saying in *The Ecologist* magazine, 'Given only a slight increase in the scope for windstorms, drought-related wildfires, and floods, the $2 trillion insurance industry would be in danger of global collapse, with knock-on economic consequences which are completely ignored in most analyses of climate change.'

It will be some years before wind, wave, biomass or solar power are in serious competition with fossil-fuel energy. But as production rises, costs will come down and fossil fuels will be priced out of the market the way that nuclear energy – with its huge start-up and decommissioning costs – already is.

There are still voices raised in defence of nuclear energy as a 'clean' alternative to fossil fuels, but no sane person could be an enthusiast for an energy whose deadly wastes will continue to threaten life and health on the planet for over 20,000 years.

The switch to clean power will not solve all the problems of an overcrowded planet, but it is one of the most urgent, and the use of clean renewable energy brings many other benefits, too.

Think of cities without a summer roofing of smog. Think of streets where you can breathe without inhaling a lungful of exhaust gases. Think of the extra money available for schools, public works and health prevention measures because it is no longer swallowed up by the huge costs of pollution. Think of hundreds of thousands of new jobs created by the flourishing renewable energy industry. Think of developing countries who can exploit their own natural resources – sunshine, wind, wave power – for their energy needs, instead of bankrupting themselves signing fossil-fuel cheques.

Think of a cleaner, greener world.

air clean energy

9 zero emission

What is the biggest polluter on the planet? There can only be one answer: the motor vehicle, environmental curse of the twentieth century.

By the year 2000, according to estimates from the UK's Society of Motor Manufacturers and Traders, there were around 750,332,811 motor vehicles on the road worldwide. Collectively they emitted an estimated 5000 million tonnes of carbon dioxide annually, as well as poisons such as nitrogen oxides, carbon monoxides and hydrocarbons, while diesel-powered vehicles spewed out millions of tonnes of deadly particulates. Any fall in these pollution levels due to new lower-emission cars has been more than wiped out by steady year-on-year increases in the total number of cars. The current western passion for gas-guzzling sports utility vehicles hasn't helped much either.

The oil on which these millions of vehicles run has fuelled wars and revolutions, turned petty sheiks into billionaires and bankrupted tiny nations. The roads on which they travel have covered millions of square kilometres of countryside with concrete. The fumes they belch out warm the planet, choke cities and poison people.

Yet which of us would be without a car? No wonder that automaking is the world's number one industry, closely followed by oil, and that in some countries it employs up to 20% of the labour force.

Governments mess with the auto-industry at their peril – which makes it all the more astounding that this industry could be in the process of saving the planet. For such a paradoxical scenario, we shall be indebted to an early Victorian invention – the fuel cell.

In 1836 Sir William R. Grove, a Welsh judge and amateur scientist, demonstrated a device of his own invention, in which hydrogen and oxygen reacted on platinum electrodes to produce electricity. This is the fuel cell, a scientific term set to become as familiar in the twenty-first century as the microchip was in the twentieth.

More than a century later, the US National Aeronautics and Space Administration (NASA) chose the fuel cell for its manned space flights: safer than nuclear and cheaper than solar. The Gemini and Apollo spacecraft were powered by fuel cells. At that time, however, nobody considered using fuel cells for cars: they would have been impossibly heavy and hopelessly costly.

Fuel cells can either use hydrogen directly, or else any fuel containing hydrogen – methanol, natural gas, petrol, diesel via reformers – or electrical energy from solar, wind converted into hydrogen or biomass, even gas from landfills and waste-water treatment.

We shall never run out of hydrogen: it is the lightest and most abundant element in the universe.

Hydrogen could also be the cleanest element in the universe, since when combined with oxygen to produce electricity and heat, there's just one by-product: water.

But there were awesome obstacles to the exploitation of hydrogen as an economically viable clean fuel. The fuel-cell technology that has been adopted by almost all leading car-makers was developed by a Canadian company, Ballard Power Systems, and needs small amounts of the metal platinum as a catalyst. But platinum is expensive because it is an extremely rare metal, much in demand for jewellery and surgical instruments as well as for the catalytic converters of conventional cars.

Hydrogen itself only remains liquid at temperatures far below the freezing point of water (-253°C), making transport and storage an almighty headache. And if vehicles ran on hydrogen alone, where would they refuel?

Events in the 1990s began concentrating the minds of auto-makers – especially in the USA. In 1990, California had passed a law that by 2003 10% of all cars sold in the state would have to be zero emission. Californians buy two to three million cars annually – a market too huge to be ignored. It was obvious that legal limits for emissions around the world would follow. And while much had been done to clean up exhaust emissions, the numbers of cars on the roads was rocketing, wiping out any gains from these improvements.

The Gulf War of 1996 highlighted the folly of a major industry dependent on oil from the powder keg of the politically unstable Middle East. Auto-makers in the USA were also under heavy pressure from a government keenly aware of the $5 billion monthly import bill for oil, and concerned about rocketing levels of greenhouse gases from exhausts. But for some time they continued to drag their feet. The feedback they were getting showed that fuel economy was low on the wish-list of wealthy American car-buyers, who enjoy the world's cheapest petrol: performance, safety and comfort were the priorities. 'Green' was an optional extra.

In September 1993, in response to the situation, President Bill Clinton's government announced the setting-up of the Partnership for a New Generation of Vehicles (PNGV), in which Chrysler (now Daimler–Chrysler), Ford and General Motors – the Big Three of the world auto industry – were partners along with government agencies, universities and national laboratories. Its objective was to develop high-performance vehicles with low emissions and up to three times current fuel efficiency. The deadline: 2004.

Early PNGV discussions pinpointed two possibilities. The hybrid car – in which on-board electricity is generated by small amounts of conventional fuel – was the easier of the two options. Today there are plenty of people in the USA happily running around in hybrid full-size compact family cars by Honda or Toyota that do 80–100 miles per gallon, with perhaps 20% of the emissions of conventional cars.

The alternative was the fuel cell, which was considered the better option. It will be a while longer before you can order a fuel-cell-powered car. Some experts reckon it will take 10–15 years before there are significant numbers of fuel-cell cars out on the streets. But Daimler–Benz AG gave a massive push to the Hydrogen Revolution when they announced in April 1997 that they were not only buying a 25% interest in Ballard but also planning to sink $150 million into creating a vehicle fuel-cell company jointly with Ballard. Beginning in 2005, they said they would be turning out 100,000 fuel cells annually, but also Chrysler has pledged to have their model ready – at a competitive price – by 2004. So the race is on and there is cut-throat competition to be first, with the governments of Canada, Japan and Germany all promoting fuel-cell development with tax credits, low-interest loans and subsidies.

'As always, progress has come through a series of breakthroughs – a combination of getting down material costs, and developing cheaper methods of manufacture to produce lower per-unit costs,' says Robert Evans of the UK's Johnson Matthey. His company's contribution has been to develop ways of cutting the amount of pricey platinum needed. 'But the real breakthrough has been Ballard's development of small, compact, low-cost solid polymer fuel cells.'

In the short term, fuel-cell cars will probably run on hydrogen generated by using methanol. In the long run, they'll use hydrogen directly – and they'll need countrywide networks of hydrogen filling stations. But even that may not be light-years away. Most of the big oil companies – almost all now becoming 'energy companies' – have hydrogen subsidiaries up and running.

The California Fuel Cell Partnership, set up in 1998, is already addressing the problems of the infrastructure that the new Hydrogen Age will call for. Already there's a Shell hydrogen filling station in Hamburg, Germany. In the *New Scientist* of 1 May 1999 a Shell spokesman explained the Shell response to the new fuel possibilities.

'We are at the peak of the oil age, but the beginning of the hydrogen age.'

This problem doesn't arise for vehicle fleets that can be fuelled at base, and the taxis, buses and delivery vans that clog city streets could be running on zero-emission hydrogen within the foreseeable future. And it's a future that is coming close thanks to the new relatively inexpensive fuel cells developed by Zetek Power.

'We work in the realm of the possible and the deliverable,' says Zetek Power Director Nicholas Abson. 'We actually manufacture our own fuel cells all the way from raw material to finished product – the only thing we buy in is the catalyst, and until recently that was platinum. Now we've developed a non-noble-metal catalyst that doesn't need platinum and that guarantees supply, because platinum is one of the rarest metals on the planet – there's only about 14,000 tonnes of the stuff between the earth's surface and one kilometre down. That's just about enough platinum for cars (at what price?) – and that's it. Our advantage is not to be dependent on platinum, so we can produce fuel cells relatively inexpensively. I reckon we'll be below the cost of conventional commercial vans in five to six years' time'.

The Zetek Power electrochemical engine uses hydrogen from air to produce water and electricity. The water is the only 'emission': the electricity is stored in on-board batteries for use by a powerful electric motor, giving the same if not better performance than conventional taxis, and once its capital costs come down, the Zetek Power hydrogen-powered vehicle will be up to 50% cheaper to run.

In the hydrogen-powered vehicle of the future, the loudest noise will be the clock: the running engine itself will be noiseless.

Sea-going vessels can also run on the Zetek Power electrochemical engine – and marine engines not only pump pollutants and greenhouses gases into the air, they make seas and rivers filthy as well.

'In poorer Asian countries, it is the bicycle rather than the truck or van that is the chief means of transport,' pointed out Marvin Maslow, head of US company Manhattan Scientific, at the launch of their prototype clean, non-polluting Hydrocycle. 'Huge amounts of goods are transported through cities by scooters powered by heavily polluting two-cycle engines. These societies are literally choking on gas and diesel.'

Cars, sea craft, commercial vehicles and bicycles are just the beginning. Cheaper fuel cells are bringing the Hydrogen Future ever closer. In that future, they won't be used simply for running cars. Your home could have its own refrigerator-sized generator in the basement running on any energy available, from solar to natural gas, and supplying electricity, heating and hot water: surplus electricity could be sold back to the national grid. Hospitals, factories, office blocks and schools could all be powered by fuel cells using one fuel that is never going to run out on us – hydrogen. Even laptops and other portable electronics could be running on hydrogen before the century is much older.

Hydrogen-powered vehicles will do nothing to save our roads and city centres from traffic congestion, but they could save the planet from the polluting emissions of millions of cars. Decades from now, we shall at last be able to dispense with polluting fossil fuels, thanks to fuel cells – which would never have made it to the market-place without the competitive pressures of the world's auto industry.

'Fuel cells have been the technology just around the corner for ages,' commented Norm Claesen of the Rocky Mountain Institute, 'now they're actually happening. A few years down the road they'll be doing everything from soup to nuts. Right now it's cutting edge; in a few years any architect planning a large building will think about them.'

The billionaire countries have already seen the writing on the wall. In an interview with the UK newspaper the *Sunday Telegraph* on 25 June 2000, the former Saudi Arabian oil minister Sheikh Jamani prophesied a sharp drop in oil prices by around 2005, to be followed at some time in the future by their collapse. The impact of new fuel cell technology, he commented, will be particularly dramatic. 'Thirty years from now there will be a huge amount of oil – and no buyers. Thirty years from now, there is no problem with oil. Oil will be left in the ground. The Stone Age came to an end not because we had lack of stones, and the oil age will come to an end not because we have lack of oil.'

10 reaping the wind

Until windmills were invented, grain had to be ground, wood sawed and water pumped by sweating manual labour or with the help of domestic animals. Then, around 2000 years ago, some unknown genius worked out a way to harness wind power. China, Afghanistan and Persia (now Iran) were the first countries to capitalize on this inexhaustible source of energy. By medieval times, windmills had reached the Middle East. Observant German crusaders took the idea back to Europe for use on their own farms and forestry businesses. And there the idea caught on fast.

Soon there were tens of thousands of windmills in England, Germany and the Netherlands. By 1650 there were around 50,000 at work in Europe. It was windmill power that finally made it possible for the Dutch to reclaim huge areas of their low-lying country from the ever-hungry seas. Simon Stevin (1548–1620), Holland's Surveyor of Water Works, devised a special windmill to pump the water from inland lakes and waterways to create polders, where life could at last be lived in some security behind huge protective dykes.

Over the centuries the design of the primitive windmill was refined and improved. The fantail was invented – an outsize version of the arrow on a weather vane – which kept the sails angled into the wind. The wooden sails in turn were updated by the use of slats like a venetian blind, which could be opened or closed simultaneously on each sail, by a lever inside the mill. Powerful mills like these supplied the energy for the early decades of the UK Industrial Revolution.

But the windmill was doomed by the invention of the steam engine. By 1900 the number of working windmills in Europe had shrunk to around 10,000. Holland alone had boasted as many as this in the heyday of the windmill; today only 800–900 survive. With plenty of cheap coal, oil and gas to supply energy, who needed windmills in the early twentieth century?

Only the far-sighted Danes stayed with wind power, a natural resource for their small northerly peninsula.

Early in the twentieth century they had developed a new technology, the wind turbine, which harnessed wind power to produce up to 1kW of electricity. Within a decade the USA, too, was producing battery-charging wind turbines.

The oil crisis of the early 1970s touched off a general reappraisal of renewable energy sources, other than nuclear. None, at this time, could begin to compete with oil or coal in economic terms, but wind power at least was developed enough to suggest it could be competitive in the near future, given enough investment.

The US government launched an incentive programme of tax breaks for the installation of wind turbines, after a government study had pinpointed three particularly promising sites in California, all of them big windswept mountain passes. In the ten years from 1982, around 12,000 wind turbines were set up in California, generating enough electricity for a city of one million people. Modern wind-turbine towers, with their triple spinning blades, convert energy directly into electricity using a generator coupled to the turbine shaft through a gearbox. The biggest wind turbines so far in action can generate up to 1MW – enough to supply 400–500 homes.

The Danes have never lost their head start in the race to improve and develop wind-power technology, greatly aided by huge public enthusiasm. Most of the country's wind turbines are rural co-operatives of 30–40 families. The turbines are connected to the electricity grid, to which any surplus can be sold back. Today, Denmark dominates the wind-energy industry, with a $1 billion share of a world market estimated at $2 billion in 1999. More than 10% of Denmark's energy needs in 1999 were being met by wind power.

Spain is a close rival. Until the mid-1990s, wind power made a relatively insignificant contribution to the country's power needs, but by the end of 1999 nearly 3000 wind turbines were feeding power into the Spanish grid. By the end of 2000 wind power was expected to yield a total of 2500MW, with Galicia expecting to generate 45% of its power from wind by 2005.

Among renewable energy sources, wind power is the big success story, just as it is the most advanced technologically. Over the 1990s its rate of expansion has been a staggering 25.7% annually – and the growth shows no signs of abating, creating thousands of new jobs in countries that have had the foresight to invest in wind. Given the world-market potential, this is hardly surprising.

The energy needs of the UK – which in 1999 had only a meagre 341MW of wind-energy capacity – could be met many times over by wind and wave power combined, according to industry estimates. A Greenpeace study suggests that over 30,000 jobs would be created. The Washington-based World Watch Institute, an organisation dedicated to the promotion of an environmentally sustainable society, believe that 'China has clear potential to become a wind superpower – with abundant wind resources in several regions, including a vast stretch of Inner Mongolia that could be the Saudi Arabia of wind power.'

Not everybody loves windmills, in spite of the clean power they offer. The earliest wind turbines drew violent objections as noisy, unsightly blots on a rural landscape – exactly the same complaints as were made about windmills in the seventeenth century. But modern wind turbines are virtually silent, and their slender towers can have an austere elegance – a claim that could never be made for electricity pylons. Offshore wind turbines – a growing sector of the industry – may be one answer to such objections.

Given the chance, many may be ready to pay a premium for the clean power of wind. In Colorado, USA, consumers have had a choice since 1996 between wind and cheaper coal power. Business-sponsored local radio commercials remind them that for every $1 they pay to their local utility it will burn 14lb of coal. If they spend an extra $10 a month on wind power, they'll keep 10,000lb of carbon dioxide out of the atmosphere. By the summer of 1998, around 10,000 Colorado families, as well as local big businesses such as Coors, IBM and the telephone giant USWest had signed up to pay extra for wind.

Given the choice, probably millions of green-minded consumers would do exactly the same.

air therapy

11 the power of conscious breathing

Take a minute to observe your breathing. Is it hurried or leisurely? Shallow or deep? Regular or ragged? And how are you breathing – through your nose or through your mouth? Few people pay this kind of attention to their breath, and why should they, they might ask? Breathing comes as automatically as – well, breathing, doesn't it?

Unlike almost any other bodily function, breathing can be a conscious as well as an unconscious process. We can take charge whenever we want to, decide to hold our breath, to slow it, or to breathe more deeply. But most of the time breathing does indeed come automatically, directed for us by centres in the brain stem in response to changes in bodily levels of oxygen or carbon dioxide. The heaving chest of the ballerina, after her five-minute solo, is her body's automatic response to a desperate need for more oxygen.

Other factors influence our unconscious breathing patterns. Emotions such as rage, anxiety, grief and terror all produce characteristic distortions of breathing harmony. So do tensed shoulders and slouched posture, or breathing through the mouth rather than the nose, or drinking too much coffee, or working in a stuffy, poorly ventilated room.

Until quite recently, it has been the view of western science that these shifts and irregularities in breathing are of no great importance:

the body continues to be supplied with enough oxygen to keep it going. Few western doctors question their patients about the way they breathe. But even at the purely physical level, it makes obvious sense to ensure that every single cell in our bodies receives a smooth and regular supply of the oxygen on which we depend. Slow and rhythmic breathing does exactly that, improving your circulation to ensure a dependable supply of oxygen and nutrients to those billions of hungry cells. Heart, respiratory and digestive systems all function better. And the consequences are not only physical.

Advances in neuroscience have demonstrated, even to sceptics, that there is literally no boundary between mind and body. Both interact in what pioneer neuroscientist Candace Pert has described as a psychosomatic information network, linking psyche – mind, emotion and soul – to our material envelope of molecules and cells. Grief, rage, anxiety, love – all the emotions that swirl through our minds – are carried around the network by billions of neuropeptide messengers. There are receptors for these messengers not just in the brain but in the immune system, the autonomic nervous system, the gut and the respiratory system. Thus changes in the rate and depth of your breathing can have a dynamic impact on your state of mind as well as your body – as anybody knows who has ever paused to slow their breathing at moments of acute stress, panic or pain.

In systems of oriental philosophy thousands of years old, proper breathing is considered so fundamental to health, and to life itself, that wise men have spent a lifetime in its study.

To them, breathing is far more than a gaseous exchange in the lungs, air far more than a mix of oxygen and nitrogen with a dash of carbon dioxide. Through breathing we take in life itself – the *prana* of the yogi, the *chi* of Chinese Taoist, the cosmic energy which sustains and permeates all life, from the smallest blade of grass to the universe itself.

The *pranayama* of the yogis means, literally, the extension or expansion of this energy through control of the breath. *Chi kung* can be translated as 'the cultivation of energy'. Instead of the jerky or gulping breathing so common today, the mind is conditioned to impose order, pattern and harmony on the process. Even unconscious breathing becomes slower and more harmonious. 'Full use of this absorption and re-absorption of energy,' wrote famous yoga teacher B.K.S. Iyengar, 'will allow one to live a hundred years with perfect health of body, clarity of mind, and equipoise of spirit.'

Yoga and tai chi (or chi kung) are forms of exercise designed to establish this control, to harness this cosmic energy through the rhythmic diaphragmatic breathing patterns they impose. Anyone who practises one of these disciplines regularly will tell you how amazingly energizing to mind and body an hour of this exercise can be.

Breathing techniques

Even a few minutes a day of gentle attentive breathing can help you feel calmer, more clear-headed, more in control of your life, and the best way to acquire good breathing habits is in the context of regular classes with a skilled teacher. Below are listed some of the most widely practised breathing techniques; exercise is too strong a word for these slow, attentive practices, which need to be done when you have time at your disposal. Most of them, you will note, start with an out-breath, the exact opposite of the 'take a deep breath' school of physical training, which can encourage gulping breathing. (See also pages 135–8).

Diaphragmatic breathing Find a quiet place and lie down on a firm surface, with a cushion under your head. Focus on areas of tension in your body and try to release them. Breathe OUT gently, as slowly as possible, and don't stop exhaling until your body spontaneously breathes IN for you. Gently and slowly breathe OUT again: exhalation should take twice as long as inhalation.

Alternate nostril breathing According to yogic teaching, this will balance, calm and revive you. Sit on your heels on the floor or in a chair, back straight, eyes closed, left hand resting on your thigh. Breathe IN slowly, then use the thumb of your right hand to close your right nostril, while you breathe OUT through your left nostril, then breathe IN again. Now release the right nostril while you use your fore- and middle fingers to close your left nostril and gently breathe OUT through the right nostril. Breathe IN and repeat the entire cycle. All these breaths should be gentle and unhurried.

Relaxation breathing Stand with your feet well apart and your arms by your sides. Breathe OUT slowly. Then breathe IN slowly through your nose as you raise your arms above your head, palms facing each other. Slowly bend forward from the hips as you breathe OUT until your head, arms and whole top half are hanging down loose and limp, arms dangling like a rag doll. Relax everything. Now breathe IN again as you slowly uncurl, vertebra by vertebra, letting your arms fall to your sides and bringing your head up last of all.

Abdominal breathing Sitting with your spine straight, eyes closed, imagine your head is a ball held aloft on a jet of water, shoulders down and relaxed, breathe OUT slowly and deeply through your nose: you will feel muscles working all the way down into your stomach as you push out the last sigh of air. Then breathe IN through your nose, slowly and quietly. Repeat seven times.

Humming breathing Sit straight and breathe IN normally. Breathe OUT slowly and evenly through your nose, make a humming sound that you will feel vibrating at the back of your head and neck. The hum should last as long as the out-breath. Breathe IN and OUT slowly without humming. Repeat the humming on alternate exhalations. This exercise will make you feel both alert and peaceful.

Tranquillizing breathing America's favourite health guru, Dr Andrew Weil, teaches this yogic breathing exercise to all his patients, asking them to do it at least twice a day, though not for more than four breaths at a time in the first month. In his book *Natural Healing, Natural Medicine*, he calls it 'the single most effective relaxation technique I know'. Many people I know have benefited from this technique, claiming it gives them more energy and a sense of control. Although it sounds complicated, most mastered it within two or three days.

Sitting with your back straight, place the tip of your tongue against the ridge of tissue just behind your upper front teeth, and keep it there during the exercise. You will be exhaling through your mouth around your tongue: try pursing your lips slightly if this seems awkward.

Breathe OUT completely through your mouth, making a whoosh sound. Close your mouth and breathe IN quietly through your nose to a mental count of four. Next hold your breath for a count of seven.

Then breathe OUT completely through your mouth, making a whoosh sound to a count of eight: this cycle is one breath. Now inhale again and repeat the cycle three more times.

The Buteyko hypothesis

We live because we breathe: the last breath of our lives will be the moment of our death. The act of breathing can be a natural, unconscious function, yet millions of people in the developed world live in constant fear of suffocation. They are asthmatic and from one moment to the next their chests may tighten, their airways constrict, and their breathing become a laboured gasp for air. In severe cases, they can never live too far from a hospital or without an inhaler at hand.

Asthma is a modern epidemic spiralling out of control. There are an estimated 16 million asthmatics in the USA, 4 million in the UK, perhaps 2 million in Australia. In clean, unpolluted New Zealand, 20% of the population is asthmatic. Most developed and prosperous countries show similar figures, and the numbers have been rising steadily over the last two decades. Australian medical authorities predict that by the year 2020, 1 in 2 people will be asthmatic. This is not surprising, since children are the most severely affected. In the UK in 1970 fewer than 1 child in 25 was asthmatic; by the 1990s, it was 1 child in 8. Among the New Zealand Maoris it is 1 child in 3. Modern medicine has no cure to offer and the outlook for an asthmatic is lifelong dependence on inhalers and other forms of drug therapy. The drugs, unlike the patients, are getting better all the time.

Why is normal breathing impossible for so many millions of people? Air pollution, particularly in busy city streets, is often cited. But asthma was relatively rare a century ago when cities choked on soot and sulphurous fumes, and pea-souper fogs were common – and higher figures for asthma in children have been recorded in the bracing Scottish Highlands than in grimy old cities.

Asthmatics are not the only people with a breathing problem. Hyperventilation – over-breathing – is a syndrome that was first identified by an American doctor studying Civil War soldiers in 1871. Few doctors are trained to recognize the disorder, but its symptoms can range from light-headedness and joint stiffness to severe chest pain and terrifying panic attacks. It is often mistaken for a heart attack: up to 40% of patients admitted to emergency rooms with suspected heart attacks turn out to have nothing wrong with their hearts. Asthma, it is believed by many, is one of the causes of hyperventilation.

When a young Russian physiologist called Konstantin Buteyko studied his own medical problems – asthma, high blood pressure and skin allergies – he realized he was hyperventilating. He trained himself to stop over-breathing – and all his problems vanished. He no longer needed drugs. For nearly 50 years since this turning point in his life, Professor Buteyko has been studying the root causes of asthma and developing his own method for its treatment.

Hyperventilation, in his view, is not one of the symptoms of asthma. It actually causes asthma, as it causes dozens of other modern medical problems. His theory of asthma, based on physiological research that goes back to the 1930s, stands conventional medical thinking on its head. According to Buteyko, when an asthmatic is gasping for air it is not oxygen that he is short of: it is carbon dioxide.

Far from being the 'waste' gas of popular belief, carbon dioxide is actually as essential to life as oxygen, and is the regulator of many vital functions in the body. Its key role is to facilitate the release of oxygen from the haemoglobin in the blood. When we over-breathe, too much carbon dioxide is removed from our bodies as we exhale. And as levels fall, the release of oxygen is also slowed or halted. All the cells become deficient in oxygen. The consequences are devastating.

The sympathetic nervous system goes into overdrive, to evoke the physical symptoms of stress. More histamine is released, triggering allergic reactions such as hayfever, and the smooth muscle in the walls of blood vessels, air passages and the intestines contract or go into spasm. This constriction of the airways in the lungs – the bronchioles – produces the typical breathing difficulties of an asthma attack.

The atmosphere breathed by the first human beings 45,000 years ago contained as much as 20% carbon dioxide. A baby in the womb today breathes in an atmosphere that is still 8% carbon dioxide. But it emerges into a world where this vital gas is no more than 0.03% of total air. In adapting to this change over millennia, human beings developed a carbon dioxide reservoir in the lungs, where the tiny air sacs or alveoli contain on average 6.5% carbon dioxide.

Asthma, says Buteyko, is the message your body is sending you to stop over-breathing.

He sees the restriction of the bronchioles not just as a result of over-breathing, but as evidence of the body's attempts to conserve carbon dioxide, as are the production of excess mucus and the swelling of the membrane lining the bronchial tubes – both of which narrow the airways. The importance of carbon dioxide in controlling spasm is recognized in one folk cure for hiccups: when you breathe into – and then from – a closed paper bag.

Normal breathing – when we take in 3–5 litres of air a minute – maintains the carbon dioxide reservoir in our lungs, but in what Buteyko calls 'hidden over-breathing' as much as 5–10 litres may be breathed in during a minute. This breathing pattern results in people breathing out too much carbon dioxide; we need to retain this carbon dioxide in our bodies so the oxygen we breathe in can be properly released into our system. An asthmatic suffering a severe attack will take in 10–20 litres, and an intake of up to 30 litres a minute will bring on an acute panic attack. Taking in so much excess oxygen lowers levels of carbon dioxide progressively. This deficiency disturbs our metabolism at the deepest levels and over 150 diseases may be the result, including anaemia, bronchitis, Chronic Fatigue Syndrome (ME), emphysema, high blood pressure, migraine, rhinitis, tinnitus and lack of concentration or memory loss.

A common cause of hyperventilation, according to Buteyko, is the deep breathing inculcated into children. This usually takes the form of conscious deep and often gasping rapid breaths – quite different from the slow, deep and even breathing of oriental physical disciplines such as yoga. Other common causes of over-breathing include hot stuffy rooms, over-eating, lack of regular exercise and excess sleep – particularly if you sleep on your back. If you breathe through your nose, it is less likely that you will overbreathe. But if you breathe regularly through your mouth, it is very likely that you will overbreathe.

Patients attending the Buteyko five-day course measure what is called their control pause. They breathe twice, gently, through their nose, and on the second out-breath they pinch their nose shut and count how many seconds they can hold their breath. If the control pause is 60 seconds or more, they are taking in the right amount of breath. At 30 seconds, they are breathing enough for two people, at 20 enough for four. In a series of gentle exercises over the five days, patients are trained to extend their control pause, breathe through their noses and take control of their breathing. Pulse rates usually go down as they progress and many patients see results from day one.

The Buteyko method is officially recognized in Russia, where it has a recorded success rate of 95%, and over 100,000 asthma patients have benefited from it. Thousands more in Australia, the USA and the UK have learned to control their asthma and other hyperventilation problems at special Buteyko or Breath Connection clinics. Doctors and respiratory specialists have been slow to acknowledge what one Australian doctor has described as 'the medical breakthrough of the century'. The Buteyko technique will not work for all asthmatics and many hotly dispute that hyperventilation is a major factor in the disease. To date, there has only been one small controlled trial, in Australia – which produced results that would have been the talk of any hospital if a new drug had been responsible. But fast-spreading word of mouth accounts of its success from former asthmatics, a number of excellent books, informative Internet websites and plenty of publicity in the media have spread its fame far and wide.

Courses are not cheap, they are not widely available and they are not generally on offer from state-funded medicine. Nonetheless, it would seem sensible to consider the mechanics of breathing in a disease chiefly characterized by breathlessness. For asthmatics, or others suffering from hyperventilation who are not comfortable with drug therapy, there are a number of books and other sources of information listed in Further Reading.

12 scents of power

The green world of plants gives us the oxygen we need for life. Many of the same plants offer us another wonderful bounty: their aromatic power. For thousands of years, the scents of fragrant plants have been used in ritual and ceremony and to promote a healthy mind and body.

Among the most highly valued plants were those burned as incense or used as sacred oils, from Yemen, Oman, Syria and Palestine to Mesopotamia, Assyria, Egypt and the Roman Empire. 'The invisible yet influential effect of odour was well known to the ancient Egyptians...,' comments Julia Lawless in her book *Aromatherapy and the Mind*, '... Kyphi [a compound of aromatic barks and resins, including cassia, myrrh, juniper and cinnamon] was burned on ritual occasions to heighten the senses and spiritual awareness of the priests, and to raise the spirits of their congregation.' Kyphi was also recognized as having psychotherapeutic powers: Plutarch reported that 'it lulled one to sleep, allayed anxiety and brightened dreams' – claims that would be thought extravagant for a modern tranquillizer.

Native Americans treated respiratory diseases, catarrh, headaches and inflammatory conditions with the smoke of aromatic plants like sage, cedar and juniper burned on hot coals, or made them into infusions to be poured over the hot stones in their sweat lodges.

When the Plague struck in the fifteenth, sixteenth and seventeenth centuries, aromatic spices were burned in public meeting places 'to destroy the corruption of the air'. For rich people, a pomander became the must-have accessory of the day – hollow gold or silver balls filled with a paste of expensive spices such as myrrh, aloes and cinnamon, whose aromas might protect them from infection. The less well-off carried oranges stuck with cloves – which are, in fact, highly antiseptic.

The idea that aromatic smells can have real therapeutic value for mind or body still seems outlandish to modern medicine, and aromatherapy is often dismissed as no more than a placebo. But given what recent scientific research has revealed about the physiology of smells, this is a pitiably ignorant view. We now know that an aroma is not just an agreeable sensation registered in the brain, but a physical presence which travels the whole body, and which can have a number of effects at physical, mental or psychic level. Some of these effects can be harmful – like those of the Volatile Organic Compounds (VOCs) discussed in chapter 6. Some are fatal: think of glue-sniffing.

Smells enter the nose when we inhale, in the form of myriad minute aromatic molecules. These penetrate the mucous membrane lining the nose to reach the ten million olfactory nerve cells, each cell sprouting a bundle of cilia, each cilia equipped with dozens of receptors. The molecules 'dock' in receptors specific to them, and their odour is transmitted by electrical impulses through the olfactory bulb to the brain.

As Julia Lawless explains, 'We can be affected by odours without even being conscious of the fact – the information has bypassed the cerebral cortex and entered directly into the innermost control centres of the limbic system.' In this, the first part of the brain to develop, odours can trigger the release of neurotransmitters: encephalins, which relieve pain and induce a sense of euphoria and well-being; endorphins, which can arouse sexual feelings as well as lowering responses to pain; serotonin, which can calm us down; and noradrenalin, which can wind us up to alertness and action.

In laboratory studies on subjects wired to electroencephalogram (EEG) machines, lavender, sandalwood and pine-forest smells produced alpha-wave patterns in the brain – the slow deep waves of the meditative state. Jasmine, basil and ylang-ylang showed up as stimulating, and lavender, marjoram and chamomile as sedative. Effects vary, of course: if the smell of lavender is associated in your subconscious with a traumatic episode in your past, it can have a very negative effect.

Dr Jean Valnet, founding father of modern aromatherapy, has described essential oils as 'the atomic power of a plant'.

Because they are so highly concentrated, some of these oils can be dangerous if taken internally, and in France only qualified doctors are allowed to prescribe them in this way. The handful of French doctors who still practise what is called phyto-aromatherapy employ them internally to considerable effect, particularly in the case of acute or chronic infection. But in the USA, UK and other countries, the use of essential oils is limited to external application, mainly through massage.

Essential oils are, however, so volatile that when applied to the skin in massage they will reach the bloodstream, to travel along it and eventually reach every system of the body. An old housewives' remedy for whooping cough in babies – much derided by doctors – was to rub the soles of their feet with a cut clove of garlic. In fact, the volatile oils enter the bloodstream and reach the lungs to do their work with great speed, bypassing an immature digestive system. And if you breathe in through your mouth the vapours of essential oils added to hot water will be taken directly into your lungs via your throat.

Using essential oils

A professional aromatherapy massage is perhaps the most direct way to enjoy the benefits of essential oils, but even if you cannot spare the time or the money, there are still many ways in which you can exploit them for your health and well-being.

Steam inhalation This is very effective for any respiratory problem, catarrh or blocked sinuses. Fill a basin two-thirds full with boiling water, add five to six drops of oil, and cover your head with a towel as you bend over the basin to stop vapour escaping. Inhale slowly and deeply for a few minutes. Choose from eucalyptus, thyme, peppermint, lavender or tea tree, used alone or in combination.

On a handkerchief or pillow Sprinkle a few drops of oil on a handkerchief to be sniffed regularly: peppermint to ward off nausea or travel sickness; rosemary to keep you alert on a long drive; eucalyptus if there are colds about. You can also put a couple of drops of oil on your pillow to help fight off an infection (eucalyptus or pine), to stop a night-time cough (cypress), or to induce restful sleep (lavender, marjoram or neroli).

Bath therapy Put up to eight drops of your favourite oil (or a blend of two of three) into a medium-hot bath. You can add them first to half a cup of milk, to disperse them properly, or to a specially treated castor oil called Turkey Red, available from specialist suppliers. If your skin is very dry, aromatherapist Franzesca Watson suggests adding them to a little jojoba oil instead. Use rosemary to get you going in the morning; jasmine for when you want to feel pampered; Scotch pine for its bracing, anti-cold properties; lavender at bedtime.

As a footbath This is an excellent way to get the systemic effects of an oil if you don't have time for a bath – and, of course, it is excellent for local problems such as athlete's foot or chilblains. Add five to six drops of oil to a basin of warm water and soak for ten minutes. For sweaty, smelly feet, try cypress; for fungal infections such as athlete's foot, thyme or tea tree; for hot, overworked feet, peppermint.

In a sauna Add a few drops of essential oil to the water before you splash it on the hot stones.

In a burner or electric vaporizer Use to freshen a room, battle the bugs in a sickroom or create an inspiring environment in your workplace. Cedar is rich and warming, basil and rosemary aid concentration, sandalwood and frankincense – long used in the East as an aid to meditation – are deep and rich; pine, eucalyptus or lavender are good sickroom choices.

Caution Essential oils should be used only with the help of a reliable guide. For useful books on the subject, see Further Reading. Many should not be used in pregnancy, some can have unexpected side-effects (clary sage combined with alcohol can give you nightmares, for instance) and all should be kept well out of the reach of children. They should never be used directly on the skin: the exception is lavender, which is especially valuable in burns when – in all but the most severe cases – it can soothe pain, prevent scarring and inhibit infection.

air

the clean air action plan

1. Bring fresh air into your house day and night. In cities particularly, night-time air is less polluted than daytime air.

2. If any member of the family suffers from asthma, or sleeps in a room with windows opening onto a busy street, invest in an ionizer for the bedroom.

3. Sleep in the raw in summertime; for the rest of the year choose light, cool cotton. Your body needs to breathe to eliminate wastes through the skin.

4. Wear natural fabrics (cotton, linen, silk, hemp) rather than synthetics (polyester, nylon, rayon, acrylic). Most synthetics can generate a positive charge of electricity when rubbed and will attract any negative ions around (see chapter 4). The looseness of the weave is important, too, making for efficient insulation and ventilation.

5. Wear the minimum of clothing. Try a light cotton T-shirt under a sweater, a scarf around your neck and a light quilted windproof jacket or waistcoat.

6. If you feel chilly, don't huddle over a heater or turn up the heating. Go for a brisk walk around the block or do some active warm-up exercises.

7. A morning wash or shower before you get dressed is important: the air between clothes and an unwashed body becomes stagnant overnight.

8. Eat locally-grown food as far as possible: the typical plate of food in the USA today has travelled 1500 miles, and every food-mile travelled adds its quota to environmental pollution.

9. Take your exercise out of doors, especially in winter, such as fifteen minutes brisk walking in the fresh air – if possible among trees, in a park.

10. Make sure you get regular exposure to normal outdoor temperatures – hot or cold, windy or calm – to promote good circulation, preserve the health and resilience of your skin and to keep you fit and alert.

11. If you're deep in demanding mental work and your brain seems to have seized up, take yourself out for a quick walk around the block.

12. Minimize exposure to electromagnetic fields produced by domestic gadgets such as irons and TV sets. Don't hold hairdryers too close to your head. Unplug electric blankets and heated waterbeds before you get into bed. If you use a handheld mobile phone, keep calls to a minimum – especially indoors or in a vehicle, where more power is required. Fit a device to protect you from excess radiation exposure (see Resources), and keep the aerial tilted away from your head. Don't allow children to sit close to the TV: they should sit as far away from the set as is practicable.

13. Avoid all synthetic fragrances in your home as far as possible. There are excellent ranges of natural, unfragranced cleaning materials and cosmetics (see Resources), and if you enjoy a scented bath use essential oils or aromatherapy products based on them.

14. When you bring clothes or bedding home from the drycleaner, remove the plastic covering and hang them in front of an open window.

15. Avoid synthetic building and furnishing materials and fabrics in your home as they may give off chemical fumes linked with health risks.

16. If you work in an office and suffer from lethargy, headaches, eyestrain or a stuffy nose, find out if such symptoms are common in your colleagues. If so, make an approach to your management to see what can be done.

17. If you work in an air-conditioned office, drink plenty of water all day long. The office management should make filtered water available to their staff.

18. If you work in an office with plenty of electronic equipment, ask for ionizers to be installed. An ionizer should be sited at least a metre away from any person, on a piece of towelling or blotting-paper twice its size on which dust particles will ground, and which can be cleaned or renewed regularly. Ideally, it should stand on a piece of metal or aluminium foil, earthed by a connecting wire.

19. If you work regularly at a computer, make sure that management assesses your work-station to make sure that it suits you personally – height of desk, glare on computer screen, etc.

20. Lobby to have plenty of green plants all around the office – and make sure that there's one on your own desk.

21. If you habitually breathe through your mouth, make a real effort to switch to breathing through your nose as nature means us to (see pages 131–3 for suggestions on how this can be done). One trick is to keep smiling.

22. Check if you over-breathe (see page 136). If you still have a problem, read one of the two good books on the Buteyko technique listed in Further Reading: *Breathing Free* by Teresa Hale or *Freedom from Asthma* by Alexander Stalmatski. If you are actually asthmatic, consider learning the Buteyko technique (see Resources).

23. Practise slow, deep breathing as an essential aid to health and spiritual awareness and as a remedy for stress. Find a good class near you and learn yoga, tai chi (or chi kung).

24. When driving in heavy traffic, keep the windows closed, and make sure your car's ventilation system is fitted with a filter to reduce pollutants.

25. Minimize car use. The twice-daily school run contributes massively to pollution. Are public transport or walking really not options? Consider helping to organize a Walking bus (see Resources) in which numbers of children walk to school two by two, with one parent as 'driver' at the front, and another as 'conductor' at the back.

'We must look into unknown dimensions, into that incalculable and imponderable life, whose carrier and mediator – the blood of the Earth that accompanies us steadfastly from the cradle to the grave – is water.'

Viktor Schauberger *Implosion* magazine, 1932

water: our world of water

1 the cradle of life

In the Transvaal of South Africa, paleontologists searching for the earliest fossil records of life on earth saw the imprint of water. In rocks over 3500 million years old, they found ripples identical to those that the outgoing tide leaves on soft sand, set forever into the rock. Where did this water come from? How did the earth acquire its oceans? And what *is* water anyway?

Every school boy knows the answer to the last question: it is H_2O – two atoms of hydrogen and one of oxygen. But the first two questions are much harder to answer, and for decades astronomers, physicists and chemists have been puzzling, speculating and arguing over them. Slowly the pieces of the jigsaw are being fitted together, thanks to the huge telescopes which peer into space, the Hubble telescope actually in orbit and sending pictures back from deep space, and the data transmitted from cameras mounted in space probes to the US National Aeronautical and Space Administration (NASA's) astrochemistry laboratory in California. At the start of the twenty-first century, most scientists now agree on the broad outlines of an answer to each of these questions.

It is now believed that the universe contains a huge amount of water and that this water continually forms in the depths of huge interstellar clouds, from a combination of the two most abundant gases in space – hydrogen and oxygen. Our sun was born when one such cloud collapsed in on itself to form a star, and the rest of the cloud – billions of particles of stardust – went into spinning orbit around this new young star. Within a million years or so, the particles cannoning into each other clumped, expanded and formed into hundreds of embryo planets. Nine planets finally locked into the young sun's inner circuit; the four innermost being made mainly of rock. The third rock from the sun was our planet earth, perhaps 150 million km distant.

Closer to the sun – too close for comfort as it turned out – were Mercury and Venus, around 58 million and 108 million km respectively. Much further away from the sun was Mars, which lay at a distance of around 228 million km. And further out still, on the far side of the Asteroid Belt, which is peopled by thousands of minor asteroids and planetary fragments, circle the giant planets Jupiter, Saturn, Uranus and Neptune. Even further out is Pluto, then about a light-year away is the Oort cloud, thought to be the source of comets.

In his book *The Restless Sea*, Robert Kunzig vividly imagines a young red-hot earth: 'A bright red ocean, the colour of the lava that flows out of Kilauea on Hawaii, under a perpetual grey fog. A boundless ocean of churning, boiling rock, stirred from time to time by the splash-down of a minor planet. ... a thick viscous ocean with no land, no landmarks at all to catch the eye, even if the eye had been able to penetrate more than a few feet through the dense, crushing fog...'.

By 3.9 billion years ago the long blitz finally tapered off – around 700 million years after the violent birth of our planet. And as the earth cooled, the cloud of vapour finally condensed into liquid form, and the first rains fell, even while the ever-thundering volcanoes continued to blast tonnes of water vapour into the atmosphere. By the time the earth had cooled, seven-tenths of it's surface was covered by oceans.

More recently, however, leading US space astrophysicist Louis Frank of Iowa University has called into question this once-and-for-all theory of how earth's oceans formed. In 1986 he announced a new theory, based on images of space captured by a space probe. Some of these images contained dark spots, and Frank and his colleague John Sigwarth suggested that they might indicate clouds of water vapour being released high above the earth's atmosphere by the disintegration of small comets composed mainly of snow. These comets might be more than 6–9m in diameter – the size of a large igloo. The idea of these regular extra-terrestrial blizzards was at first ridiculed by other astrophysicists but, undeterred, the two scientists have continued to develop their theory, speculating that these small comets were hitting the earth's atmosphere to deposit their cargo of water at the rate of 1000 an hour – enough to add a couple of centimetres of water to the earth's oceans every 20,000 years, or fill them over billions of years.

Some interstellar water still reaches our planet encapsulated in small meteorites from within the solar system. One such meteorite, which fell to earth in Texas in 1998, was examined at the NASA laboratory in Houston. When researchers carefully cracked it open, they found crystalline deposits inside holding tiny amounts of water of the same age as our solar system – 4.5 billion years.

But wherever our oceans come from, they cover about 70% of the earth's surface today, to an average depth of about 3 km, and the total amount of all the water on the planet has been estimated at around 1230 million cubic km. These huge bodies of water are always on the move, powered by enormous currents such as the Gulf Stream, which shifts 1.6 million cubic metres of water a second to deliver a temperate climate to north-western Europe. Oceans respond, too, to the extraordinary gravitational pull of the moon, which literally causes their waters to bulge outwards at the point nearest the moon and to spread at the point furthest away, creating the twice-daily tides that rise and fall around the world's coastlines. The sun also exerts a tidal pull, although a much weaker one than that of the moon.

According to the Gaia hypothesis developed by space scientist James Lovelock, the earth behaves like a living organism, with the atmosphere its respiratory system, the rock its skeleton that holds everything in place and the oceans its life-blood. Just like blood, the oceans and all the water in the world have their own circulatory system: it is called the Hydrological Cycle and it is solar powered.

As surface water is heated by the sun, it evaporates into an invisible vapour that rises into the atmosphere. More water vapour rises from plant leaves when they transpire. As this water vapour rises, it cools and condenses to form a liquid again. Clouds are collections of these water particles. As air currents drive clouds through the air, the water particles are precipitated to fall to earth as rain, hail or snow.

Water falling back to earth as rain or snow may have lost the salts of the ocean when it evaporated, but as it falls from clouds it can pick up airborne contaminants to carry them down to earth: the infamous acid rain is an example of this. Some of the rain reaching the earth becomes surface run-off, flowing back through streams and rivers to the sea; some soaks into the ground to be taken up by plants; and some percolates down through cracks and crevices in rock or soil to reach the subterranean reservoirs of ground water. Much of this will re-enter surface waters eventually or be tapped by wells.

Endlessly recycled over billions of years, the water in the shower you took this morning may have formed those ripples in the ancient rocks of the Transvaal. In those same rocks, paleontologists found the fossil evidence of earth's earliest known living organism, an ancient, single-celled bacterium born in the seas.

Without water, this life on earth could never have existed.

2 body of water

Did you know that when you step on the scales, around 70% of the kilos you register are water? Did you know that inside your envelope of skin – and within that skin – around 40–50 litres of water is circulating? Why don't we hear it sloshing around? Where is it all?

It's everywhere. The plasma which makes our blood liquid and bathes every single cell in our bodies, the lymph which is a key component of our immune system, the mucus which lines and protects our respiratory and digestive tracts, the tears we weep, the saliva that starts the digestive process in our mouths – all these form part of the seas within us. There is more water inside every one of our cells. When we are dehydrated our skins dry out, too, far beyond rescue by 'moisturizing' creams. Our muscles contain water, as does the cartilage that cushions our joints – even our bones contain water. Our lungs need water to function, which is why our moist breath can make a mirror mist over. Our brains are always thirsty: brain tissue is 85% water and it uses 5% of the body's total supply.

Like the Hydrological Cycle (see page 149), the water within us cycles endlessly through our bodies, purified by the tireless kidneys. Part of our body water – the cerebrospinal fluid that circulates within the brain, the brain stem and the spinal cord – even has its own 'tide' according to William Sutherland, the founder of craniosacral therapy. This fluid, he suggests, is a living, pulsing sea with its own ebb and flow, whose energy and amplitude are an index of health.

Of the 40–50 litres of water each of us contains, we lose one or two daily as urine, and about another litre is lost in faeces, sweat and breath – the soles of our feet alone produce a half to one cupful of water every day. Heat and exercise both lead to water loss: spend an hour in your car in a crowded city and you could sweat out half a litre. This water must be replaced.

Your food will supply plenty of water – steak is 60% water, hard-boiled eggs are 75%, while broccoli, peaches, strawberries and tomatoes are over 90%. Orange juice, milk and herb teas are all good sources of water, too. But there's nothing like pure water to satisfy your body's craving for the stuff: wine, beer, tea, coffee and fizzy drinks don't count. Alcohol in the first two, and caffeine in the remainder, will dehydrate your body, however long the drinks may be.

Sodium is just as essential to our health as food or water, as our bodies need it to regulate water balance and to maintain normal heart rhythms. The transmission of nerve impulses and the contraction of muscles are sodium-dependent, too, and a normal body contains around 70–100g of sodium. When patients lose too much blood, doctors will order a saline drip as a matter of urgency to replace the salt they have lost in their blood (which, like tears and sweat, is salty.)

Excess sweating can also cause severe dehydration, and athletes who overdo it can go into salt deficit, signalled by cramps, dizziness and exhaustion. But few people – apart from athletes – ever run into serious sodium-deficiency problems. Much more common are the medical problems caused by too much sodium in our diets.

A normal healthy diet supplies all the sodium we need – around 1–3g a day, the amount our kidneys can process. There are 45mg in a small serving of spinach, 122mg in a cup of milk, 54mg in an egg, 50mg in a stalk of celery. But modern food processing adds huge amounts more: the average bag of potato crisps contains over 1g, a helping of salted peanuts 150mg, ten pretzels over 1g, a cupful of chicken noodle soup just under 1g, a quarter-pound cheeseburger over 1200mg. Most of us grow up salt-addicted. To make matters worse, the salt so liberally added to modern processed foods is not natural mineral-rich sea salt, which contains 14% of the vital minerals calcium, sulphur, magnesium and potassium, as well as trace elements, and is only 84% sodium chloride. It is a highly refined salt from which all the minerals have been removed, leaving 97.5% sodium chloride, with 0.6% of iodine added by law in most countries, and additives to improve its running and moisture-free qualities. One cause of today's epidemic of hypertension may be excess intake of this concentrated salt.

When an Iranian physician, Dr Batmanghelidj, was thrown into Tehran's notorious Evun jail for alleged political crimes by the revolutionary government of Iran in 1980, the guards appointed him prison doctor. In the hideously overcrowded prison, the commonest medical problem he had to deal with was acute stress and the gnawing ulcers it caused. But he had no medical supplies and when he was called to see an ulcer patient in agonizing dyspeptic pain, he could only prescribe two glasses of water. To his amazement, it brought almost instant relief. For the next 25 months he made a systematic study among his stressed fellow prisoners of the water treatment. At his trial he presented an astonished judge with an article on the water treatment of over 3000 cases of peptic ulcers and he was freed in order to continue his research.

Later, he fled to the USA, where he has continued his research ever since, becoming a fervent advocate of the use of water in a wide spectrum of disease. His message is simple.

'You are not sick, you are thirsty. It is chronic water shortage... that causes most of the diseases of the human body.'

In his book *The Body's Many Cries for Water*, Dr Batmanghelidj suggests that digestive problems including ulcers and hiatus hernia, joint and back pain, stress and depression, high blood pressure and high cholesterol, asthma, allergies, obesity, even diabetes can all result from chronic dehydration, and plenty of water should be the first line of treatment.

London-based Danish biopath Gudrun Jonsson has a starry list of famous clients who depend on her counsels to keep their digestive systems functioning sweetly. Part of the daily routine she enjoins on all her patients is to drink 1.5–2 litres of water every day – in hot or arid climates much more – unless they are constipated, in which case the total should be increased to 3 litres a day. 'Water,' she points out, 'is needed for every bodily function. Without it enzymes and nutrients could not be transported around the body. It helps to dilute acids, makes the blood more alkaline, helps the kidneys excrete acids and us to digest nutrients, and provides moisture for the skin.' Dehydration, in fact, is ageing: 'A sure sign that we are not drinking enough water,' says Gudrun 'is the condition of the skin. In a well-watered body this will be soft to the touch. In a dehydrated body it will be dry and wrinkly.'

Some naturopaths insist that the body sends out clear signals about thirst and that we need only drink in response to these. But our modern lifestyle can distort these natural signals. Cravings for food are not always an accurate indication of real need, and most of us have learned to ignore the fatigue or sleepiness which tells us when our bodies need rest, long before we're ready to leave the party. And when we're thirsty we're more likely to reach for a cold beer, a soft drink or a cup of tea than a glass of water – any of which can actually dehydrate us.

To most people, a real thirst for water is not a common sensation. 'Drinking eight glasses of water a day sounds quite boring and difficult,' as Alice Kavounas remarks in her book *Water: Pure Therapy.* She began obediently doing so herself after a cranial osteopath suggested she do so as part of his treatment for the migraines which had plagued her for years. 'Strangely, the more I drank, the thirstier I became. I began to feel lighter, my eyes and skin looked clearer, my hair seemed to thicken again. Most important of all, my migraines diminished. Now, drinking eight glasses a day is as natural as breathing. Without it, I feel like a dog in a hot car: dehydrated.'

But if we must all drink at least eight glasses of water a day, what type of water should we be drinking? Tap water? Filtered? Still or sparkling? Spring or spa water? In chapter 7 we will consider the options.

3 the weirdness of water

Water is weird stuff. Depending on the circumstances, it can be a liquid, a solid or a gas. And from the outset it has gone its own way, in defiance of the conventions governing the rule of liquids and solids. Unlike most liquids, for instance, water doesn't shrink as it gets colder: it actually expands, which is why water pipes burst as they freeze and that bottle of bubbly you left too long in the freezer exploded in a mess of glass. But then again, water is more dense as a liquid than it is as solid ice – which is why icebergs float, and ice stays on top of water rather than sinking to its depths. This is lucky for us, since ice acts as an insulating lid on water in very cold weather, allowing life below it to continue even in arctic conditions.

Water is also a great solvent – an enormous range of substances dissolve in it, making it a wonderful means of transport exploited by all living organisms. And living organisms, as we saw in the preceding chapter, are themselves largely made up of water. Chemists and physicists around the world are struggling to understand these peculiarities of water in terms of its molecular structure, and the ways in which those molecules form clusters.

But water continues to defy science in other ways.

Scientists now find themselves faced with the question – does water have a 'memory'?

Homeopathic medicine strongly suggests that water does have a memory: the 'potentized' drugs of homeopathy are remedies which have been diluted in water so many times that in the highest potencies not a molecule of the original drug-substance remains. It is for this reason that homeopathic medicine has been a thorn in the flesh of science since the nineteenth century, when Samuel Hahnemann first developed it. Or rather, it would have been a thorn – if science hadn't simply chosen to ignore it.

But in 1988 the moment arrived when this particular weirdness of water – its ability to 'remember' substances it had once contained – was forced on their attention by a French biologist, Jacques Benveniste. His name is now as much anathema in scientific circles as that of Galileo must have been in early seventeenth-century Rome.

Benveniste was Research Director at the French National Institute for Medical Research (INSERM) and a high-profile specialist in the mechanisms of inflammation and allergy. In a paper submitted in 1987 to the prestigious science journal *Nature*, he presented evidence from experiments conducted in his own and other laboratories over six years in which water containing an antibody had been both vigorously shaken – or 'successed' as it is called in homeopathic drug preparation – and diluted until no molecule of the antibody remained. Nevertheless, using his ultra-sensitive equipment, he found that this highly diluted solution elicited a reaction just as if a molecule of the antibody had still been present in it. Benveniste thus appeared to be producing a validation for homeopathy.

All hell broke loose. The editor of *Nature*, John Maddox, descended on Benveniste's lab as leader of a three-man fraud squad bent on debunking the biologist's work. The third member of the team was actually a magician whose most famous coup had been to debunk the fork-bending Uri Geller. If Benveniste were taken literally, thundered his peers, it would mean the collapse of the physical or chemical worlds. Later experiments conducted in other labs confirmed the high-dilution effect, claims Benveniste, but no reputable journal would publish them. Benveniste eventually lost his job, his laboratory and his position as director of INSERM.

The whole episode raises huge questions about the nature of scientific censorship, but Benveniste has refused to be deflected from his research. 'Life depends on signals exchanged among molecules,' he says in an article published in *Nexus* in September 1999. Current biological orthodoxy states that molecules can only exchange information if they are in physical contact. Not so, says Benveniste, on the strength of his studies. Every atom of every molecule, in this new view, emits a group of specific radio frequencies as a 'signal' to other molecules 'tuned' to the same frequency, even if they are not in physical contact.

None of this communication would be possible without water. 'It is,' says Benveniste, 'the vehicle for information. This cannot be avoided since there are 10,000 water molecules in the human body for every molecule of protein.' Molecules do not transmit their signals directly: they are relayed and perhaps even amplified by water. And Benveniste believes that water can memorize and store the information one molecule is conveying to another.

More controversially, and based on research carried out at his new Digibio Laboratory in Clamart, France, Benveniste now claims that this 'information' can be picked up electromagnetically from water, digitized and stored on a computer via a standard sound card. This stored signal can be relayed through a computer, or even sent over the Internet, and played back into water, which will then store the same information to exert the same biological effects. Benveniste claims that signals from molecules of heparin, an anti-coagulant, do in fact slow down the coagulation of blood when transmitted over the Internet from a European laboratory to one in the USA.

These claims have provoked outrage in the scientific community. The 'memory' of water can be dismissed as a hypothesis of manifest absurdity which flies in the face of established knowledge, but science still has to deal with the fact of homeopathy, which relies on this very phenomenon, and for which the only kind of evidence that scientists will accept – double-blind trials – is beginning to accumulate. In a paper written for a homeopathic website, the Australian biophysicist and homeopath Paul Callinan describes some of this evidence: it includes a tightly controlled randomized double-blind trial of remedies for hayfever, carried out at the Glasgow Homeopathic Hospital in Scotland in 1986. In the trial, the effects of a homeopathic preparation of mixed grasses was compared with those of a placebo (a dummy pill) in 144 patients with active hayfever. The patients getting the homeopathic remedy did significantly better – in their view and that of their doctors – than those getting the placebos.

The remedy in question was what homeopaths call a 30C potency, one in which dilution had been so great that no molecule of the original drug-material remained: here, unquestionably, the 'memory' of water was in action. When the results were published in the *Lancet*, as Callinan records, it provoked a storm of correspondence: 'Although some of the more far-sighted of the correspondents suggested the possibility that a new chemistry and a new physics had been born, the reliance on pharmacology in the allopathic way of thinking showed its dominance.' The experiment, it was claimed, was simply testing one placebo against another. 'The fact that statistical significance was obtained for one of the "placebos" was apparently deemed of no consequence, and indicates that the issue may not be a scientific issue at all, but more an economic and emotional one.'

Scientists who are not prepared to be open-minded about the work of a distinguished biologist, carried out with colleagues over years in a reputable laboratory, certainly won't be inclined to pay much attention to the ideas of Theodor Schwenk: his work and that of Viktor Schauberger, whom we shall meet in the next chapter, have been dismissed as 'romantic fancies'. A German physicist who had been greatly influenced by the ideas of Rudolf Steiner, Schwenk's book *Sensitive Chaos* reflects his belief that water is far more than a vehicle for conducting intermolecular signals. He believes that it acts as a medium through which cosmic forces find their expression in the physical world. If for 'cosmic forces' you read 'Creator' – that least unscientific of all concepts – then exactly the same idea is expressed in the very first lines of Genesis: 'In the beginning God created heaven and earth. And the earth was void and empty, and darkness was upon the face of the deep; and the spirit of God moved over the waters.'

John Wilkes is a sculptor, not a biologist, but his whole artistic career, you might say, has been shaped by water, and by ideas such as these about its importance. While he was studying at London's foremost art school, the Royal College, he was intrigued by the ideas of George Adams, a Cambridge scientist, who was working closely with Schwenk. Wilkes subsequently went to Germany as Adams' assistant at the Institute for Flow Sciences in the Black Forest set up at the beginning of the 1960s.

Adams' direction of research related to the use of special mathematical surfaces which have been named path-curve surfaces and which, he discovered, form the basis for many organic forms, such as cones, buds, eggs and even the shape of the heart. The objective of the research was to move water over such surfaces, and follow the effects of this process.

In order to determine any quality changes in water after planned treatments, Schwenk developed a new test method. This has become known as the Drop Picture Method and uses water's capacity to move in rich vortical patterns as an indicator of its overall regenerative quality. In a flat, polished glass dish the water sample under test – which might be 'pure' or might carry the effects of a prior process – is mixed with a small percentage of glycerine. Into this, drops of distilled water are allowed to fall from a specific height at controlled intervals. If there was vital energetic water in the dish, it would send out the raying star-like pattern formed by the rich vortical movement of good quality water. But if the water was contaminated by as little as 0.0005% detergent, you would see only shallow concentric rings spreading outwards. Schwenk thus demonstrated that under undesirable influences, water loses its capacity to generate rich movement within its volume and thus is unable to mediate the sensitive influences of the environment to the living organism. This embedding of the organism within the environment is water's task and without it there is little chance of survival.

Central to this work and to Wilkes' own understanding is the idea of water as a carrier and mediator of the rhythmic forces which shape life. 'Water,' he writes, 'is the basis for all fluid rhythmical life-sustaining processes... all life-forms exist by virtue of the rhythms and surfaces mediated by water.' Any life-form displays these rhythms: the pulsing circulation of blood and the expansion and contraction of our lungs as we breathe are two obvious examples.

In 1970, some years after Adams' death, Wilkes discovered a method of generating rhythms in streaming water. This was done by causing water to flow through vessels that offer a degree of resistance precisely calculated for specific purposes. This has become known as the Flowform Method, and it draws on a combination of Adams' research into path-curve with the capacity of rhythms to allow water repeatedly to swing over and intimately caress such surfaces in a streaming process.

The object of the Flowform is to enhance the activity of the Hydrological Cycle (see pages 149 and 150) which has maintained water's quality for millennia. In our time, it is under grave danger from intensive technological and domestic degenerating influences. 'Our most wonderful experience of water,' Wilkes suggests, 'is the mountain stream – clear, fresh and sparkling , constantly spiralling and moving in vortices, generating myriads of rhythms. Water needs movement – it needs oxygenation.'

Over 1000 Flowform projects have been installed worldwide, in more than 30 countries, and for a wide variety of functions. Among these are the biological treatment of sewage, the air conditioning of offices, food processing, the mixing of preparations for biodynamic organic farming (see Earth, pages 57–60), for swimming pools, and children's recreation areas and private, public, interior or exterior situations. Wherever possible, research is undertaken to monitor the effect and influence of rhythms and surfaces whether empirically or mathematically designed.

It is easy to see that an attractively designed Flowform installation in the middle of a big city office could raise spirits and diminish stress and absenteeism. The sound of running water is happier music to human ears than the clatter of fax machines and the buzzing of phones, cascading water generates lots of healthy, happy-making negative ions, and every air-conditioned office could do with the refreshing and humidifying effect of running water.

It is much harder to work out, though, what could be going on at the big Demeter bakery in Fulda, Germany. Demeter is one of the big names in the healthfood movement in Germany, specializing in biodynamically produced food: the Fulda bakery produces excellent wholemeal bread for shops within half a day's journey. Since 1999, their water supply has been piped to the top of a 13m tower, from which it descends over slabs of granite and finally through a series of Flowforms to the bottom where it enters the factory. When maintenance halted the process for a few days, and normal piped water was used instead, the bakery received dozens of enquiries: 'What happened to that wonderful bread you were making last week?'

On the mysteries of water, it seems, science has not had the last word.

4 the energy of water

'You may have lived a calm and contented life,' it has been said, 'but from the moment you come face to face with the ideas of Viktor Schauberger, you will never again have peace in your soul.' Exaggeration perhaps, but more than any other thinker of our times, Schauberger's teachings call into question almost every assumption on which our comfortable western lives are based. As early as the 1930s he foresaw the environmental destruction and degradation for which he held scientific technology responsible. The cancers to which 1 in 3 of us is now doomed, soil salinity, acid rain, the problems of monoculture in field and forest, catastrophic flash floods, desertification, arid infertile soils, reduced groundwater quantity and eventually water wars: Schauberger predicted them all.

Viktor Schauberger was born in Austria in 1885, the son of generations of foresters. As a child, he was fascinated by the virgin forests near Lake Plochkenstein of which his father was Master Woodsman. But it was water, not trees, that fascinated him, and over the next decade water became for him the subject of long and almost obsessive study. He studied its sources deep in the forest, and its preference for courses shaded by overhanging banks and greenery. He noted the swirling spirals and vortices that characterized its flow, and the meandering course that streams and rivers naturally took. He learned from his father that heat is the enemy of water's energy: 'Water exposed to the sun's rays is tired and lazy and therefore curls up and sleeps. At night, however, and especially in moonlight, the water becomes fresh and lively...'

Towards the end of the 1920s, Schauberger was criticising the management of the Rhine and Danube rivers, as their curves and meanders were obliterated by concreted banks in a misguided attempt to prevent them silting up. In his view, such treatment of rivers could only be disastrous because it failed to take into account the natural behaviour of springs and streams and nature's own way of regulating their flow.

Modern water treatment, according to Schauberger, is totally at odds with the natural way that water behaves.

Collected in large open reservoirs, where rapid warming destroys its health-giving energies and encourages the proliferation of pathogenic bacteria, it is then forced through many kilometres of straight metal pipes and chemically treated to disinfect it. 'All of life,' he wrote, 'is dependent on stale and unhealthy water.'

For Schauberger, the straightening of riverbanks was just one more example of misguided modern technological thinking. As he had learned years earlier, there are no straight lines in fields and forests. 'In [nature's] systems involving dynamic energetic processes,' explains Callum Coats, who has devoted 15 years of his life to the study of Schauberger's work, 'she always appears to select a spiral form of movement and its vortical derivatives.' These spirals and vortical movements are omnipresent in the natural world, from the swirling nebulae of galaxies down to the shaping of snail shells, antelope horns and pine cones, and the twisting double helix of DNA.

This is nature's way of creating energy, which Schauberger christened implosion. Implosion – vortical power – can be observed as the force at the heart of 'twisters', strong enough to lift buildings bodily off the ground, or in the powerful suction felt when you press a hand over the plughole as your bathwater drains away.

Schauberger contrasted implosion with the destructive and wasteful explosive processes of modern energy generation. Friction, overheating and rising resistance make the internal combustion engine startlingly inefficient. 'Our modern technology,' scoffed Schauberger, 'behaves like a farmer who...plants seven potatoes, and...harvests one.'

As well as the polluting by-products, coal and oil were themselves valuable resources. Nuclear energy was for him the culminating stupidity of explosive technique, and the last years of his life were spent in a struggle to develop viable forms of implosion energy. This culminated in a disastrous move to the USA in 1958, in the hope of having full research facilities at his disposal. He returned to Austria after only three months, but not before he had signed away to a US company full rights not only to his data, sketches and prototypes, but to his future thinking on implosion. He died five days after his return.

Perhaps the secrets of implosion energy production are locked in an American company safe. But interest in Schauberger's revolutionary ideas is rising steadily. In a number of small research institutes in Europe, his ideas are being studied and developed. Some day soon, perhaps, the enormous investment needed to assess and perhaps realize his dream of limitless cheap energy from water may be made available. At the Centre for Implosion Research in Plymouth, Devon, in England, Jonathan Stromberg and Dolly Knight are meanwhile exploring another dimension of implosion energy, with another objective: that of restoring to water its lost energies.

At the Centre they have constructed an implosion machine in which water is subjected to very powerful vortices – like the inside of a tornado. By this process, they claim, water is revived to its natural vibrant energetic state and regains its life force. Filled with this imploded water, their copper spiral – the Vortex Energizer – can be attached to an incoming water pipe to recharge a household's drinking water or energize water in a closed system such as a refrigerator or heating system, while small personal harmonizers, filled with the same imploded water will, they claim, protect the wearers from electromagnetic radiation.

To sceptical ears, energized water sounds about as credible as the elixir of eternal youth. But hundreds of testimonials flowing in from happy users tell of some remarkable results. A beautiful 230m circumference lake had become unbearably foul-smelling and algae-infested when overcolonized by Canadian geese, whose excrement removes oxygen: within two hours of being energized by a personal harmonizer, the algae sank to the bottom and within days the lake was crystal clear again. When an energizer was attached to one radiator in a ten-year-old heating system, the water inside turned within three weeks from inky foulness to sparkling clean and the radiators became more efficient. And in 1998, plant trials carried out at the One World Garden Centre in Northern Ireland showed a 50% reduction in required feed and an overall 250% increase in yield for plants watered with energized as opposed to ordinary water.

Water is weird stuff.

water

turning on the tap

5

the thirsty planet

The New Valley Canal in Egypt has been described by its construction workers as a modern pyramid – or the president's folly. When it is complete, the canal will stretch a green arm into the Egyptian desert, diverting 5.5 billion cubic metres of water a year from the Nile into the badlands to create a fertile valley and 400,000 hectares of farmland.

The idea has been discussed in Egypt for the last 40 years, and now President Hosni Mubaruk claims it is finally going to happen. Neighbouring states point out that Egypt already uses all the Nile water it is allocated by international treaty, mostly to irrigate its crops. Egypt has had the lion's share of the Nile waters for many years, and now upstream Sudan and Ethiopia are indicating strongly that they want more.

Egypt cannot allow that to happen. Unemployment is already high, more than half its food has to be imported, including about 10 million tonnes of grain annually, and any new projects to boost the economy – especially agriculture – may require even more of the Nile's waters. But within Egypt itself, sceptical scientists have pointed out that the last thing this parched country needs is a $2 billion project that will give water to farmers virtually for free in an unsustainable attempt to turn the desert green.

The project may threaten more than the waters. In 1991 the Egyptian defence minister said that his country would not hesitate to use force to defend its control of the Nile. And every nation of the Nile basin has now classified access to the waters of the river as a vital national interest over which they would be willing to go to war.

In 1999 the United Nations (UN) issued an international warning. If no immediate action is taken, they said, it would not be impossible to imagine war breaking out within the next 30 years between nations that have exhausted their most precious and essential resource: water.

But how is this possible? If the earth's water were to be spread evenly around the whole globe, we would all be living beneath 2.5km of H_2O. The problem is that most of that is saltwater. The freshwater, the stuff that makes up our bodies and without which we cannot survive more than a day or so, is less than 3% of the world's supply, and we can only access a sixth of that.

For comfortable westerners, the idea of being more than a stroll away from a cold drink is unthinkable. But according to the UN, more than half the world's population is already living in unsanitary conditions without access to clean water. The UN expert, Brian Appleton, has put it in very specific terms: 5000 children die every day from water-borne diseases. That is the equivalent of 12 jumbo jets crashing every single day. And it's going to get worse.

By 2025, 17 countries in the Middle East, as well as South Africa, Pakistan and parts of India and China, will all face 'absolute water scarcity'. They will not have enough water to produce the food that they are producing now. A further 24 countries, mainly in sub-Saharan Africa, will face 'economic water scarcity'. They'll be able to produce the water, but only after huge development projects which will cost money that they just don't have. We are sleepwalking our way towards disaster.

When we look at the figures, of course, the facts are staring us in the face. The world's population has trebled since 1900; 85 million more people arrive every year; and global water consumption at home, in industry and on the farm has increased even faster – sixfold in the last 100 years.

In both developing and developed countries we are using water as if it will last forever.

We need to start thinking of it as a mineral resource, just as precious as silver or oil, and just as finite. Perhaps we can begin by looking at the world as one gigantic water filter: every year 120 trillion litres of water are cycled from the sea through our atmosphere to the land. The rivers and lakes that fill with rain are known as surface water. Beyond this resource there is also groundwater, drawn from huge underground aquifers from previous ages, containing billions and billions of litres of freshwater. These refill, but at a far slower pace than surface water. For millennia these two sources have been more than sufficient. Unfortunately, this is the century when demand starts to overtake supply. The quantity of water that is being cycled by the earth remains stable, but water use is expected to carry on increasing.

We draw too heavily on the resources – if Saudi Arabia continues to pump up water from its underground sources at the present rate, it will have none within 50 years. We're diverting rivers and lakes away to farms and cities, but that means that people downstream get nothing. For the last 15 years, the Yellow River in China – one of the four great rivers of the world – has run dry and failed to reach the sea.

And we go on to use these resources wastefully. More than two-thirds of all the water used is for irrigation purposes, but it's long been known that irrigation is enormously wasteful. Only about 15–35% of the water poured onto our fields actually gets to the roots of the plants, while the rest just drains away, taking vital nutrients in the earth with it. We waste water in our domestic lives as well: think about the river of water that runs through your home every day from dripping taps, half-full dishwashers, toilets being flushed every five minutes, deep baths, sprinklers. And don't forget that a leaking tap – one drip per second – will waste 9800 litres of water in a year.

The future, clearly, has to be better management of the world's water supplies. In the longer term, the UN water assessment makes it clear that policy decisions will have to be made at an international level about water allocation, and large amounts of money will have to be invested in getting access to new sources and making sure the water reaches the people who need it. But before any step can be taken it's vital to change the way people think about water.

Israel is almost the only country in the world to have tackled this problem seriously in the last 20 years: the result has been that its water use has actually declined. In 1987, the Middle East faced severe droughts. Israel immediately began improving its water system, modified the flush toilet system to allow for lighter flushing, clamped down on businesses and industries, and priced water higher and higher.

By the time the drought ended, Israel had managed to push water consumption down by 10% and the policy has continued. Israeli agriculturists have adopted the 'drip' irrigation system, which uses perforated plastic tubing – installed on or below the soil surface – to drop water straight onto the roots of the plant, cutting water use by up to 70%. They also recycle 55% of their sewage water, after treatment, for inedible crops such as flax and cotton.

There's a basic pragmatism about this approach which makes a huge amount of sense. I particularly like the fact that all car washes in Jerusalem use recycled water. It's that sort of attention to detail which will make all the difference in the end.

Efficient water use is, clearly, the best method of conserving our limited supplies.

Irrigation of crops uses up a staggering two-thirds of the world's available water. Drip irrigation has consistently been shown to cut water consumption by 30–70% and crops do better: yields can increase by as much as 90%. So far only about 1% of the world's crops are grown this way, but those crops include sugar-cane and cotton, and low-cost systems are being developed in the USA which would pay for themselves within a fairly short time.

There is one final possibility. The main five crops that humans depend on – wheat, corn, rice, potatoes and soybeans – will not survive if exposed to salt. But there are those huge and tantalizing expanses of seawater, as well as plenty of water inland that is brackish (too salty) for use: the obvious answer is to find some way to get the salt out and end water shortages forever.

Desalination plants around the world already produce up to 18 billion litres of water daily. Millions of people on Caribbean islands drink desalinated water, the USA is increasingly turning to this technology to meet its insatiable thirst, and for the Middle East and countries in North Africa it seems the logical way ahead.

Jordan's water deficit was estimated at 155 million cubic metres in the year 2000. Desalinating brackish water in the Jordan Valley and the Hisban area could provide around 70 million cubic metres. But Jordan is also studying a much bolder plan: to construct a canal through the desert which would transport water from the Red Sea to the southern end of the Dead Sea, and use the electricity generated by the fall of the water from a higher elevation to power desalination. The problem with desalination is that it leaves a 40% residue of very salty water. But, of course, the Dead Sea is to hand to dump it in.

Desalination has always been an expensive process, in terms of both cash and energy. The two leading technologies currently available are distillation, which produces freshwater from steam, and reverse osmosis, which uses permeable membranes to separate out salt and other impurities. Oil-rich Middle Eastern countries, who can afford the steep prices and who have the energy resources, can help themselves to all the water they need. But for poor countries literally dying of thirst, salvation by desalination is far beyond their means.

However, a solution may be on the horizon. Israeli researchers have just proposed a design for a solar still that can produce freshwater from saline or brackish water. Output from the unit would be 40% higher than from conventional desalination systems, they claim, and the consumption of fossil fuels would be nil. They are still working on the prototype, but if it comes off the implications will be spectacular. New technologies for exploiting wave energy may also solve the problem by producing surplus on-the-spot energy for desalination (as we shall see in chapter 9). But it could be decades before these technologies bring relief to the areas suffering most.

By that time, hopefully, we shall have mended our ways, and learned not to squander water as if it were... well, water.

6 poisoning the water

Flying into Rome a few years ago, the captain announced that, as usual, there would be a slight delay before we were allowed to touch down at Ciampino. As we circled out over the Mediterranean, my husband nudged me and pointed down towards the sea. 'Look at that,' he said. All along the coast, we could see a dull pink bloom in the water, flowering out from the heavily populated beaches. This is eutrophication, a phenomenon that has been slowly killing off rivers, lakes and now seas around the planet for the last 40 years.

The issue of water pollution has become one of the most hotly contested battlegrounds for environmentalists, agriculturalists and industrialists alike. Complex in the extreme, all sides throw stones: no one wants to take the blame for what is clearly happening to our water. There are even some who claim that there is no problem at all and it's just that we have different tools to measure pollution with these days. And it is undeniably true that in important ways our water is better today than it has been for many centuries.

As late as Victorian times, Parliament in London was often compelled to suspend its sittings on hot summer days, so unbearable was the stench from the Thames flowing past Westminster, carrying its cargo of corpses and raw sewage down to the sea. And a Dr Snow in London's East End stopped an epidemic of cholera in its tracks simply by removing the handle of the parish pump.

For centuries, in most European countries human excrement was dumped in holes in the ground, or left lying around in backyards or city streets. Heavy rains washed it into wells and groundwater, and 'drinking' water as a result was so foul that few people dared touch it: they drank milk, beer or wine. Stately homes and castles reeked of the wastes accumulating in cesspools beneath them.

A terrible fate befell the assembly summoned by the Emperor Frederick Barbarossa to his castle at Erfurt in Germany in 1183. 'This was perhaps the greatest assembly of princes and knights the medieval age had ever seen...,' wrote Are Waerland, who told the story in his book *In the Cauldron of Disease*. Just as this troop of gorgeously clad and important noblemen piled into the Great Hall at Erfurt, the floors finally gave way, '...rotted by the fumes and moisture rising from a century-old accumulation of manure in a semi-fluid state of decomposition in a cellar below.' The emperor managed to scramble to safety – but almost all his guests fell headlong to a dreadful death.

If we could travel in time, the first thing to hit us in past centuries would be the smell. To our delicate twenty-first-century noses, accustomed to deodorized bodies and fragrant laundry detergents, it would probably be unbearable. Our drinking water no longer reeks of human wastes, but before we become complacent about its safety and quality we should remind ourselves of a few other things that we are now putting – or allowing to be put – in it.

Dying forests first forced the problem of acid rain on our attention in the 1980s. The noxious clouds blowing out of our factory chimneys were actually affecting rainwater falling hundreds of kilometres away. Emissions of sulphur dioxide and oxides of nitrogen from fossil-fuel-burning factories react in the atmosphere with water, oxygen and oxidants to form various acidic compounds, which fall to the earth as rain or snow, or just blow around as gas and particles. It all ends up in the water, poisoning our rivers, our lakes and eventually even the ocean.

In some lakes in the USA, acidification has completely eradicated fish species and left waters barren, and although stringent controls have abated some of the atmospheric effects, it looks increasingly as though the lakes will never fully recover. At the Institute of Ecosystem Studies in Millbrook, New York State, they call this the Tums effect. Just as antacids in the stomach can help neutralize the effects of excess stomach acid, so certain compounds from the bottom of the lake used to buffer the effects of acid rain. But years of exposure have depleted these compounds, and the researchers think that it may be decades, or even centuries, before the buffers rebuild themselves.

Among the hundreds of thousands of polluting chemicals that end up in our water systems, pharmaceutical drugs – exiting our bodies in urine – make a hefty contribution. A study by the Royal

Danish School of Pharmacy suggests that 30–90% of the antibiotics we take go into the water system: there is no monitoring of the actual amount or of its effects, and no filtering.

Mervyn Richardson, of Thames Water in the UK, analysed sewage flows to discover that there were more than 170 different drugs flowing down the River Lea in northeast London, ranging from aspirin to morphine derivatives. If it doesn't end up in our drinking water, it could end up being sprayed over a field, and from there it's a short trip back into an animal. And thence back to us?

Industrial farming, with its heavy use of pesticides sends millions of litres of chemicals into nearby rivers every day. In 1999 the US Geological Survey studied 20 of the largest river basins in the USA and found 83 pesticides and breakdown products in the water, and 32 pesticides in fish or streambed sediment. The surveyors pointed out that due to budgetary restraints there were many other pesticides they weren't even able to test for.

Swiss studies have found that rain, too, comes laced with pesticides – so much so that rainwater regularly fails standards set nationally for drinking water.

The effects of these pesticide residues on human health is a favourite topic of environmentalists (see Earth, chapter 6). But beyond their effect on us, what are they doing to the planet at large? The eutrophication that I saw from the plane into Rome is the result of phosphorus and nitrogen – from farm fertilizers, industrial waste and human and animal waste – seeping into our water supply. It is slowly choking many stretches of water to death.

In 1999 the World Wildlife Fund released a horrifying report which stated that 51% of freshwater species are declining in numbers. Increasingly rivers and lakes around the world are suffocating because phosphorus and nitrogen function as fertilizers. If left alone, algae in rivers and lakes will bloom briefly in season, but given an all-year-round supply of fertiliser, algae will bloom continually: the result is that other species in a given body of water become deprived of light and oxygen, and eventually die.

Even oceans are vulnerable to this problem, though for years scientists had assumed they were too large and fast-moving to succumb. In the shallow waters around Denmark, the sea grass is being smothered by macro-algae. Every summer 18,000 square km of the Gulf of Mexico become 'the dead zone', as the deep waters fill with dead plant matter which is unable to receive light or oxygen through the thick layer of plant life covering the surface. Other seas being affected include the Baltic Sea, the North Sea and the Lagoon of Venice.

Marine life is vulnerable to other threats, including the toxic anti-fouling paints that coat ships' hulls, radioactive discharges from nuclear power stations like Sellafield and Dungeness near the sea in England, and oil spills or deliberate discharges from ships at sea.

The problem of water pollution is hugely complex. Take phosphates, which became public enemy number one for environmentalists in the 1970s and 1980s. Phosphorus is one of the five elements which make up DNA, along with carbon, hydrogen, oxygen and nitrogen, all essential building blocks for life.

The amount of phosphorus present in our soil determines the amount of food we can produce: most crops draw phosphorus from the soil without replacing it. As a naturally occurring element to plant growth, it is available only in limited amounts. Science-fiction author Isaac Asimov writes: 'Life can multiply until all the phosphorus has gone and then there is an inexorable halt which nothing can prevent.'

In the Middle Ages, agricultural techniques throughout Europe would have exhausted the phosphorus in soil, and in his book *The Shocking History of Phosphorus* John Emsley suggests that this may have been the reason for stagnating population numbers and general poor health. The invention of artificial fertilizers supplying phosphorus and nitrogen in the nineteenth century meant that, for the first time, we could add phosphorus instantly, instead of using more arduous techniques like letting the soil rest, planting certain crops and using organic materials as compost. Although fertilizer use was initially fairly small scale, after the Second World War it took off, sending huge quantities of fertilizer run-off into our waterways. Simultaneously, phosphates were being used in our detergents: Procter & Gamble launched phosphate-rich Tide in 1946 – 'the new washing miracle' –

and by 1950 it was outselling all other brands. On top of all these sources, phosphates are also present in human and animal waste.

The result of this tidal wave of phosphorus was, as already explained, to fertilize the plant life of our waterways. Preventive action can sometimes succeed. Lake Erie, one of the five Great Lakes of North America, which was diagnosed as dying in the 1960s and 1970s, seems to have been brought back to life by a huge coordinated effort from the US and Canadian governments. Together, they enforced a ban on phosphate use in detergents in the area, as well as improving water treatment locally. It worked, and the lake (which has the quickest clean-through period of any of the Great Lakes – just three years) has almost completely recovered. And gradually, most detergent manufacturers began to replace the phosphates with alternatives, which seemed to work just as well.

But some studies in the intervening years have suggested that phosphates are not the only culprit for eutrophication. It turns out that industrial pollution by heavy metals, oils and insecticides was killing the zoo plankton, tiny organisms which would have fed on the algae and kept it manageable. And just to complicate matters, phosphate can occasionally be the solution instead of the problem. In the 1990s workers at the Netherlands Organization for Applied Scientific Research added phosphate to unpolluted waters: the result was an upsurge in algae growth, zoo plankton and, eventually, fish.

For long years it was assumed that pollutants dumped in fast-flowing rivers or out at sea would be carried off to remote depths where they would trouble us no longer. We now know better. Heavy metals such as mercury and cadmium can also travel seawards attached to grainy sediments in riverwater. Once they reach the sea, they settle to the seabed, where they are taken up by mussels and oysters. In the 1960s, over 40 people died in the Japanese town of Minimata from mercury poisoning, and many more of the 50,000 inhabitants suffered lingering ill-effects. Over 30 years of dumping, the mercury had accumulated in the fish that featured on Minamata's daily menu.

Industry certainly isn't the only polluter.

Almost everything that makes life in 'advanced' western countries easy, trouble-free and agreeable contributes its own whack to water pollution. The shampoo, shower gel and soap we use for our morning bath or shower, and the deodorants, aftershaves, toilet waters and cosmetics that later make us ready to face the world; the bleaches, detergents, spot removers and fabric softeners that take care of our laundry; the solvents that our friendly local dry-cleaner will use to get the grease out of our clothes; the dozens of chemicals including fragrances that go into our impressive array of cleaning materials; the weed killers, fertilizers and insecticides we use in our gardens; the aerosols we use to blast household pests; the residues of paint and paint thinner – these are just some of the dizzying cocktail of chemicals that all of us contribute via our household drains to pollution of the waters we could one day be drinking.

Then there are the septic tanks widely used for households not connected to mains sewage systems, not to mention toilet cleaners, disinfectants and cesspool or septic tank cleaning products, which can leak pathological bacteria, viruses and parasites out into local groundwater. According to J.C. Jenkins, who has written the ultimate work on shit and its disposal, *The Humanure Handbook*, in nine US states septic systems are the primary source of groundwater pollution.

Want to hear more? Not really, but let's just briefly cite leaking landfill sites – the ones that were just huge holes in the ground, before present-day regulation – hazardous waste dumps, oil spills, leaking underground storage tanks and the salts and other chemicals dusted over icy roads in winter.

There are more than 8 million cubic km of fresh groundwater stored in the earth, half of it within 0.8km of the surface. It's a frightening thought that much of it is already too polluted to drink, that thousands of wells and boreholes, which once tapped into crystal-clear, clean drinking water, can no longer be used.

Groundwater is the reserve that countries will increasingly be drawing on as streams and rivers dry up and demand for water increases. But as Fred Pearce pointed out, writing about just one pollutant, solvents, in the *New Scientist* of 21 September 1996, 'Rivers can be cleaned up quickly once the source of contamination has been dealt with: solvents in groundwaters will remain for hundreds, and perhaps thousands of years.'

There is good news, too. In the past, industries dumped their poisonous waste products into the nearest brook, stream or river, and nobody paid too much attention unless the water actually started to smell bad. Today there are tight controls in place and, although in practice they may be widely disregarded, and fines for polluting industry are too often derisory, the legislation is there, together with a growing political will to make it work. Politicians listen to public opinion, which is now swinging increasingly behind clean-up initiatives and tough anti-pollution legislation.

Activist bodies, too, have impact on public opinion and political action to an extent far beyond their wildest dreams of 30 years ago. Thanks to the Internet, such movements – not just the big league players like Greenpeace and Friends of the Earth, but smaller local groups like the US-based community Groundwater Guardians – are growing in strength, in numbers and in influence. The huge information resource of the Internet is also making it steadily more difficult for big polluting industries to get away with it.

And finally, since every one of us is a consumer of water, there is plenty we can do. For suggestions on actions that will help clean up our water resources see the Pure Water Action Plan on pages 210–211.

7 fit to drink?

You could put five experts in a room together to discuss drinking water safety, and probably leave them there for a couple of days, safe in the knowledge that they'll still be arguing when you come back. Issues like fluoridation, chlorination and bottled versus tap raise every sort of hackle and, ultimately, it's up to individuals to make their own decision.

Unsurprisingly, the quality of our drinking water is an issue of great concern. The USA and UK are both fortunate enough to have tapwater that is basically safe to drink, that is unlikely to carry water-borne diseases like cholera and hepatitis that cripple poorer countries. In fact, the UK claims to have some of the best drinking water in the world: the chief inspector of drinking water recently revealed that 99.82% of the country's drinking water met his tough tests in 1999.

But this may be something of an illusion. Both the USA and the UK have been plagued by occasional outbreaks of water-borne bacteria, and, according to *USA Today*, about a million Americans suffer gastro-intestinal sicknesses every year from contaminated drinking water. Apparently as many as 1000 may die, while water contamination is suspected in cancers, miscarriages and birth defects.

In fact, tapwater can carry a number of things which may be dangerous to your health. The issue of fluoridation is discussed in chapter 8, but chlorination is almost as contentious: chlorine, a highly effective disinfecting agent used extensively in the UK and USA to treat water supplies, is increasingly being linked to heart disease and cancer. This is a tough one, because chlorination has undoubtedly saved countless lives, and is regarded by some as the most important health advance of the twentieth century. In 1900, before chlorine was in use, there were about 35,000 deaths from typhoid, a water-borne disease, but by 1955 the death rate had dropped to just 50. Moreover, a cholera epidemic in Peru hit 300,000 people in 1991, was blamed by many on Peru's refusal to chlorinate drinking water.

It would all seem very clear cut if it were not for the fact that, after analysis in the 1970s showed that chlorine may produce chloroform if it reacts with organic matter, the US National Cancer Institute found links between chloroform and cancer. When they looked at the pattern of bladder, rectal and colon cancer rates across the USA, there was clearly a link to areas with chlorinated drinking water. Other studies have since found that chlorinated water may affect blood cholesterol levels, which would link it to heart disease as well.

The debate over chlorinated water has raged fiercely for the last 20 years and Greenpeace have called for a total global ban. But the alternatives – ozone or ultraviolet treatment – are just not as effective as disinfectants. What should we do? Water filters may be one answer and these are covered in detail on page 178.

Other worrying elements in your tapwater may include lead. UK scientist, Dr. Eric Millstone, Senior Lecturer at Sussex University's Science Policy Research Unit, estimated that 1 in 10 children in the UK has learning and behavioural difficulties as a result of lead pollution. The UK allows higher ratios of lead to water than the WHO advises, although a European Union (EU) Directive states that we must change that, and all water companies now offer to replace lead pipes free of charge. The situation in the USA is as bad: it is possible that as many as 20% of Americans are exposed to dangerous levels of lead in their drinking water. It is worth finding out what your pipes are made of and looking out for lead solder or metal alloys containing lead.

Then, as we saw in chapter 6, there are all the substances that can seep into groundwater, and hence into our drinking water. Nitrates and pesticides can both be found, usually from farm run-off, and they can have a whole spectrum of harmful effects.

Occasional outbreaks of parasites and bacterial infections always make the headlines. In the UK in 1988, almost 500 cases of cryptosporidiosis – an illness caused by a water-borne parasite that causes acute diarrhoea – occurred in Swindon and parts of Oxfordshire in the West of England, probably caused by faeces from infected cows washing into a local river. And the US Centers for Disease Control have found that over 900,000 people in the USA become sick every year from water contaminated with biological organisms.

Yet another worry is a possible link between drinking water with high levels of aluminium and Alzheimer's. Focusing on 3777 people aged over 65 in 75 different villages in the Dordogne and Gironde areas of France, a report by the government-funded medical research institute INSERM found that people who drink water containing more than 100 mg of aluminium per litre double the risk of contracting Alzheimer's.

To round it all off, there is the occasional accident like the incident in Camelford in Cornwall in 1988, England, which made 20,000 people extremely ill. When a relief tanker driver came to deliver a batch of aluminium sulphate to the Lowermoor water treatment plant, he found the plant unstaffed, and mistakenly poured his solution into the reservoir of treated water. Local residents suffered acute metal poisoning and acid burns and, although the Health Advisory Group set up to investigate the incident concluded that no long-term effects on health could be attributed to the incident, some locals still complain of joint and muscle pains, malaise, fatigue and memory loss.

However, before you swear never to drink straight from the tap again, think about what water was like 150 years ago.

In 1854, cholera, a water-borne disease, killed 10,765 people in the UK. There are now a lot of regulations in place to keep water relatively healthy. In Europe we have the EU Directive on drinking water, which set standards for 46 different substances, as well as various other sets of regulations, while in the USA there are a host of acts, such as the Clean Water Act and the Safe Drinking Water Act of 1974, which the Environmental Protection Agency (EPA) is now empowered to enforce.

There are other options. Bottled water has become one of the fastest growing industries around: consumption in the UK rose by 25% between 1998 and 1999! If you're drinking 'natural mineral water' in Europe, then you're drinking water which has come from an underground unpolluted source without being treated (apart from getting the sand out), which is a very appealing idea, apart from the wastefulness of all those plastic bottles. It's worth hunting out glass bottles just because glass is so much more recyclable.

But other types of bottled water may not be quite so ideal: concerns have been raised in the USA about sanitation levels at bottling plants after the EPA checked out the facilities at 25 chosen at random. They found that about 1 in 10 bottles contained bacteria from handling without gloves, leaving the bottles uncapped, and other lapses in hygiene. It's not what you want, really. And remember, bottled water costs up to 1000 times more than tap water.

The other possibility is to install water filters, either portable or in-line (the filters are attached to one of your taps – more convenient and longer-lasting, but much more expensive). The most traditional filter type is carbon: sailors noticed centuries ago that drinking water stayed fresher and tasted better if stored in charred barrels. Filtering water through carbon removes Volatile Organic Compounds (VOCs – see Air, chapter 6) like some pesticides and industrial chemicals, most of the chlorine, water hardness and some heavy metals including lead. It's not effective for nitrates and, if you fail to change them pretty regularly, it may even encourage bacteria. Irritatingly, it's impossible to tell when their time is up, but most manufacturers do supply guidelines.

If you are buying portable jug-type filters remember that, as a general guideline, the longer the filter itself the better: the more contact time the water has with the carbon, the more efficiently impurities will be removed.

The question of hardness or softness in water can be one of the most difficult problems to resolve.

Depending on its degree of hardness, water can cause a build-up of scale in pipes, radiators, water heaters and kettles, shortening their life and upping the running costs, as well as increasing the amount of detergents your clothes will need for a proper wash and sometimes depositing an irremovable white scale on glasses. On the other hand, soft water, being very acidic, can corrode pipes and leach hazardous metals such as cadmium, copper, lead and aluminium out of them into your water supply. In an extremely hard water area, a water softener will pay for itself by giving your appliances a longer lease of life, but it doesn't remove chemicals or heavy metals – what it does remove is minerals and trace elements which may be beneficial to your health, such as calcium and magnesium. The British Regional Heart Study compared water hardness and cardiovascular deaths in 253 towns in the UK. The report concluded that there were 10–15% more cardiovascular deaths in areas with very soft water compared to areas of medium hardness.

The commonest softening system uses ion-exchange, but one big snag with this is that it adds salt to the softened water, and most of us have more than enough sodium aboard already (see also page 151). Newer systems, such as nanofiltration or a copper-zinc redox system patented under the name KDF, are more expensive but don't have this drawback.

If it all sounds too technically daunting, there is plenty of advice and information available to help you make the best choice (see Resources).

8 the fluoride saga

Frederick McKay was fresh out of dental school when he opened his first practice in Colorado Springs, Colorado in the USA in 1901. He hadn't been long in town when he began noticing chocolate-brown stains on the teeth of many of his patients, a condition he had never come across in dental literature. Intrigued, he began researching the problem.

Together with a leading dental researcher, Dr G.V. Black, he spent the next six years investigating those brown-stained teeth. He made two discoveries. The first was that the curious mottling only happened while teeth were developing: once the permanent teeth were through unmottled, they would never develop the disfiguring stains. The other discovery was even more thought-provoking: the stained teeth seemed impervious to decay.

At a small town called Bauxite in Arkansas they finally found their answer. Bauxite was a company town belonging to the Aluminium Company of America, and a report by the two dentists landed on the desk of the company's chief chemist, H.V. Churchill. After analysis of the local water using sophisticated new technology, in 1931 Churchill reported that sodium fluoride in the water – a waste product of the aluminium industry – could be the explanation.

McKay began correlating levels of fluoride in the Colorado drinking water samples with the appearance of the brown staining. They matched up, again and again. The condition was now christened fluorosis and research took off at the highest level, led by Dr Trendley Dean, head of the Dental Hygiene Unit at the US National Institutes of Health. Dean was soon airing an astonishing proposal: what if enough fluoride could be added to the nation's drinking water to protect the all-American smile from decay without causing unsightly brown stains?

The rest, according to the National Institute of Dental and Craniofacial Research at the National Institutes of Health, is history, and pretty glorious history at that: '...a scientific revolution that shot dentistry into the forefront of preventive medicine... the story of how dental science discovered – and ultimately proved to the world – that fluoride, a mineral found in rocks and soil, prevents tooth decay... '

Other people don't see the story quite that way. In their view, the half-century and more of water fluoridation is a shameful saga of political stitch-ups, medical swindles, intrigue, bribery and corruption, and bent or bought science.

Before fluoridation could be officially launched as public health policy, it obviously needed testing. Accordingly, in 1945 Grand Rapids in Michigan became the first city in the world to have an artificially fluoridated water supply. For the next ten years, researchers monitored the rate of tooth decay among almost 30,000 young Grand Rapids children. As a control, children in the non-fluoridated city of Muskegon also had their teeth checked. After only five years, Dean was able to announce a sensational finding: the decay rate among Grand Rapids children born after the start of fluoridation had shown a significant fall. The Grand Rapids study became the cornerstone of the fluoridation campaign. (Only later did it leak out that the rate of tooth decay in the non-fluoridated Muskegon area had fallen at the same rate over the five-year period: it was quietly dropped from the study, and its water fluoridated, too.)

Backed by the American Dental Association, the American Medical Association and other high priests of medical science, fluoridation was adopted nationwide. Then manufacturers of toothpastes and other oral hygiene products clambered aboard, and today in the USA, UK, Canada and Australia, it's quite hard to find a toothpaste on sale that doesn't have fluoride added to it. Today 200 million Americans and 5.5 million people in the UK drink fluoridated water whether they like it or not, and dentists in countries still committed to fluoridation get hot under the collar if you even suggest that it might not be the obvious solution to tooth decay.

The pro-fluoride case rests on the proposition that the addition of fluoride to drinking water at the accepted rate of 1 part per million strengthens the enamel of developing teeth to give lifetime protection against tooth decay. Pro- and anti-fluoridationists have been hurling studies at each other for over 50 years, to sustain or contest this view – but there are some figures it is surely hard to dispute. In 1986–7 the US National Institute of Dental Research conducted the biggest-ever study on the question, tracking 39,000 schoolchildren aged five to seven. One-third lived in fluoridated areas, one-third in partially fluoridated, and the remaining one-third in non-fluoridated areas. A panel of experts, convened by the Massachusetts town of Natick, concluded that the study showed no statistically significant differences in tooth decay between the fluoridated and non-fluoridated areas.

British Columbia has the lowest rate of dental decay in all Canada – yet only 11% of its inhabitants drink fluoridated water, compared to 40–70% in other regions. Less than 2% of Europeans now have fluoridated water. It was banned by Sweden and West Germany in 1971, by Norway in 1975, by Holland in 1976, by Denmark in 1977, and by France in 1980. Yet plenty of studies suggest that dental decay rates in Europe have gone down quite as much as – possibly more than – they have in the USA. In other words, fluoridation may protect the developing teeth of young children but other factors – perhaps improved oral hygiene, changes in diet or the addition of fluoride to almost all toothpaste – are equally responsible.

Dr John Colquhoun was for years Chief Dental Officer of New Zealand's largest city Auckland, and one of the world's most ardent advocates of fluoridation. Then statistics started coming up that made him pause: tooth decay was decreasing just as fast in New Zealand's non-fluoridated cities. He called for fresh studies, more statistics, and, finally, figures for all New Zealand. Those for 1981 showed that in most health districts, the percentage of 12- to 13-year-olds who were free of tooth decay – that is, had perfect teeth – was actually greater in the non-fluoridated part of the district.

Alarmed, Colquhoun wrote to colleagues in the USA to ask them what their most recent figures showed. His queries were met by a perplexing silence. Finally, Dr John Yiamouyiannis got hold of the 1986–7 figures by invoking the US Freedom of Information Act. They showed that there is little or no difference in tooth decay between fluoridated and non-fluoridated areas. Numbers of large-scale studies since then have made the same point: there is no real benefit to teeth from fluoride in drinking water. Increasingly disturbed, Colquhoun looked at figures going back to the 1930s and discovered a surprising truth.

The rate of tooth decay had begun its decline long before fluoridation.

Studies showing a positive effect for fluoridation continued to appear in dental journals, however. But when Colquhoun examined these he found that many of them had been carefully rigged: in one study, school dentists in the experimental area were actually instructed to change their method of diagnosing tooth decay, so that they recorded much lower figures for decay after fluoridation began.

Fluoridation had achieved one effect on teeth, however: in fluoridated Auckland, 25% of children now had the mottled teeth of fluorosis – the first sign of fluoride toxicity – as compared to only 3% in places where the water had been untreated. Similar figures are now turning up elsewhere: according to the Centers of Disease Control, at least 22% of children in the USA now have dental fluorosis. But even in non-fluoridated areas, fluorosis is becoming a common problem.

One explanation could be the yummy, amusingly packaged and brightly coloured toothpastes for children, containing fluoride, now heavily promoted – in the interests of dental hygiene. In the USA those tubes carry health warnings that no more than a pea-sized amount should be used each time, and that the child must on no account swallow this. A spokesman for Procter & Gamble, makers of Colgate toothpaste, famously admitted in 1984 that a small tube of toothpaste 'theoretically' contains enough fluoride to kill a child.

The recommended daily intake of fluoride for children to prevent fluorosis was set at 2mg a day in 1995. Even if the child doesn't swallow a single drop, much of the fluoride will be absorbed into the bloodstream through the mucous membrane of the mouth. It has been reckoned that children can absorb up to 0.5mg a day from toothpaste. And the family dentist may suggest that children be given fluoride supplements in non-fluoridated areas, while children with real dental problems may be given a treatment in which a fluoride gel is held in trays surrounding the teeth for minutes at a time.

Advocates of fluoridation often talk as though the fluoride added to our drinking water is one of those good-guy minerals, like calcium and magnesium, that our bodies need regularly. But the US Food and Drug Administration does not recognise fluoride as an essential nutrient. An adult's body contains around 2.6g of the non-metallic mineral fluorine, but since there are many food sources – especially fish and cereals – deficiency is unknown, and has never been produced in experimental animals. Average daily intake in the UK – apart from water – has been reckoned at 1.82mg, of which 70% is supplied by tea: fluoridated water adds around 1.1mg extra.

What is added to fluoridated drinking water, however, has never been this naturally occurring fluorine. Originally it was sodium fluoride, a waste product of the aluminium industry, which is lethal at doses 50% lower than naturally occurring fluoride and is more toxic than lead.

The stuff being added to water in the USA and UK, however, is no longer the sodium fluoride produced as waste by the aluminium industry: it is the toxic waste produced by the phosphate fertilizer industry. During manufacture, huge quantities of hazardous chemicals including fluoride are emitted via the chimneys. To comply with tight US Environmental Protection Agency (EPA) regulations, this waste is 'scrubbed' – or washed down with water. The pollution scrubber liquor contains 19% fluoride in the form of hexafluorosilicic acid (H_2SiF_6), together with unspecified amounts of arsenic, cadmium, beryllium, mercury, lead, sulphides, iron and phosphorus, as well as radioactive compounds.

This form of fluoride – fluosilicic acid – was a lot easier to handle than the sodium fluoride. Being liquid and readily soluble in water, it could simply be dumped into water as it was. No clinical or safety studies were carried out, and in 1983 the EPA triumphantly declared: 'In regard to the use of fluosilicic acid as a source of fluoride for fluoridation, this agency regards such use as an ideal environmental solution to a long-standing problem. By recovering by-product fluosilicic acid from fertilizer manufacturing, water and air pollution are minimized, and water utilities have a low-cost source of fluoride available to the communities.'

The fertilizer manufacturers were very happy: the cost of trucking this stuff to a class one landfill has been reckoned at up to $7000 a truckload. Water authorities actually pay them to take it off their hands.

Dr William Hirzy, Senior Vice-President of the EPA's own Professional Headquarters Union, summed it up: 'If this stuff gets into the air it's a pollutant, if it gets into the river, it's a pollutant, if it gets into the lake it's a pollutant; but if it goes right straight into your drinking water system, it's not a pollutant. Amazing!'

How did these astonishing facts come to light? An American investigative journalist from Florida, George Glasser, stumbled upon the pollution scrubber story when workers at a phosphate plant asked him to help them fight for compensation for industrial injuries. He was appalled by what he learned. 'After publishing their stories', Glasser later said, 'I spent the next two years researching official regulations and the PSL itself, and turned up some very frightening facts... Arsenic and beryllium are classified as Group 1 'known human carcinogens'. There is no 'safe level' for arsenic – it's a cumulative poison... Why would anyone advocate adding known human carcinogens to the public drinking water for any reason at all? To promote it for a claimed reduction in tooth decay is utterly preposterous.'

In March 2000, Jane Jones, energetic Campaign Director of the UK's National Pure Water Association, wrote to Thomas Reeves, the US Chief Fluoridation Engineer, asking him to confirm or deny that the fluoridating agent is pollution scrubber liquor, and to provide Safety Testing Data for the product. Months later, as this book goes to press, she has received no satisfactory answer. Incidentally, studies designed to assess the effects of long-term fluoride consumption and its possible toxicity have all been carried out with pharmaceutical-grade sodium fluoride: in none has the pollution scrubber liquor been used.

But evidence is mounting that far from being an innocuous health measure, fluoridation is having a catastrophic impact on the health of thousands of people.

Weakened bones can be one consequence. Studies from all over the world, based on statistics from huge computerized data banks and published in journals which carry real clout – such as the *Journal of the American Medical Association* – show that people living in fluoridated areas are more likely to have hip fractures. Researchers have found that at strengths as low as 1 part per million, fluoride decreases bone strength and elasticity; about half of the fluoride we ingest is retained in the body and stored in bone, where it displaces calcium.

Testosterone is vital to the growth of bone in males, although not in females. It now seems that even at low levels fluoride may interfere with testosterone function. A dramatic rise in the incidence of a once-rare cancer of the bone, osteosarcoma, is now being found in areas where water is fluoridated. Its victims are boys aged 9–19. In 1992 the New Jersey Department of Health reported that osteosarcoma rates were three to seven times higher in its fluoridated areas than in those where the water had not been treated.

It was evidence like this that has turned Dr John Colquhoun from enthusiastic advocate to outspoken opponent. 'Even more chilling,' he wrote in 1997, 'is the evidence from China that children with dental fluorosis have on average lower intelligence scores.'

Andreas Schuld in Canada is founder of a campaigning body called Parents of Fluoride Poisoned Children. He can cite over 100 published studies which may be relevant to the Chinese findings. Many of them strongly suggest that fluoride is a direct cause of iodine deficiency leading to thyroid problems. Iodine is a non-metallic mineral essential to the production of the thyroid hormones, which in turn are vital to the growth and development of both brain and body. When iodine is deficient – as it is in the soils of many countries, including India, China and Italy – children are stunted, mentally retarded and apathetic, and pregnant women are at risk from stillbirth or miscarriage.

So well known is fluoride's antagonistic action on iodine levels that it was for long used as an antithyroid drug. 'Is it really coincidence,' asks Schuld, 'that many areas of the world identified with the greatest iodine deficiency are also the areas with the greatest occurrence of fluorosis?'

The York Review, set up in the UK in 1998 to consider the whole question of fluoridation, refused to consider these papers collated by

Schuld. They have also refused to consider animal studies and fluoride intake from any source other than drinking water. For these reasons the conclusion of their final report in Autumn 2000 – that fluoridation presents no threat to health – has been severely criticised by scientists around the world.

Some of the most bitter criticism of fluoridation has come from those working for the EPA in the USA, which itself is a leading advocate for the policy. Their union represents some 1500 scientists, lawyers, engineers and other professional employees at EPA headquarters in Washington, and members were becoming increasingly uneasy about what they saw as heavy political pressure, rather than good science, influencing the EPA's decisions. The union's treasurer, Dr William Marcus, was actually fired for going public with his concerns about the cancer risk. This was too much.

Using the EPA's own standard method for controlling risks from toxic chemicals, they found that people drinking no more than a litre of fluoridated water, and not exposed to any other source, would already be receiving 100 times the reference (or safe) dose.

On this basis, the EPA union have called for 'an immediate halt to the use of the nation's drinking water reservoirs as disposal sites for the toxic waste of the phosphate fertilizer industry'.

To many people, however, the fluoride issue isn't even a medical matter: it's a question of individual freedom.

If a white-coated medical man appeared at your door with a small glass of medicine in his hand and told you that you had to swallow it, no choice, sorry, the government said so, and the same tomorrow and the day after, too, you would be contacting your favourite national newspaper within minutes to denounce this tyranny. But in effect, that's what has happened with fluoridation of public drinking water. No choice. And definitely no guarantee that the stuff is safe.

As Dr Hans Moolenburgh, leader of the successful anti-fluoridation battle in the Netherlands, put it: 'Freedom is a blessing that is acquired with great difficulty and lost with great ease. Fluoridation is one of the ways of taking that freedom away.'

water: the power of water

9 harnessing the waves

It has been estimated by the Marine Foresight Panel, an advisory body to the UK's Department of Trade and Industry, that if less than 1% of the renewable energy available within the oceans could be converted into electricity, it would satisfy the present world demand for energy more than five times over. The potential is vast but, unlike wind power, there has been little major investment in the technology.

There are three leading technologies for exploiting water power: hydroelectric, tidal and wave.

Hydroelectric power is generated by dams, and the second half of the twentieth century was boom time for dam builders. Hoover dam in the USA, completed in 1946, was the trail-blazer. A stupendous curve of concrete 221m high across the Colorado River, on the borders of Nevada and Arizona, it was hailed as one of the wonders of the world. And thereafter, as Patrick McCully suggests in his book *Silenced Rivers*, dams were regarded as 'potent symbols of both patriotic pride and the conquest of nature by human ingenuity'.

Today Hoover would be dwarfed by the 300m-high Nurek dam in Tadjikistan, the 285m Grande Dixence dam in Switzerland and a dozen others. More than 45,000 large dams have been built in the last half-century – over 300 of them in the same league as Hoover. If the highly controversial Three Gorges dam across China's Yangtze River is ever built, it will be monster-sized, stretching nearly 1.5km across the fertile valleys of the Yangtze, with a reservoir 560km upstream flooding agricultural land and displacing more than 1.5 million people.

Dams now account for more than half the energy in over 66 countries, supplying 20% of world energy: 56% of Canada's energy comes from hydropower, with 27% in Mexico and 13% in the USA. Latin America is particularly dependent on hydropower: it meets 87% of Brazil's energy needs, 59% in Venezuela, 53% in Chile and 43% in Argentina.

If this energy gap had been filled by fossil fuels, global warming might already be a hideous reality.

Millions of smaller dams and hydropower structures – perhaps two million in the USA alone – provide for the energy needs of smaller communities, or create reservoirs of drinking water. They are the descendants of the watermills developed in ancient Rome which, together with windmills, helped power the Industrial Revolution.

But recently big dams have become targets of what dam-builders bitterly call 'eco-fundamentalists'. They attack dams on many counts, and you can see their point. Tens of millions of people have been evicted from cherished homes and land, there has been a huge loss of life when dams have broken, great rivers are dying, freshwater fisheries are being lost, species have become extinct, millions of hectares of fertile flood-plain soils have been irreparably destroyed.

The swelling chorus of opposition includes economists and hydrologists, as well as activists representing the rural communities threatened by them or greens appalled by environmental damage. Hundreds of kilometres of rivers around the world, reports McCully, are now legally protected against dam building, including almost all the rivers that still flow freely in Norway and Sweden. In the USA numbers of smaller dams are already scheduled for removal: in June 1999, the 162-year-old Edwards dam across the River Kennebec in Maine was demolished and scientists, anglers and environmentalists celebrated as salmon, sturgeon and striped bass returned to a river renewed and revitalized.

In a clean, green, future Eden, perhaps even the largest dams will be torn down and rivers restored to their former glory.

Meanwhile, growing energy needs have to be satisfied, and it is to oceans rather than to rivers that the energy-makers of tomorrow are turning.

So what about tidal power? This is the modern update of the old tide mills once common around our coastlines. And as early as 1910, the suggestion of a monster tide-mill, or barrage, across the Severn Estuary between England and Wales was first mooted. Both the estimated costs and the technical problems were enormous, so no more was heard of it until the 1970s, when it surfaced once more, with enhanced appeal as a source of renewable energy.

The Severn Estuary was one of eight possible sites around the UK coastline; the others included the Thames, the Humber and the Solway Firth. A 16km-long barrage between Cardiff and Weston-super-Mare began to take shape, on paper at least, in a number of government-funded studies. It promised a staggering 8600MW output, the equivalent of two large conventional power stations. But environmentalists grew increasingly dismayed by the impact it would have on the whole ecology of the estuary, and estimates of its cost – £11.8 billion in 1992 – were the *coup de grâce*. In 1996 the government withdrew its support.

The French had achieved a much more modest project in the 1960s, with the pioneering 240MW tidal-power station at La Rance in Brittany. But it has remained the only one in Europe, the French themselves turning to nuclear for their energy future when the oil crisis hit.

Canada also exploited tidal power for its still more modest 20MW station on the Bay of Fundy in Nova Scotia – but Fundy is a long, long way from the big centres of power demand. And the Australians have been toying with a project of their own, at Doctor's Creek, outside the Kimberley town of Derby in Western Australia. Like Fundy, however, Kimberley is hardly a throbbing centre of power-hungry life – and the costs, once more, are daunting.

The trouble with big tidal-power schemes, in the end, is that each one is unique, so the technology cannot simply be adapted from similar schemes. That makes them much more expensive. And even if they do not pollute, they can be highly damaging environmentally.

This leaves wave power, which for a number of years has been the technology that's just around the corner.

With their coastlines pounded by the long fetch of the Atlantic, Ireland and the UK – particularly northwest Scotland – are naturals for wave power. The energy contained in the waves off the Scottish coast could supply almost three times the electricity needs of the whole UK, according to Greenpeace estimates.

Like other sources of renewable energy, wave power began attracting both funds and good research brains in the mid-1970s, prompted by the oil crisis. Even the British government was prepared to dig into its pocket for a contribution to funding – although they withdrew their financial support in 1982. Undaunted, a number of engineers and designers continued to work away at improving the technology to a commercially viable point.

In 1990, some of these engineers and designers formed a company, Wavegen, which is today agreed to be the world leader in wave power. Hopes rose when, in 1993, the first offshore commercial wave-power station, a 2000kW generator christened Osprey, was towed out to its appointed site, in shallow waters just off the coast of Dounreay in north Scotland. But before its steel ballast tanks could be filled, a freak storm blew up and broke Osprey's back. 'It was a good learning curve,' says Wavegen business development manager David Langston staunchly.

Undaunted, Wavegen went on to develop their new offshore Limpet station, which was installed on the island of Islay in the summer of 2000 and went into commission in November 2000. Waves smashing through a gully will force air through two turbines to produce 500kW of electricity – enough to power over 300 homes as well as some of the energy needed for the island's famous whisky distilleries.

Wave energy development in the UK was given an unexpected boost in 1998 when Tom Thorpe, the government's leading adviser on wave power, authored a new report on the outlook for wave energy technologies. The potential was huge, he pointed out; the

International Energy Authority estimated that wave energy could eventually supply 10% of the world's energy needs and, as an additional bonus, wave energy generators could help solve a world shortage of drinking water by powering reverse-osmosis desalination plants (see also page 167). There was a potential market in excess of £100 billion. Efficient new designs and technological breakthroughs had slashed the cost of wave power to one tenth of what it had been in 1982: it was already economically competitive in niche markets. It could cost as little as 2.6p per kW/hour: almost competitive with electricity generated by a new gas-powered power station and nearly half the price of nuclear. He also advised strongly that the way ahead was to start small: wave energy needed to prove itself by a number of successes.

To the new young Scottish Parliament, wave energy is particularly attractive, offering jobs as well as power – a point emphasized by Greenpeace when they launched their New Commission for Wave Power in Scotland. 'Scotland,' said Greenpeace renewable energy campaigner Ian Taylor, 'has the world's most innovative wave-power companies, one of the world's best wave climates and some of the world's leading wave research scientists.'

The Scottish Office is now officially backing three different wave energy machines, of which Wavegen's Limpet is one. The British government is also investing several million pounds in wave power over the next 15 years. The US company Tidal Electric has proposed the most ambitious tidal-power project yet – an artificial hollow 'island' off the coast of Wales at Rhyl, which, at a cost of around $500 million could meet a seventh of Welsh energy needs. Other governments around the world have their eye on the vast job potential of wave power and have launched well-funded research programmes: among them are Denmark, Sweden, Norway, Portugal, France, Japan and Ireland. But no one, so far, apart from Scotland's Wavegen, has got much further than prototype stage.

The Danes achieved their spectacular lead in wind power by starting small, developing wind turbines just big enough to power a farm or a small village and honing the technology as they went along (see Air, pages 128–9). Given the investment, and serious government backing, the UK can do the same for wave power.

water therapy

10 the water cure

'An Amazing Discovery,' trumpeted the front page of *The European* newspaper in April 1993. 'The Romans did it. Charles Darwin lectured on it... Now scientists have proved for the first time the therapeutic benefits of cold-water bathing.' The article went on to document the studies being carried out by Professor Vijay Kakkar at the Thrombosis Research Institute in London, England, with 100 human volunteers. While they bravely submitted to a carefully graduated series of cold baths, monitoring of these men and women had shown up some extraordinary changes. Levels of sex hormones – testosterone in the men, oestrogen in the women – had climbed significantly as they graduated to the colder baths. Circulation improved dramatically, and levels of an enzyme that prevents blood from clotting also rose. And white blood counts had climbed, indicating improved immune function.

For one volunteer in particular, the results of the trial were spectacular. She had been suffering for years from Chronic Fatigue Syndrome (ME), spending up to 18 hours a day in bed and hardly able to crawl upstairs. She had been reluctant to join the trial, but was amazed by the effect of her daily icy plunge: '...as if it had freed my body from imprisonment in an iron jacket.... With each passing day, the feeling of well-being is increased.'

Professor Kakkar's study had been prompted by his discovery that victims of ME have poor blood circulation, which reduces the supply of oxygen to brain and muscles, while immune function declines. Cold-water therapy reversed these trends. How? Brace yourself.

Take a one-minute cold shower followed by a quick, brisk rub-down and you will feel, in rapid succession, a shocking sensation of cold, followed by a rushing return of warmth as you rub down, followed by a glow of energy and well-being.

That shock of cold closes skin-surface blood vessels, and blood is driven inwards, relieving congestion. The body's thermostat reacts by rushing warm blood back to the surface, blood vessels reopen and tissues are flushed with fresh oxygen-rich blood. And as an early nineteenth-century physician put it, '...the nerves, blood vessels and all the organs of the body are excited to a more healthy and energetic performance.'

By speeding up cutaneous circulation, the treatment also boosts elimination through the skin of bodily wastes: an instant detox. When there is fever, the surface cooling is the therapy, as any mother knows when she sponges the limbs of a feverish child with tepid water.

Although the water cure – or hydrotherapy, to give it its proper name – is now being 'discovered' by modern medicine, there are records thousands of years old of its use as a medical treatment by the doctors of ancient China and India, Egypt and Mesopotamia, Greece and Rome. Its spectacular renaissance in the early nineteenth century was fathered by a peasant farmer called Vincent Priessnitz from Silesia in Poland. Following local methods, Priessnitz had been treating his own animals with cold-water therapy when they were sick or injured. A fall under the wheels of a runaway cart left him with three crushed ribs. Priessnitz reset them himself and treated himself for weeks afterwards with ice-cold wet packs, drinking plenty of cold water. A year later he was completely recovered, and began treating his neighbours.

Gradually his circle of patients widened and in 1826 he opened a clinic in Graefenberg, Germany, for patients who needed long courses of treatment. Soon it was famous and fashionable all over Europe. Among the hundreds of patients taking the cure in 1841 were an archduchess, 10 princes and princesses, 100 counts and barons, military men, professors, lawyers and a number of doctors. The regime they paid to endure was spartan in the extreme: straw beds in plain stone huts, coarse peasant food, day-long exercise in open air – and, of course, cold water.

Priessnitz' favourite treatment was the wet pack: patients were stripped and swathed in a cold wet sheet while they lay down on a thick blanket. More covers were piled up on top and they were left to sweat for up to two hours, during which time fresh wet sheets were sometimes applied. The 'disagreeable colour and smell' of the sheets and bandages when removed were evidence of the heavy discharge of what Priessnitz called 'the bad stuff' – as any modern nature-cure establishment, using the same technique, would verify.

Afterwards, patients were sponged down with cold water or put in the cold plunge-bath for a minute or two, then quickly dressed – without being dried first – and sent to take brisk outdoor exercise. It sounds like a sure prescription for pneumonia. But what Priessnitz knew – and other practitioners have verified – is that as long as the body is wrapped warmly enough to prevent chilling, continuing contact with cold water stimulates it to produce more heat, and thus speed up the circulation to produce a delightful glow of well-being.

Other cold-water treatments included simple sponging-down with cold water, sitz-baths and douches constructed from local mountain springs trained through showers that fell from as high as 6m.

Priessnitz kept no records, but his results in almost every disease imaginable were so spectacular that a regular procession of doctors turned up at Graefenberg to study his methods. Soon there were hydrotherapy institutions all over Europe.

Among Priessnitz' many followers was the famous natural healer Father Sebastian Kneipp (see also Earth, page 78), whose work *My Water Cure* explained the principles and practice of hydrotherapy in clear, simple terms for laymen. It became a huge best-seller, and was translated into English in 1891. Kneipp considered cold-water treatment not just as a cure, but as a marvellous way to improve health and increase resistance: a process he termed 'hardening'. In his view 'hardening' couldn't start too young. He suggested that babies should be given a quick cool or cold dip after their warm bath, and that children be encouraged to run about barefoot. Walking on wet grass, in newly-fallen snow or in a bath filled ankle-deep with cold water were other suggestions.

In 1990 the Hanover Medical School ran a six-month study of the Kneipp 'hardening' theory with 50 student volunteers. Half the students took an early morning shower, the temperature of which was gradually reduced over the first weeks until it was cold; the other half took a daily warm shower. When the six months was up, the cold-shower volunteers were recording only half as many colds as the control group, and those they did have were milder and cleared faster.

By the end of the nineteenth century, the water cure was the subject of serious study at hospitals and in medical practices all over Europe.

Professor Winternitz of the University of Vienna in Austria ran a hydrotherapy clinic where he made dozens of careful observations of patients. The American Dr Baruch studied under Winternitz and went back to New York to apply and develop what he had learned.

At a time when infectious diseases were usually lethal, Dr. Baruch claimed to have lost fewer than 1% of 1223 typhoid fever patients treated by his hydrotherapy method at Manhattan General Hospital in New York. He would wait until the patient's temperature had climbed to over 38.3°C, and then immerse him or her up to the chin in a cool-to-tepid bath (18°C) for 15 minutes, followed by a rub-down. In a massive treatise called *The Principles and Practice of Hydrotherapy*, published in 1898 and written after years of applied hydrotherapy, Baruch lamented that the water cure had been so much neglected. In this he chose to ignore the nature-cure practitioners of the USA, who had been promoting hydrotherapy with enthusiasm for decades at sanatoriums such as the famous Battle Creek in Michigan, home to Dr Kellogg and his Corn Flakes.

Dr John Harvey Kellogg published his own 1193-page work, *Rational Hydrotherapy*, three years later in 1901. It was based, like Baruch's, on years of practice and careful observation. Although it remains the outstanding text on the subject, it seems to have damned hydrotherapy in the eyes of the medical profession by association with 'quackery' – an association already established by the spread of 'Kneippism', with its dozens of sanatoria in Europe and the USA.

Today, professional hydrotherapy treatment is only on offer at a few Kneipp 'cure-houses' in Europe, and, apart from a limited use in physiotherapy, this wonderfully effective therapy has been consigned to near-complete medical oblivion. We can still profit in our own homes from its 'hardening' powers. To modern ears, the mere idea of cold showers, chilly baths and icy rub-downs seems masochistic in the extreme. But nobody feels cold weather more keenly than those who spend their lives cocooned in modern comfort. Moreover, central heating offers no pleasures to rival the wonderful tingle and glow of a cold shower followed by a quick rub-down and a brisk walk.

11 sweating it out

The sauna habit has a long history. As therapy or hygiene, for social pleasure or ritual purification, this bracing combination of hot air, sweat and cold water has been enjoyed worldwide for thousands of years. Remains of stone bath-houses, built near running water with telltale heaps of blackened stones, have been found at Bronze Age sites in the UK. In Ancient Greece, the hot-air bath followed by a cold dip was a regular feature of an athlete's conditioning programme, and every gymnasium had its well-equipped bath. The Romans adopted the bath and the *hypocaustum* – the manner of heating it by flues under the floor. Soon they rated its health-giving powers so highly that wherever the Roman legions made permanent camp, bath-houses were immediately built for the troops. Bath-mania reached its height in the enormous *thermae* built by Caracalla in Rome, lavishly decorated with marble, granite and mosaics: there were marble seats for 3000 bathers and the water flowed through massive silver taps.

In the Byzantine world, luxurious hammams (steam baths) built of marble and tiles combined that healthful sweat with a long and sensuous massage: they can still be found in the Middle East today. And passing English travellers noted this extraordinary habit in Russia, China and Japan. 'Scores of individuals mingle together in one 'heated apartment,' reported a nineteenth-century visitor to St Petersburg, 'and after being sweated, switched and half-boiled, rush into the open air like so many frantic satyrs and plunge into the coldest water.'

Until well into the nineteenth century, the sauna – usually a log cabin – was the weekly social gathering place of every Scandinavian village. Men, women and children all undressed together and, armed with a bucket of ice-cold water and a besom made of birch twigs, climbed up to a big platform to lie down on fresh clean straw. The women took it in turns to play attendant, throwing boiling water at intervals over the huge stone stove so that the cabin filled with steam.

When the sweat ran down their bodies, the sauna-bathers dipped their birches in iced water and beat themselves till they were lobster-red. The Swedish naturopath Are Waerland noted that, according to archaeological records, the sauna tradition was at least 9000 years old. As a boy of nine, visiting relatives in Finland, he could remember afternoons of wonderful fun at the sauna, revelling with the village boys and rushing out at intervals to gambol in the deep snowdrifts. 'This great treat ended with a general scrubbing with soap and hot water... after which the woman in charge poured a bucket of icy water over our heads and bodies, and sent us into an adjoining room to dress. At suppertime – what an appetite! And in bed – what wonderful, deep, invigorating sleep!'

There were other fans of the sauna: Celts, Teutons, Polynesians, the tribes of New Guinea and Melanesia among them. Visiting the Aztecs of Latin America, one traveller reported that '...the favourite remedy for almost every ill of the flesh was the vapor-bath.' Indigestion, snake bites, dangerous fevers and crippling joint pain were among the ailments for which the Aztecs resorted to sweat therapy. As Virgil Vogel has recorded in his epic *American Indian Medicine*, many of the Native Americans used sweat-baths regularly, either for super-cleanliness or as therapy, plunging into the nearest icy lake or stream afterwards. Even critical white observers were obliged to concede that the therapy appeared to be highly effective. It was, according to one eighteenth-century missionary, '...their general remedy for all disorders, small and great... and in many cases the cure is complete.' Some of the bolder settlers ventured to imitate them and were often struck by the efficacy of the treatment.

Scandinavia has provided the prototype for the modern western sauna: a pine-built room lined with wide slatted shelves for bathers to lie on, heated by a brazier of glowing coals. Since heat rises, the upper shelves are the hottest. A loofah is the modern soft option – instead of the traditional birch twigs – used to slough off the dead skin. Sometimes cold water is thrown on the glowing coals to create a cloud of steam – and even greater heat. When the heat becomes unbearable, sauna-users take a cold shower, plunge into an icy pool – or, wherever possible, roll in the snow outside.

Why is the heat-sweat-cold treatment so good for us? Because it boosts the skin's eliminative activity while at the same time giving the whole metabolism a terrific shot in the arm. Our 1.7 square metres or so of skin helps maintain body temperature at a steady 36.9°F by the action of its built-in cooling system of over two million tiny sweat glands. All day long, silently and efficiently, these glands spurt out microscopic jets of water – an average total of 0.8 litre per day, which helps cool the skin as it evaporates. But 2% of that liberal outpouring of sweat in the sauna is bodily waste – salt, lactic and uric acids, heavy metals, nicotine, alcohol, environmental toxins and other junk you're better off without. (The Turkish Baths in London's Jermyn Street used to have a regular early morning rush of gentlemen who had indulged themselves too liberally overnight.)

A sauna followed by a cold shower or dip is thus a wonderful detox for the whole system, upping the body's waste disposal rate dramatically.

Circulation improves, skin, muscle and joint problems can respond spectacularly, headaches and indigestion are relieved, and tensions ease as mind and body relax. Enjoy this exhilarating and tonic treatment, ending with a relaxing massage, whenever you can.

Caution Don't take a sauna if you suffer from diabetes, a heart problem, high blood pressure, asthma or any other serious medical condition. Don't take a sauna within the hour before you take a meal or for two hours after. And don't overdo it, especially the first time.

12 taking the waters

On 5 February 1910, England's Edward VII gave a public dinner for some leading civil servants. He ate his way enthusiastically through a nine-course meal of turtle soup, salmon, grilled chicken, saddle of mutton, several snipe stuffed with *foie gras*, asparagus, a fruit dish, an enormous iced concoction and a savoury.

Nothing unusual in that: all his life Edward VII was a voracious eater, bolting his food – he lacked the patience to chew, he told his doctors – and washing it all down with vintage champagne or fine old brandies. Breakfast, lunch, tea, dinner and supper were all solid meals on his daily agenda – and the king's chef was instructed to send some cold roast chicken to the royal apartments at bedtime, in case His Majesty should feel peckish before retiring. The digestive price of such habits can be imagined, and in late summer every year Edward would retire for a month or so to Marienbad, Germany, to take the waters and give his digestive system a badly needed rest.

Marienbad is one of hundreds of spas dotted all over Europe, many of them tracing their origin back to Roman times; some, like Bath, are even older. The legend goes that around 860BC there was a Prince Bladud, son of Lud Hudibras, the eighth king of the Britons, who suffered from leprosy and so was cast out of the royal family. He became a swineherd, but unfortunately his pigs all developed an unpleasant skin disease. Happily, one day they came across a steaming swamp near a river, the pigs went in for a good wallow, and came out cured. The prince immediately jumped in to see if his leprosy could also be cured, and came out as good as new. He returned to the castle, was warmly welcomed, and eventually built a spa at the site of his cure – he called it Bladud, which over time evolved into the name Bath. The hot springs of Bath have since been enjoyed by many, not least the Romans, who created magnificent buildings there.

The history of spas goes further back still: every great civilization has made use of medicinal mineral-rich springs, often emerging ready-heated from the depths of the earth. But it was the Romans who elevated the spa into an integral part of healthy living, a preventive medicine as well as cure for this or that malady, and Europe's wealth of spas is the legacy of a time when the Roman Empire was almost as extensive as today's European Union.

The UK can boast as many medicinal springs as any country in Europe, and in their day they made spa towns like Bath, Harrogate, Buxton and Tunbridge Wells wealthy and famous. Anglo-Saxon prejudice against any form of medical treatment other than pharmaceutical drugs or surgery closed down the springs in almost all of them, following the birth of the National Health Service. In recent years there has been a resurgence of interest and money has been raised to rebuild and reopen at least three of the most famous: Bath, Buxton and Strathpeffer in Scotland.

On the Continent interest has never waned. In France, Germany, Italy, Spain and Austria, considerable amounts of the annual health budget go towards subsidizing visits to spas. In fact, in 1972 the then West German government conducted an investigation: it had spent 2% of the Gross National Product on sending patients to take the waters in the previous year. A thorough study concluded that the length of illness was shorter, absenteeism dropped, and long-term effects were sufficiently favourable to justify the money. In 1999, France announced that it was considering abolishing the grants for spa treatment still available through the national health insurer: the furore rumbles on.

There must be a spa to suit every illness as well as every pocket.

The range of spas is huge, from small villages with a single modest spring to huge resorts like Montecatini in Tuscany, Italy, where accommodation ranges from five-star grand hotels to *pensiones* of spartan simplicity, and the life of the whole city revolves around its luxuriously housed medicinal springs. Every spa has its own medical establishment, where those there for purely medical reasons are assessed by resident specialists before their schedule of treatments – drinking the waters, baths, massage, high-pressure showers – is prescribed.

Once installed, visitors are quickly sucked into the gentle common routine, starting their day without breakfast since the first of the daily doses of water is usually gulped on an empty stomach, and ending with a three or four-course dinner, since spa hotels and *pensiones* rates almost invariably include full board.

Depending on the nature of the spring, spas tend to specialize in particular disorders. The waters of Schwalbach, Spa, Pyrmont and St Moritz are rich in iron, those of Vichy and Contrexeville unusually alkaline, the waters of Homburg naturally effervescent because of high concentrations of carbon dioxide. Over the years observers have divided the types of illness that different waters may be able to treat into a couple of groups. Alkaline waters are generally recommended for dyspepsia, liver and gall-bladder disease, while effervescent waters are sometimes found to be effective for the treatment of stones in the kidney and bladder. Chalybeate (iron-rich) waters are, obviously, recommended for anaemia.

Many spas have more than one kind of spring. At Lanjaron in the mountains of Andalucia in Spain, which receives an annual influx of 10,000 customers, there are five different springs, each recommended for different conditions. The iron-rich Capilla spring is considered excellent for the anaemic, the diabetic and those with high cholesterol. The effects of the Capuchina spring on chronic constipation are often so instantaneous that a handy row of lavatories has been installed nearby, while sufferers from kidney stones or bladder problems are sent to the San Vicente spring.

Other spas specialize. Vichy advertises its 'thermalism for rheumatic and digestive pathologies' as well as 'preventive thermalism for stress relief and improved well-being'. Arthritis, respiratory problems and digestive ailments (especially those affecting the liver) usually top the list of health problems treated at spas. High blood pressure, diabetes, kidney problems, osteoporosis and, increasingly, stress and fatigue are other common candidates.

Skin disorders often respond spectacularly well to spa therapy. The Avene treatment spa in the southwest of France has only been open for ten years: it draws its waters from the Sainte Odile spring and has had astounding results with eczema and psoriasis. French scientists recently reported that after double-blind testing, comparing Avene water with three other mineral waters, that of Avene was more effective than conventional treatments in 58% of cases and produced striking improvement in the severity of flare-ups in eczema and psoriasis. And the Dead Sea between Israel and Jordan has consistently proven itself in this field: the mineral-rich waters of this inland sea have had quite amazing results with psoriasis.

A distinctive sub-category of spas, developed in France, are those offering thalassotherapy – literally, the sea treatment. Developed early in the twentieth century, thalassotherapy grew out of the findings of a famous French biologist, Rene Quinton. The plasma in our blood – that straw-coloured liquid which makes up almost two-thirds of its volume – has a composition extraordinarily close to that of seawater in its mineral content. 'In the internal environment of our human system, and only there,' he wrote in the early twentieth century, 'do we find the same mineral make-up and the same physiognomy as that of seawater.'

The sea within us became the all-consuming object of Quinton's study more than a century ago. Over years of painstaking research, he studied the composition of that water – and he found that, with rare exceptions, in almost every living being descended from that first single-celled organism, born in the oceans billions of years ago, the same *milieu marin* still bathes every cell.

Inspired by these findings, Dr Louis Bagot opened a Marine Institute at Roscoff in Brittany in 1899, where he treated cases of chronic rheumatism with hot sea-baths. Sea air, he explained at a Climatology Congress in 1905, was a giant aerosol composed of gaseous molecules of marine salts and the iodine emitted by seaweed. So successful was thalassotherapy that the list of ailments for which it was prescribed rapidly lengthened – anaemia, rickets and nervous exhaustion among them. The reputation of thalassotherapy is solidly established – the perfect combination of therapy and pampering for mind and body, the skin and *la ligne* – and the leading thalassotherapy establishments in France have lists of rich and famous regulars.

In departments of dermatology and rheumatology at medical schools all over continental Europe, balneology is often a recognized speciality, and a huge body of clinical work on the efficacy of spa treatment has built up over the years, published in dozens of Continental journals. Unluckily, almost none of this appears in the prestige journals read by the Anglo-Saxon medical establishment, who tend to assume that most of the evidence of spa efficacy is anecdotal, or – even more damningly – that benefits are 'purely psychological'. Well, of course, the sense of leisure, the pleasant surroundings, the sunshine (in many cases) and the feeling of being on a rather pampered holiday are all part of the spa experience. Given what we know about the huge component of stress in most of the disorders it claims to benefit – particularly those of the skin and gut – that seems to me to present one more unanswerable argument in the defence of the medical benefits of spa therapy.

For a country who came to the idea so late, spas have now caught on in the United States in no uncertain fashion. The International Spa Association – based in the USA – publishes a list every year of 'What's hot and what's not'. Top of the list in 1999 was 'one-stop shopping' – spas where you can be pampered, counselled, have 'a manicure that's practically a work of art', or a 'deeply spiritual encounter that changes your relationship to the world around you', all in the same place. Other services people wanted to find at their spa were business advisors, marriage counsellors, nutritionists, or alternative therapies that can include anything from Native American sweat lodges, labyrinth walking or Javanese body massage. Have I missed out anything?

Well, yes. The oddest thing about the spa craze that is, undoubtedly, sweeping the USA, is how very far it is from what we think of as a spa. The element often conspicuous by its absence is ... water.

13 the therapeutic bath

Maybe it's our unconscious memories of the time when we were rocked and cradled in the waters of the womb, maybe it's genetic recall of our oceanic origins – but there is no denying the fact that immersion in warm water is as remarkably soothing to the spirit as it can be agreeable to the senses. At times of stress, many people agree, there's nothing like a long hot soak, preferably scented with some natural fragrance, with candles and soft music as optional extras.

A bath can be actively medicinal, with the use of plant or aromatherapy oils. It can also be an excellent all-over skin and beauty treatment. But before you splash out on beautifully packaged and pleasingly coloured and scented stuff to add to your bath, remember that during long immersion in hot water any chemicals it contains may be absorbed through your skin, and that the sodium laurel sulphate which turns up in so many potions for adding to your bath enhances this absorption. Go for the pure natural stuff: check labels and packaging carefully. Robert Tisserand, one of the UK's leading experts on aromatherapy, sees red when a bottle of cheap oil, highly coloured and scented with synthetic aromachemicals, is sold as an aromatherapy product. 'An aromatherapy product,' he says, 'should use only essential oils as its fragrance, otherwise it is no different from any other scented toiletry on the market.'

Temperature is a key factor in the therapeutic bath. A cold or very cool bath is bracing and invigorating (see chapter 10), toning skin and muscles, increasing the metabolic rate and boosting the immune system. Tepid baths – warmed to blood heat – are best for a herbal medicine or aromatherapy treatment as essential oils evaporate fast if the bath is too hot. Hot baths relax you, soothe aching muscles and help to promote the skin's cleansing action. But don't overdo it: very hot baths are enervating, and an especially bad idea if you suffer from high blood pressure, heart problems or varicose veins. End hot baths with a quick tepid or cool shower if your bath has a shower attachment, or by pulling out the plug, running the cold tap hard, and rinsing yourself with the rapidly cooling water. You'll feel much more relaxed.

Before bathing, give yourself a quick head-to-toe scrub with a special dry skin brush or loofah, working upwards in long sweeping strokes from toes to neck: brush towards the heart area but not too near the heart itself, and if you have varicose veins, stroke over them very gently. Then wipe yourself all over with a flannel or sponge and warm water. Now you're nice and clean and you won't be sitting in your own dirt.

A friction rub with a loofah or rough mitt is a wonderful tonic for you and your skin and helps slough off dead cells. A sea-salt rub is an even more effective way of invigorating your skin: before you get into your drawn bath, add a cupful of sea salt to a bowl, add enough water to turn it into a sludge, and buff yourself all over with it before sitting down in the bath and letting it dissolve around you.

There's a huge range of enjoyable or beneficial products you can buy to put in your bath: among the most useful are those based on seaweed and Dead Sea or Epsom salts, which are cleansing, bracing and revitalizing. Beauty guru Bharti Vyas is a passionate believer in the health benefits of Dead Sea salts in your bath. She believes that they encourage gentle detoxification of the system, reduce fluid retention, help combat stress, boost resistance and, at the end of a gruelling day, induce restful sleep by quelling anxiety and restoring calm. Dead Sea salts are extremely rich in minerals, some of which are absorbed through the skin, which they also help to smooth and refine. You can buy packets of Dead Sea salts at most chemists.

Here are some suggestions to make bath time soothing, stimulating, relaxing, healing or just plain blissful.

Ginger for aching joints, stiff muscles or low spirits Add two teaspoons of powdered ginger or a few centimetres of grated fresh root into a big pan of boiling water. Simmer until the water turns yellow, then pour it into your bath. This bath is very stimulating so don't take it just before you go to bed.

Lime-flower tea to induce sleep Make up a strong tea with a big handful of lime-flowers (or four to five tea bags) and add to a tepid bath. This is also highly effective for nervy children who can't get to sleep, or for fretful babies, but two lime-flower tea bags will be enough for children.

Apple cider vinegar for dry, itchy skin This softens and helps to preserve the acid mantle of the skin and it's also a great tonic when you're feeling tired and jaded. Add one cup to the bath. You can also make a herbal vinegar for your bath by half-filling a screw-top jar with aromatic herbs, filling it up with cider vinegar and leaving it to macerate in a quiet dark corner. Strain out the herbs and store the vinegar in a pretty labelled bottle. Sage is tonic and bracing, peppermint is wonderfully refreshing, marjoram is so sedative you might fall asleep in the bath and thyme is helpful if you feel a cold or chill coming on.

Oatmeal as a treat for the skin If you have just arrived back from a happy holiday orgy of sunbathing, a handful of oatmeal flung into a warm bath will put some of the life and resilience back into your sun-dried skin and will soften the bathwater. Use the special colloidal oatmeal that is sold in chemists and good herbal suppliers. If you can't get this, blend ordinary oatmeal to the finest powder. You can also use ordinary oatmeal in a bath bag made out of a square of muslin tightly closed with an elastic band: suspend it from the running hot tap, and use it like a sponge during your bath.

Marshmallow or comfrey for softer skin This is also wonderful for tired, sunburned skin. Add one tablespoon of the powdered root of either marshmallow or comfrey to a pan with three cups of milk, stir well, heat very slowly and simmer over the merest ghost of a flame for 15 minutes. Strain into your bath.

A warming pine bath Pinecones can be collected during a country walk and can be used to make a wonderful bath for cold weather. Soak them overnight in a panful of cold water, and then bring to the boil, simmer for a minute, and leave to infuse for 15 minutes before straining the liquid to add to your bath.

An essential oil bath A bath is one of the best ways to enjoy all the benefits of essential oils for general health, as well as for your skin: the warmth dilates the pores of your skin to allow the oils maximum penetration, while at the same time you breathe in the aromatic vapours. Most aromatherapy handbooks suggest five to eight drops for a bath, but Dr Jean Valnet who can be considered the founding father of modern aromatherapy, suggested 20 drops, although eight to ten drops will still give you a wonderfully aromatic bath. These should be diluted beforehand in a special oil base, since oils do not disperse in water, and direct contact with some essential oils could irritate your skin. There's an excellent Bath Base in the Valnet Aromatherapy range or you can buy a specially treated form of castor oil called Turkey Red, to which you can add the essential oils of your choice: you will need about a tablespoonful for a bath. You can also add essential oils to a cupful of milk, which will help soften the bath water into the bargain. The following are some of Dr Valnet's suggestions for baths with essential oils, which can be blended with a tablespoon of oily bath base or a cup of milk.

To boost circulation, or to relieve symptoms of the menopause: ten drops cypress; five drops juniper and five drops lemon.

For a soft satiny skin: fifteen drops geranium and five mandarin.

To help you unwind: fifteen drops Lavender and five drops sweet orange.

A tonic and aphrodisiac bath: fifteen drops rosemary (not to be used during pregnancy) and five drops ylang-ylang.

To ward off winter germs: five drops each eucalyptus, ravensara, niaouli and thyme.

To enhance the softening and cleansing effect of a salt rub: In a small bowl, mix two tablespoons of coarse sea salt and enough almond, olive or jojoba oil to turn it into a sludge. Then add two to three drops of a favourite essential oil – perhaps geranium or lavender. Mix well. Run your bath and, standing up in the bath, slather your body briskly with the mix, avoiding your face and genital areas, before you sit down.

Caution Essential oils should be used only with the help of a reliable guide (see Further Reading for books on the subject).

water
the pure water action plan

1. You are more than 70% water: make sure that any water entering your body is of the highest quality possible. In your home choose a good filtration system, either jug or plumbed in. Bottled spring water is a good option when you're on the move, but for everyday use it is very unfriendly to the environment: think of the energy that the manufacture and transport of all those plastic bottles represents.

2. If you live in an area where the water has been fluoridated, campaign for an end to this contamination. If there is no local campaigning organization, join the National Pure Water Association (see Resources).

3. Washing-machine powders and fabric conditioners make a massive contribution to water contamination. Detergents contain phosphates which can encourage the growth of algae, when they end up in streams or rivers. Use one of the environmentally friendly ranges of laundry detergents. If you have no choice but to use conventional detergents, experiment to see how much less you actually need than the suggested dose on the packet. And ask yourself if you really notice the difference when you add quantities of synthetically scented fabric conditioner to your wash.

4. Think of energizing the water in your home or garden chapter 3 and 4. For details of energizing devices, see Resources.

5. The pesticides you use in your garden will end up draining away into groundwater and polluting it. Make your garden organic (see Further Reading).

6. All the toxic stuff that goes down your drain ends up in the water that will eventually re-emerge from your taps as drinking water. Most household cleansing products, as well as personal toiletries, are full of chemicals that will contaminate water. As far as possible, use cleansers and toiletries made from natural non-polluting ingredients (see Resources).

7. Water is precious: don't waste it. There are lots of simple things you can do to save it, for instance:

- Close taps tightly.
- Don't clean fruit and vegetables under a running tap: fill a basin and then turn the tap off.
- When you clean your teeth, shave or wash your hands, never leave the tap running. Fill a glass or bowl with water for rinsing the mouth, shaving or brushing.
- Next time you have to replace a toilet, switch to one of the new low-flush economical kind.
- When you cook vegetables, save the nutrient-rich cooking water for stock, or drink it, or use it to feed your plants.
- Washing your car with a hose uses up about 400 litres of water: use a bucket and sponge instead.
- If you have a garden, install a drip-watering system with a timer. It will save you time – and many litres of water.

'Truly the light is sweet, and a pleasant thing it is for the eyes to behold the sun.'

Ecclesiasticus

light

the world of light

1 the colour of life

Green is the colour of life on earth. The tender green of wheatgrass and the silvery green of olive trees, the sad green of cypresses and the acid green of apples, the luscious greens of the jungle, the deep green of parsley and the commonest colour on the planet, grass green.

Stored in the chloroplasts of every tiniest leaf or blade of grass is the green pigment chlorophyll, which enables every plant to harvest and exploit sunlight energy for its growth and nourishment. And through this miracle of photosynthesis, sunlight energy powers the whole of our planet.

Without photosynthesis there would be no food for us to eat, no oxygen for us to breathe.

A process of awesome complexity, photosynthesis has been described as the most important biological reaction on earth. The process is powered by light, which is why plants left in darkness lose their strength and colour. It is dependent on carbon dioxide, which diffuses in through the open pores of the leaf; and it is dependent on a supply of water, hauled up from the plant's roots: without water, plants first stop growing, then shrivel, then dry out and die.

The energy of light is absorbed by the green pigment chlorophyll in plants and, through a complex chain of reactions, simple organic sugars are produced using carbon atoms from the carbon dioxide in the air. It has been estimated that photosynthesis produces more than 150 million tonnes of these sugars every year. Oxygen is the useful 'waste' product of this process.

Why is it that plants appear green? Because the green pigments in them absorb light from the red and blue ends of the rainbow spectrum of electromagnetic waves, which has colours ranging from ultraviolet through indigo, blue, green and yellow to orange and red, each with its own wavelength. The green-yellow light in the middle of the visible spectrum is reflected back, which is why we see most plants as green. If plants absorbed only the green-yellow wavelengths, we might find ourselves admiring a landscape of violet and red, like the skies at sunset. Or if – appalling thought – plants absorbed light right across the spectrum, we could be living in a world of black.

There are other coloured pigments in many plants which absorb in the green-yellow wavelengths and reflect back other colours. And a glimpse of a might-have-been world is given us every autumn when the chlorophyll in leaves dies down, leaving those other pigments to turn trees into spectacular displays of reds, yellows and oranges.

2 the rhythm of life

In 1729 a French astronomer, Jean Jacques de Mairan, locked up a heliotrope in his study overnight. The heliotrope, with its sweet-smelling flower, is named for its habit of – quite literally – following the sun: its English common name is turnsole. It opens in the morning facing east, and during the course of the day slowly turns westward, to close its petals at dusk. With no rising sun to cue it, de Mairan was confident that after a day, he would find the heliotrope still firmly closed. He was wrong: it continued to open and close at its accustomed times. He was intrigued, but he never completed his research.

Not until more than two centuries later was the modern science of chronobiology called into being, when 20 Swedish 'rhythms enthusiasts' met in 1937 in the small spa of Ronneby, in southern Sweden, and established a Society for Biological Rhythm Research. Over the next decades interest grew and the pace of their research quickened. It eventually led to the discovery that the life of virtually every living creature runs to an internal clock which is cued by light and set to the natural 24-hour cycle of night and day. These rhythmical physiological changes were christened 'circadian' rhythms – from *irca* (about) and *dies* (day) – by American researcher Franz Halberg. Not all biological rhythms run to a 24-hour cycle, however. There are ultradian cycles, such as menstruation in women, and infradian, such as the 90-minute sleep cycle, which we all experience.

The energy that powers and synchronizes our biological rhythms is light.

This sunlight energy travels to our planet in the form of electromagnetic waves. Many of the waves are filtered out by the earth's atmosphere – including our precious ozone layer – and the light that reaches us is only about 1% of the total light created by the sun. For billions of years, life on earth has evolved in the presence of the rainbow spectrum of light these electromagnetic waves create, in which every colour has been shown to play a vital biological role. But ultraviolet (UV) – which has the shortest wavelength – also packs more energy and thus has a more powerful impact on health. It is UV that can burn us – or heal us.

This rainbow spectrum of light enters our eyes and travels to an area with a jaw-breaking name, the suprachiasmatic nuclei (SCN), located in the hypothalamus in the brain. Entrained by light-signals, and routing its own signals through the hypothalamus and the pituitary glands, the SCN works like a master-clock, controlling hundreds of circadian rhythms throughout the body, as well as seasonal biological rhythms cued to changes in day length over the year – thus giving the signal for migration or hibernation in birds and animals.

Every system in the body is cued to these signals. Over ten years George Brainard, Professor of Neurology at Thomas Jefferson University in Philadelphia, USA, and his colleagues subjected Syrian hamsters to a series of light and darkness conditions, changing not just the intensity of the light but even its colour wavelengths. They found that simply by manipulating the quality and quantity of light they could affect a startling range of biological functions, including the secretion of key hormones like cortisol (the action hormone), the thyroid hormones, oestrogen and testosterone, as well as levels of cholesterol and free fatty acids. Sleep, appetite, heat regulation, growth and repair are all subject to these rhythms: so is reproduction.

We may not be hamsters, says Brainard, but we have evolved under the same sort of environmental conditions, alternating light and darkness on a daily basis and subtle changes in day length on a seasonal basis, depending on the latitude at which we live. And numbers of neurophysical studies carried out in human beings are confirming that, yes, Syrian hamsters and ourselves have a lot in common.

From the hypothalamus, light energy is relayed via the spinal cord into the pineal gland, a tiny pea-sized organ shaped like a pine cone – hence its name – and buried deep in the brain. At night-time, when little or no light is entering the eyes, the pineal gland secretes a hormone called melatonin, which signals a change in activity patterns throughout the whole body: the cue for restorative sleep, for repair, for physical inaction. Melatonin is the messenger of darkness: when bright light enters the eyes again, melatonin production shuts down.

Melatonin was first identified and christened by dermatologist Aaron Lerner at Yale University in 1958 and research has made clear its unique importance.

Just as light is the daytime cue for our circadian rhythms, melatonin is the night-time signal.

Receptors are found all over the body, including the SCN operations centre. Like many other key body chemicals, levels of melatonin decline with age: one reason the elderly can have difficulty sleeping.

A number of well-respected scientists became over-excited about melatonin and from the mid-1990s on, in a couple of best-sellers and countless articles, it was touted in the USA as the ultimate wonder-drug, able to slow ageing, prolong sexual vitality, cure insomnia and jet lag, combat cancer, AIDS and Alzheimer's, and generally boost our resistance. A cover story in *Newsweek* confirmed its celebrity status, and by 1996 the US retail market was reckoned to be worth up to $350 million annually.

Most of these claims have not been substantiated by good scientific studies and respectable research has focused on just two problem areas where it is proving of real use – jet lag and sleeping disorders based on disturbed circadian rhythms. Since these are problems afflicting millions of people – for which no 'natural' and truly effective drug exists – there is already a huge market for melatonin, and drug companies, who cannot patent a natural substance, are rushing to produce their own synthetic analogues and hoping they'll work as well.

Circadian rhythms are regulated by the alternation of light and darkness, but millions of years of evolution have patterned the timing of these clocks firmly into the genes of living creatures as well, instructing them when to forage and when to sleep, when to be sexually active and when to hibernate, when to eat and when to fast. The reason why progesterone surges around midnight to send women into labour may date back to the times when foraging males were likely to be around and able to take protective charge at this vulnerable moment. Growth hormones are secreted at night, when the body can devote its metabolic energies to the process, and vital repair and maintenance work is also carried out in these quiet, inactive hours.

By 6am, body temperatures are rising in preparation for an active day ahead: so are levels of the adrenal hormone cortisol, ready to spur us into action. Blood pressure and heart rate rise in readiness, too – many heart attacks happen at this early hour of the day.

By noon all this energy has peaked; by 2pm you're flagging as heart rate and blood pressure are beginning to decline again. By 7pm, as daylight fades, melatonin production starts up again, peaking just before midnight, to send us into the first deep, dreamless sleep of the night, when heart rate and brain waves both slow.

Even when subjects are locked away from light-and-darkness cues, the genetic clocks controlling their circadian bodily rhythms tick on, as de Mairan discovered with his heliotrope experiment. But in these conditions, rhythm cycles tend to lengthen, up to as much as 28 hours, thus gradually getting out of synch with the light-and-darkness cycle – with consequences that can be painful, if not fatal.

For hundreds of thousands of years, human beings – like all other living creatures – lived their lives in harmony with nature's clock. Only the very rich enjoyed a night-life, and even then the most lavish supply of candles or oil lamps couldn't match the blaze of light emitted by a 100W or 150W bulb. Most of humanity worked while the light lasted and, when it faded, thankfully downed tools.

This world of natural rhythms changed forever in 1879, with Thomas Edison's development of the light bulb. Night could be turned into day, the poor could dine as late as the rich, shops, offices and factories could stay open for hours longer. A century on, we live in a world turned upside down for many people. Few people get up at sunrise any more, except in summer, and even fewer people go to bed when it is dark. Summer may have longer days, but most people's working rhythms hardly change over the length of the year – except that they may go to bed slightly earlier in winter.

The night is no longer only for sleeping. It is also the time for partying, for clubbing, for hanging out in bars: it is the time when coffee-fuelled students do their last-minute swotting, when theatres, cinemas and restaurants do much of their business, when we take in some late-night TV before turning in. And it is fast becoming the time when more and more of us, at ever-later hours, do our shopping. Because of all this frenzied activity, around one-third of the workforce works shifts instead of a morning-to-evening day, sometimes changing between day, evening and late night, and more and more often a yawning 12-hour night of work followed by a 'day' of sleep and rest.

So it is hardly surprisingly that sleep disorders are increasingly common. A Gallup survey commissioned by the US National Sleep Foundation in 1995 found that half of all US adults had trouble sleeping at least one night a week, and 1 in 8 slept badly at least four nights a week. The Foundation's Omnibus Sleep in America poll five years later reported that nearly two-thirds of adults – 62% – had experienced a sleep problem a few nights a week during the previous year.

As well as finding it harder to get to sleep, we are also sleeping less than our grandfathers and great grandfathers. At the beginning of the twentieth century nine hours of sleep a night was normal. Now it is seven hours – or less. For a minority of hyperactive achievers this may be more than enough. For most people, eight hours is much nearer their real need. And sleep deprivation is turning into a real problem in Latin countries, where global business hours have ousted the siesta without any compensating change in long-established habits of dining and socializing late at night. Only 1 in 6 Spaniards still knocks off for a long break after lunch.

The UK now has its own Sleep Foundation, launched in 1999, which is lobbying parliament for recognition that this is a huge national problem. In truth, lack of sleep is a killer. A quarter of all fatal road accidents are caused by weary drivers nodding off for a critical moment at the wheel, and every summer brings its tragic accounts of whole coachloads of tourists killed or badly injured in motorway accidents. Lack of sleep is also responsible for a huge burden of general ill-health, since it is during those quiet melatonin hours that our bodies carry out critical repair and maintenance work. Our brains need that long spell of shut-eye, too.

Recent research has shown that missing out on just one hour of sleep could cause a drop of a whole IQ point, along with a slide in language skills and reasoning ability.

The worst-affected victims of our rhythmless modern world are those working around the clock, for whom, much of the time, there is no real night or day any more. Working shifts is catastrophic for health and well-being, and no one who has had to work right through the night even once will find this hard to believe.

When two doctors in the 1920s decided to set up a social club in a working-class district of London called Peckham, so that they could study health rather than disease, they identified a condition they named hypotonia, or general devitalization. Among its leading features were low blood pressure, low blood sugar, ineffective muscular tone, low respiratory capacity, chronic constipation and social inertia. Even in healthy, robust individuals of both sexes, they noted, acute hypotonia developed very rapidly as a result of night duty, and even nine hours' of daytime sleep was unable to rescue these unfortunates from their zombie-like state.

Statistically, shift-workers are at greatly increased risk of heart attacks, strokes, digestive disorders, depression and infertility. Animal studies suggest that they could be cutting short their life expectancy and weakening their immune systems, too. And one factor that is seldom considered for those who often work nights is the number of days in their working lives of which not a single hour is spent in the living daylight. How critical a factor that might be we shall see in the next chapter.

3 the light of life

'You are the sunshine of my life,' says the song, and no lover ever uttered a finer compliment. For sunshine literally *is* our life, and we are as dependent on it as is the smallest blade of grass or bacterium.

The sun has been worshipped throughout history. The Greeks honoured their glorious young Apollo, the Egyptians painted the big blood-red orbs of Ra the Sun God all over their pharaohs' tombs, while the aboriginals of Australia, in their Creation myths, celebrated the great Mother-Goddess, in whose footprints on the cold dark earth the grass, the shrubs and the trees sprang up. In Japan, Land of the Rising Sun, emperors always claimed descent from the Sun Goddess Ameratsu Omikame, and the red sun blazes from the national flag. The Incas of Peru considered themselves the Children of the Sun and the heart of their huge empire was the Sun Temple at Cuzco; further north, the Aztec emperors offered human sacrifices to their potent and dreadful Shining God Tonatiuh.

Louis XIV of France liked to identify himself with the giver of all life, and at Versailles, which was crammed with solar emblems, he was almost worshipped by his courtiers as Le Roi Soleil, the Sun King.

For Christians, God and light are almost interchangeable terms: 'The Lord is my Light,' sang the Psalmist. 'In Him was life and the life was the light of men,' according to the Gospel of St John. 'I am the light of the world,' Jesus told his apostles.

Light is a metaphor for eternal life. 'They are all gone into the world of light,' lamented the seventeenth-century mystical poet Henry Vaughan, remembering his dead friends: in an evening's vision he saw eternity '...like a great ring of pure and endless light'. During the Requiem Mass of the Catholic Church, the congregation prays that the dead may enjoy *lux perpetua*, 'light everlasting'.

Among the hundreds of near-death experiences reported, one feature constantly recurs: the bright and desirable light at the end of the tunnel – and that last phrase is another way of expressing hope.

Human instincts – those honed over hundreds of thousands of years of history – tend to be reliable. A healthy respect – in many cultures a religious reverence – for the sun and its unique gift of light is one of the most profound and enduring of these instincts.

When summer in temperate climates is a succession of grey, cloudy and overcast days, we experience a deep craving for the sun's light and warmth. Denial of this craving, day after day, brings on gloom, low spirits and despondency, even states of clinical depression (see chapter 10). And then the sun shines – and people smile at strangers in the street, walk with a spring in their step, feel a creative surge of energy at work and the moment they're free, rush to the nearest park or pavement café to bask in the lovely warmth, the glowing light which makes everything look so much better.

This craving for sunshine should impress on us our profound need for the living daylight. Not only does daylight prompt our biological clocks to order our days for us, it is vital to our health and well-being in ways which we have long known instinctively, but which are now being confirmed in scientific studies.

Since 1925 it has been known that sunshine is vital for healthy bones.

Photons of ultraviolet light penetrate into the skin, where by a three-step process cholecalciferol – vitamin D3 – is formed: this in turn is converted to calcitriol in the liver. Without adequate vitamin D, normal blood levels of calcium and phosphorus, both crucial to bone health, cannot be maintained. The childhood disease rickets – that fatal softening of the bones which leads to buckled ribs, knock knees and bow-legs – was once common in the sunless slums of Victorian London. Its adult version is osteomalacia, and the victims it claims in the modern world include devout Arab women who only emerge from their homes veiled from head to foot. A lack of vitamin D also increases our chances of contracting osteoporosis (see also pages 230–231).

Vitamin D can also be found in dairy products and certain animal foods, including liver, or bought as a supplement, but sunshine is our most reliable source. And while vitamin D from food sources can be toxic at levels not much above the recommended limit of 400iu, a day in the sun can give a one-off boost of 10,000iu.

About 60% of osteoporosis patients have abnormally low levels of calcitriol and trials using supplements have been promising: in one study, patients given extra calcitriol for two years showed an average increase of 1–2% in bone mineral density, while a control group had an average loss of 2–3%. In the second and third years of the trial, only 6% of the calcitriol group had bone fractures, against 15.5% in a control group being treated with calcium supplements.

Since 1970 vitamin D has actually been recognized as a steroid hormone rather than a vitamin, and its activity may go well beyond its contribution to strong bones. Receptors for calcitriol have shown up at different target sites all over the body, including the pancreas, the pituitary gland, the T-lymphocyte cells of the immune system, the breasts and the skin. When dermatologists gave oral doses of calcitriol to patients with acne, dermatitis and other skin problems, the results were disappointing and there were some side-effects. But when they applied it directly to the skin, the results were impressive. According to Dr Michael F. Holick at the Vitamin D Skin and Bone Research Laboratory at Boston University School of Medicine, USA, topical applications of calcitriol – and analogs made by pharmaceutical companies – may replace steroids in the treatment of mild psoriasis, since they are just as effective without the skin-thinning effect.

Just like our bones, our teeth need that regular dose of sunshine.

At one north Canadian school in Edmonton, Alberta – where the days are short and dark from October to March – a group of 102 Grade 5 children spent 22 months in classrooms where the cool, white, fluorescent lights had been replaced by full-spectrum lighting – as close as artificial lights can get to natural sunshine. At the study's end, the children in the classrooms lit by fluorescent lighting had nearly four times as much tooth-decay as the children from the full-spectrum-lit classrooms. Studies involving thousands of children spell out the same message: more sunshine, less tooth decay – and more cavities in the winter time than in the height of summer.

'For all our advances in science, we still remain humbly, pitifully dependent upon the forces of nature: air, water, food and sunlight,' wrote an American physician. His name was Dr Zane Kime and he published his classic work *Sunlight* in 1980, in support of his deep conviction that '...separation from sunlight will result in disease just as surely as will separation from fresh air, food and/or water'. He treated many apparently hopeless cases with doses of sunlight.

He was particularly impressed by its results in heart problems. One elderly lady who consulted him had a high cholesterol count of 333mg/dl, with triglycerides – another blood fat – at 299mg/dl. Kime prescribed sunlight treatment for the next four days, following which, without any change in diet or exercise, her cholesterol and triglycerides plunged to near-normal levels of 221mg/dl and 197mg/dl respectively. In one study he quotes, 30 patients with hardening of the arteries were given a single sunlight treatment. Cholesterol levels were measured just before and two hours after – and the average drop in cholesterol was 13%.

An even more suggestive study, quoted by Kime, was published in the *New England Journal of Medicine* in 1953. Of a bunch of rabbits fed a high-fat, high-cholesterol diet, half were kept under standard lighting, while the other half had regular sunbaths. They were the lucky ones: at the end of the study, they had clean arteries with little or no sign of damage, while the rabbits from the cages with standard indoor lighting had arteries clogged with cholesterol.

Vitamin D and a compound in the skin called squalene are very similar in composition: it has been theorized that in the presence of sunlight, the squalene converts to vitamin D: in the absence of sunshine, it converts to cholesterol instead.

'Exposure to the sun,' wrote Oribasius, a physician in ancient Greece, 'is especially indispensable to people requiring restoration and increases of musculature.' Greek athletes trained in full sunshine: we now know that sunshine increases the oxygen-carrying capacity of the blood so that more oxygen reaches tissue and muscle, and it has been pointed out that many of the outstanding runners of our time come from countries with hot, sunny climates.

'There seems to be conclusive evidence,' wrote Kime, 'that sunlight produces a metabolic effect in the body that is very similar to physical training. Tuberculosis patients being treated by sunbathing have been observed to have well-developed muscles with very little fat, even though they have not exercised for months.'

George Byng, Director of Coaching for the Scottish Amateur Weight-lifters' Association, needs no convincing. Early in 2000 he installed 16 big full-spectrum lights in the gym where he trains twice a week – he also trains once a week out of doors. Weight-lifting is one sport where improvements in performance can be accurately measured. Six months after installing the lights, and a few months away from his sixty-fourth birthday, he competed in the Glasgow Open Weight-lifting Championships, and broke four Scottish and one British record. 'Nothing else about my training changed in those six months,' he reports, 'but in that time my performance improved 12%.'

When Burnett Park Zoo in Syracuse installed Vita-Lite sunlight-simulating lights to discourage vandalism, there was an unpredictable side-effect. 'The zoo became a veritable maternity ward,' related director Charles T. Cliff. 'The cougars fell in love all over again and produced their fourth litter, we collected five goose eggs, at last eight lambs were born, and the deer population increased by 20. Big Lizzie gave birth to a bear cub, the wallaby produced a new mini-kangaroo and the chimpanzee got pregnant.'

In another landmark book on the benefits of sunshine, *Daylight Robbery*, Dr Damien Downing explains just why sunlight can affect animals in this way. 'Sunlight falling on the skin can raise the level of sex hormones in the blood... When researchers gave doses of ultraviolet to subjects in Boston, USA, they found that a course of five doses, of increasing duration, each of them sufficient to produce slight reddening of the skin, could double the male hormone output.' Studies have shown, Dr Downing points out, that levels of testosterone rise by about 20% throughout the summer, reaching a peak in September – and the greater the amount of skin exposed, the greater the effect.

The menstrual cycle is also regulated by the sun: 'I am not the only doctor,' notes Dr Downing, 'to have seen female patients in whom light deficiency appears to disrupt and even completely stop the menstrual cycle, and in whom regular sunlight treatment produces an improvement.' Dr Kime, who confirms this, tells of one female patient who had not menstruated for two years of living almost entirely indoors. He prescribed regular sunbathing, starting very slowly, and within three months she was having normal periods again.

The reproductive system of human beings – including the ovulation cycle in women and levels of testosterone in men – is just as much subject to light cues as that of, say, the Syrian hamster, star of so many light experiments. So for this problem, too, Dr Downing packs his patients off to Greece, having noticed during a spell in the Solomon Islands, just south of the Equator, that many a supposedly infertile European couple would leave clutching a new baby after a long spell in the hot sunshine. 'There is no doubt,' he points out, 'that the level of fertility is higher in tropical climates for all living beings.' Hence the soaring populations of India, Africa and Latin America – and the falling birth rates of northern Europe.

Faster wound-healing, antibacterial activity, an insulin-like effect, an immunity boost and a boon for aching joints are among other well-documented effects of sunshine, which prove that it is no luxury, to be enjoyed once in a while, but a year-round necessity.

Staff in the cardiac unit of a hospital in Alberta, Canada, noticed that patients recovering on the sunniest side of the room seemed more likely to survive. This prompted a serious study, reported in the *Journal of the Royal Society of Medicine*, in which researchers, led by Professor Peter Hayes, looked at the records of 628 people admitted to the ward after a first heart attack, over a four-year period. Half had been in rooms on the shady north side, half in rooms on the sunny south side, where sunshine levels were up to ten times higher. Thirty-nine patients on the north side died: in the sunnier south rooms, 21.

Deprivation of sunshine may be literally a matter of life and death.

light

light and darkness

4 light starvation

The sex life of his pumpkins gave John Ott a lot of trouble. He was a banker with a spare-time hobby of time-lapse photography and Walt Disney had asked him to produce a sequence showing a pumpkin swelling into full growth for their film *Secrets of Life*.

In time-lapse photography a camera is set up to take hundreds of pictures of growing plants at regular intervals, over weeks or even months. When the pictures are shown as a sequence, plants appear to grow and buds to open into flower within a matter of seconds.

But the pumpkins were tricky customers. They have the sexual peculiarity of sporting both female and male flowers on the same vine. In Ott's basement studio, where the light from a skylight was supplemented by a fluorescent light, the vine with its pollinating male flowers grew according to schedule, but the female flowers turned brown and dropped off. When he tried again a year later, the hardware store was out of the regular fluorescent tubes, so in a hurry he bought some daylight tubes which gave a bluish light. This time the female flowers grew beautifully – but the male flowers in turn withered and fell off. With a pressing deadline, Ott eventually had a pumpkin vine covered with male flowers specially flown in to Chicago, where he lived, the flowers were successfully 'mated' and Walt Disney got their pumpkin sequence.

Other subjects proved just as tricky. Disney wanted a sequence of apples swelling and ripening. So John Ott built a glass box around a branch covered with apple blossom, installed his cameras, and waited. The little apples swelled to full size on the tree and inside the box. Then the apples on the tree began turning red – and the apples inside the box stayed green but kept on growing and growing. He tried again the following year – and the same thing happened, until he replaced the glass with a special clear plastic which, unlike glass, transmits ultraviolet (UV) light. The apples obligingly turned red and Disney, again got the required film.

Ott had a questioning mind, and he began breeding and rearing small animals under different types of light.

During his research Ott learned that different coloured lights could slow or hasten reproduction, produce male or female litters, hasten or stunt growth.

Ott also learned of other experiments in which different types of light had been shown to promote the development of tumours in mice or protect against them. Since men, women and children spent much of their lives working under artificial light, he began to wonder if 'malillumination', as he christened it, might not be affecting people in just the same way as it was affecting his animals.

Ott moved to sunny Florida in a quest for more sunshine and died there in May 2000. His original and meticulous research into what has come to be known as photobiology, continued over long years when most men are retired and taking things easy. It was reported in books, lectures and broadcasts and – rarest of achievements for a layman – it has inspired a whole generation of scientists and doctors. Among them is George Brainard, whose work with hamsters subjected to different colours of light takes up where Ott left off (see also page 215).

Over and over again, Ott asked questions which remain largely unanswered. What is malillumination doing to us? Does it matter that we spend so little time in ordinary natural daylight? Do specific kinds of artificial light have negative effects on our health?

If malillumination really does matter, then most of us are at risk. We don't spend a lot of time outdoors in ordinary daylight, complete with its powerful UV wavelength. We do spend hours of our time behind glass that selectively filters out UV from the spectrum: the windows of buildings, cars, buses, trains, even the spectacles that millions wear. UV is filtered out of by the plastic of ordinary contact lenses, too. For city dwellers, pollution smog can drastically reduce the levels of UV light getting through. And during winter it can happen that whole days go by – even months for the elderly – in which we hardly spend ten minutes out of doors in full daylight.

On a summer day, light from the sky alone can exceed 10,000 lux – the standard unit of light measurement. Add direct sunlight and illuminance can go over 100,000 lux. But even in the most brightly lit office the light level may not rise any higher than 1000 lux, while ordinary indoor lighting in the home may be no more than the equivalent of twilight – from 100 to 200 lux.

Experts estimate that the optimal light for human beings, to cue their circadian and seasonal rhythms, is over 2000 lux for up to eight hours. A group of ten healthy young male volunteers had light meters attached to their foreheads over a 24-hour period. On average, they experienced light brighter than 2000 lux for just 90 minutes a day.

For many people, the light they work by during the day may not be bright enough to suppress melatonin completely in the morning, leaving them feeling sleepy and under motivated. At the end of the day, by contrast, bright lights till late hours may suppress melatonin production, eventually leading to insomnia and other sleep disorders,

The colour of artificial lighting may be a problem, too. In the rainbow spectrum of sunlight, all the colours are evenly represented, including UV. By contrast, artificial lighting is highly unbalanced. Incandescent lights, which are the most common bulbs used in lamps in the home, are rich in red and yellow light but relatively poor in blue or green. Cool-white fluorescent lights put out most of their energy in the green and yellow bands of the spectrum, to which eyes are particularly sensitive: eyestrain is a common complaint of people who work all day in such lighting. Full-spectrum lights come nearest to the balance of sunshine, though they have more blue than the rainbow, but they also transmit the traces of UV light – as in natural light – which are lacking in other artificial light.

When John Ott suggested in the 1980s and early 1990s that lack of natural light and regular exposure to artificial light might be a factor in cancer, heart disease and hyperactivity in children, nobody paid a lot of attention. Today, suggestive evidence is accumulating from laboratory studies around the world that he might have been right. Among the major health problems in which it is beginning to look as though light – or lack of it – could be a factor are cancer (particularly of the breast and prostate), heart disease, diabetes, osteoporosis, infertility, obesity, depression, fatigue, stress, menstrual and menopausal problems and hyperactivity in children: a daunting catalogue of the diseases of western civilization.

Evidence that the sun might actually protect against cancer started coming in 1980, with the first of a series of population studies by Doctors Cedric and Frank Garland.

The Garlands had hypothesized that vitamin D might be a protective factor for both breast and colon cancer, an effect that had shown up in some studies. In one, dietary intake of 150iu a day or more was shown to halve the risk of colon cancer. And when they correlated cancer and sunshine records around the world, a startling pattern emerged. Mortality from both breast and colon cancers was generally higher in areas of the world where there is least sunlight – or worst smog pollution. Polluted Milan has a death rate from colon or rectal cancer more than three times higher than sunny Messina in Sicily. Breast cancer is nearly twice as common in the north west of the USA as in the south east, and the northern Baltic states of Estonia, Latvia and Lithuania had more than twice the rate of breast cancer as the southern desert republics of Uzbekistan, Turkmenistan and Tadjikistan.

Could artificial light at night-time be another factor in breast cancer? There is evidence that melatonin regulates the amount of hormones in a woman's body: if melatonin output, which is thought to peak between 1am and 3am, is constantly checked by light, rising oestrogen levels might be a problem. How much light does it take to suppress night-time melatonin output? Perhaps not more than the light from bright street-lamps filtering through bedroom curtains, thinks Brainard.

The fact that breast cancer is five times more common in countries rich enough to turn their night into day was suggestive in itself.

Even more suggestive was research showing that blind women have a much lower rate of breast cancer than those who can see. A study by Dr Richard Stevens, a US cancer epidemiologist, and Finnish colleagues found that women who were completely blind had 60% fewer breast cancers that normally sighted women or those who were only slightly blind. Another study, this time carried out at the Karolinska Institute in Stockholm, Sweden, compared cancer rates in general in 1600 completely blind men and women with those in 13,000 people who could still register light. Once more, those who were completely blind had only 70% of the cancer risk of those who were partially sighted.

When doctors measured the blood levels of vitamin D in 290 elderly patients in hospital, they were shocked to find that nearly one-quarter of them were severely deficient, while over half had less than adequate levels. Were they not eating enough of the reliable food sources – eggs, milk, cheese, fish? Well yes, one-third of those deficient actually were, according to nutritionists' calculation.

Lack of this bone-building vitamin can lead to crumbling, thinning bones, and hence the fractures which can be a sentence to immobility and dependence for the elderly. According to Dr Michael F. Holick, an authority on vitamin D (see also page 222), research has shown that up to 40% of elderly men and women with hip fractures are vitamin D deficient. And elderly women worrying about wrinkles, who never stir out of doors without the high-sunscreen moisturizers plugged by leading cosmetic companies, are at even more risk: even Protection Factors as low as 8 in sunscreen can block 95% of the vitamin D activation process.

Without adequate vitamin D, our bodies can't absorb calcium or magnesium efficiently, which are both equally vital to healthy bones. Dr Richard Wurtman of the Massachusetts Institute of Technology in

Boston, USA, enlisted volunteers at an old people's home. They agreed to remain indoors for seven weeks from the beginning of winter under ordinary artificial lighting. At the end of this period, it was found that they were absorbing only 40% of the calcium in their diets. Another month indoors and it fell by another 25%. Since many elderly people never move from their homes in cold winter weather, their brittleness of bone is thus hardly surprising.

Joints as well as bones and teeth need vitamin D, it seems. When John Ott stopped wearing his spectacles and began consciously spending as much time as possible out in the sunshine, he found that his sight improved and a hip that had seized up to the point where he needed a stick to get about became normally flexible again. Of 500 patients with osteoarthritis of the knee studied at Boston University, researchers found that those with the lowest intake of dietary vitamin D and the lowest levels in their blood were three times more likely to have a worsening of their disease than those with the highest intake and blood levels.

During long overcast winters we all pine for the sun, and in some people this sun-starvation tips them over into a state of clinical depression appropriately known as SAD (Seasonal Affective Disorder), which can be treated with natural light (as we shall see in chapter 10). Psychiatrists are beginning to use the bright-light treatment for other forms of depression, too: Dr Daniel Kripke treated a group of 25 veterans suffering from severe depression with bright light for a week and another 26 with dim red lights. The patients actually expected the dim red treatment to be more effective than the bright light, but within one week – far faster than with conventional antidepressant treatment – it was the light-treated patients who were showing marked improvement. Is depression yet another result of our sunless indoor lives?

Diabetes and obesity are western diseases which are becoming more problematic, thanks to the huge amounts of starchy, sugary foods in western diets. When you eat an over-sweetened cereal for breakfast, follow it up with toast, butter and jam, and wash it down with a cup of sweetened tea, your blood-sugar levels will rocket and this is why diabetics have to watch their carbohydrate intake like hawks. Your pancreas will then secrete insulin to bring your blood sugar down, but it's exactly this drop that will have you reaching for the mid-morning sugar-fix.

Lack of vitamin D compounds the problem by reducing insulin secretion, thus putting you at risk of diabetes. In experiments with rabbits quoted by Dr Damien Downing (see also pages 224–5), and confirmed with human beings, different colours of light had completely different effects on blood-sugar levels. Red light sent them up sharply – and it is red light that peaks in ordinary incandescent light bulbs. UV light, on the other hand, caused a rise in glycogen – the stored sugar which we use for energy – while the level of glucose in the blood fell at the same time. In diabetics, as Dr Kime noted (see also pages 223–4), this fall could be dramatic, and one diabetic friend of his ended up in hospital with severe hypoglycemia after a long sunbathing session. The UV effect on blood glucose is well established, and diabetics need to monitor their insulin needs very carefully while sunbathing.

In his comprehensive survey *The Healing Sun*, Richard Hobday notes that the results of a pan-European trial published in the journal *Diabetologica* in 1999 suggest that vitamin D supplements taken in infancy protect against, or arrest, a process that can lead to insulin-dependent diabetes in later childhood. 'If this is the case,' he writes, 'it seems reasonable to suggest that exposure to sunlight in early childhood may be important in preventing the onset of this disease.'

If someone ate a daily diet of bacon and eggs for breakfast, cold chicken for lunch, grilled steak for dinner, a single serving of vegetables, a little cheese, and half a slice of bread, we should say that his diet was severely unbalanced – much too much protein, far too little carbohydrate, not nearly enough fruits, vegetables and essential fatty acids, and grossly lacking in vital nutrients.

The artificial lighting under which we choose to spend much of our lives is just as unbalanced and deficient as this. And it may be quite as disastrous for our health.

5 junk light

Schooltime is stressful for children. Cooped up hour after hour in stuffy classrooms, denied the joyful activity which comes naturally to them, seated at low, flat desks and on chairs almost guaranteed to give them backache, they have to endure – as well all the pressures of school work – the uncongenial subject, the boring teacher, the tough competition and the sweat of exams. In most modern schools, moreover, they do so under the chill, unfriendly glare of cool, white, fluorescent lighting. Do we have to make it so hard for them?

Education authorities in North Carolina, USA, are discovering that in schools lit mainly by natural daylight, not only are there huge savings in energy, but children are happier, healthier and work harder. There are now four daylit schools within the state, all designed by the same architectural firm, Innovative Design of Raleigh. The latest, Durant Middle School, was nominated one of the USA's top ten most environmentally friendly buildings in 1997. When its pupils were asked what they thought of their school, they replied enthusiastically: 'It's comfortable. Open. Sort of like being at home or outside.'

Its architects planned the building to maximize the use of sunshine, orienting it along an east–west axis, and mounting north- and south-facing monitors on the roof to funnel light inside through a series of translucent fabric baffles, which diffuse light evenly into classrooms, cafeteria and gymnasium. For two-thirds of the school day, no artificial light is required.

Both air-conditioning and lighting costs have been slashed dramatically: the building came in $700,000 under budget, while annual energy savings are reckoned at around $165,000.

A much bigger bonus in human terms is the change in the children themselves. The pupils of Durant Middle School have a more positive attitude to their work, and both their attendance rates and their grades are significantly above average.

When academic performance at the three earlier schools was analysed and compared with 'normally' lit schools, it was higher by an average of 14%. Sceptics objected that perhaps the newness of their surroundings was motivating pupils: but students at another equally new, non-daylit school actually did worse than average.

This study looked at energy savings and academic performance only. An earlier study, in Alberta, Canada, which compared children attending elementary schools fitted with full-spectrum lighting and those at schools with conventional lighting, came up with even more startling results. At the full-spectrum-lit elementary schools, the children were significantly healthier, school attendance was up 3.8 days a year, the children were noticeably more positive about their studies, they had nine times less dental decay and, over a two-year period, they grew an average of 2.1cm more than children at conventionally lit schools.

There have been other patchy studies of the effect of artificial light on health and behaviour in human beings. In a controlled experiment with two groups of schoolchildren attending schools with normal fluorescent lighting, one group had regular doses of UV light as well. Compared to the control group, the children who had doses of UV worked harder, complained less of fatigue, got better grades, had clearer vision, grew faster and put on more weight.

Other studies have found that university students working under full-spectrum light complained much less often of lethargy than those studying under ordinary cool, white, fluorescent light, and that both hyperactivity and the repetitive behaviour of autistic children were markedly better under full-spectrum than fluorescent light.

Why are we happier, better at our work, healthier in daylight than under incandescent or cool, white, fluorescent light?

Why is fluorescent light in particular so unpopular with those who work under it? What is the difference? How important to our health and well-being are these missing wavelengths of light and colour?

Incredibly, there has been almost no research to establish the physiological effect on human beings of this junk light, but the results of one clinical trial are highly suggestive. In the early 1980s, Dr Fritz Hollwich exposed human subjects to long periods of cool, white, fluorescent light, then to periods of full-spectrum lighting. Under the fluorescent lights, their blood levels of two adrenal chemicals – ACTH and cortisol – rose to levels consistent with severe stress. Under full-spectrum lighting, there were no such changes. 'These findings,' wrote an appalled Hollwich, 'explain the agitated mental and physical behaviour of children staying the whole day in school under artificial illumination with strong spectral deviation from sunlight.'

Is it surprising that the universal complaint of schoolchildren and students today is of fatigue? And that truancy, hyperactivity and lethargy are increasingly common?

6 darkness deprivation

On a clear, winter evening many years ago I saw an astonishing sight: the canyons of central Manhattan's skyscrapers lit only by pure cold moonlight. A massive power failure had extinguished the lights in the middle of the evening rush-hour and, gazing up at the skies above them, we saw stars. Thousands of them. Stars that were normally hidden from sight by the bright lights of the city.

The sight of a starry sky was once the birthright of every human being. Children felt a sense of wonder flower within them as they gazed up at those uncountable points of twinkling light, saw the hazy swirl of the Milky Way, learned to recognize the Plough and the Dog Star, Orion's Belt, the Great Bear and the North Star. Contemplation of this starry immensity has always lent perspective to human affairs.

Millions of city children today have never seen the stars in all their glory, and millions more grown-ups are fast forgetting what a starry sky looks like.

If they live in a big city, what they will probably see as they gaze skywards is a wash of orange and purple, the dismal smog of a thousand street lights which spill their ghastly orange or blue-white upward as well as downward, where it is actually needed.

Motorways trail orange ribbons of glare across the remotest areas. Under pressure from ex-townies, village high streets are becoming as bright as any city thoroughfare. Airports light up many kilometres of countryside around them. Office blocks pour out light from dusk to dawn, carparks remain brilliantly illuminated long after the last car has left. Wealthy householders floodlight dark corners of their gardens in case a burglar might be lurking there, and ring their properties with 500W security lights, turning night into permanent day. And more and more cathedrals, public buildings, even parish churches are now ringed by floodlights.

Light is also a prime advertising medium and there are no controls on advertising in space, so night-time laser displays of coloured logos are already happening. And one day, perhaps, corporate sponsors of space missions will want to beam their corporate image onto the face of the moon by way of pay-off.

Astronomers were the first to start worrying, as this glare in the skies began to blur their view of the stars. In the 1950s the Royal Observatory moved from the bright lights of London to the clearer skies of the Sussex coast. But 30 years later they were compelled to move again – this time to a site 1800m up in the Canary Islands resort of La Palma. Astronomers the world over face similar problems. Today, they talk of 'light pollution' or 'intrusive light': the proliferation of artificial illumination which is steadily depriving much of the world of darkness.

'The night sky, by its very nature a site of special scientific interest and an area of outstanding natural beauty, has been quietly and gradually taken away over the last 50 years, from those dwelling in towns and urban fringe areas, throughout the developed world,' says Bob Mizon, coordinator of the Campaign for Dark Skies launched by the British Astronomical Association in 1990. The CfDS works closely with the International Dark-Sky Association (IDA), set up in 1988. Both associations came into being following surveys which found that a high percentage of astronomers were experiencing increasing difficulties from light pollution. Their objective was to build public awareness of the problem and to work towards quality outdoor lighting. Millions of street lights, for instance, could be shielded so that their light isn't sent upwards.

Apart from the aesthetic and cultural importance of losing our night skies, lack of darkness may be injurious to millions of earth's living species – from human beings to moths and earthworms – whose biological clocks are tuned to the rhythms of nature and the steady alternation of day and night, light and darkness (see also chapter 2). At the end of a day when our eyes have been stressed or over-stimulated by long exposure to bright artificial lighting and the flickering screen of the TV, we crave the soothing comfort of darkness. But for millions of people, night-time darkness is only available behind thick bedroom curtains or blinds. Should you wish to fling your windows open to the warm summer night, your bedroom may well become distractingly bright.

This absence of darkness, and the chronic disruption of melatonin production it can induce, may have more profound consequences for our long-term health than we imagine. What it does to birds is a matter of record. In the middle of the night, in my all-too-well-lit north London bedroom, I hear bemused song-birds launching into chorus, as the bright street lights and dozens of security lights convince them that dawn is at hand.

Light pollution is actually fatal to millions of migrating birds, as a thoughtful article by Joe Bower, in the March/April 2000 issue of *Audubon* magazine, made plain. Many hundreds of species of migrating birds set their nocturnal course by the stars and bright artificial lights may lead them astray – to their death. 'Numerous reports have been documented of birds flying off course towards lights on buildings, towers, light-houses, even boats,' noted Bower. 'On a rainy, foggy Labor Day weekend in 1981, more than 10,000 birds collided with the floodlit smokestacks at Ontario's Hydro Lennox Generating Station near Kingston.'

Light pollution is hugely wasteful. The Campaign for Dark Skies calculates that approximately 30% of street lighting in the UK goes straight up into the sky, wasting at least £53 million-worth of energy annually – as well as generating the greenhouse gases of millions of tonnes of polluting fossil fuels (see Air, pages 119–121). The Illuminating Engineering Society of North America studied artificial lighting and concluded that many companies use five times the amount of light necessary.

But there are signs that public awareness of the problem is slowly building. Many sectors of the lighting industry have shown themselves both informed and highly responsible, struggling to educate their customers about well-designed night lighting. The Italian design company iGuzzini has been running an eye-catching campaign against wasteful intrusive light since 1982.

In December 1999, when a night club in Guildford, Surrey, appealed against a ban on the two 7000W searchlights it had been beaming into the sky over the town, Planning Inspector Ava Wood turned them down: the beams, she said, were 'unwelcome intrusions... detrimental to the amenity of the surrounding rural areas'. In a two-page feature in January 2000, *Time* magazine noted that light pollution was fast becoming a national concern, with legislation to 'bag the beam' pending in four states including New York and Massachusetts, while Texas and Mexico had already passed tough laws to restrict outdoor lighting.

The world's first Dark Sky Reserve has been created in the province of Ontario, Canada. The reserve has been built on 2000 hectares of government-owned land that's largely undeveloped, about a two-hour drive north of Toronto. There will be no new buildings, no roads, and any development that would bring lights into the reserve will be prohibited. Standing on an 18m slab of granite that rises above the treeline, star-lovers can gaze their fill.

Astronomers are hopeful that our dark skies may not be lost for ever. 'The Chileans are particularly interested,' says Elizbeth Alvarez, Associate Director of IDA. 'There are three major observatories in their country, and they are helping sponsor a national campaign of public education. They have realized that freedom from light pollution can even be a tourist attraction: that night skies with all their stars are a wonderful resource which will last for ever – or could be wiped out the way the view has been wiped out in so many places.

'We aren't talking about trade-offs, the way we might be with other forms of pollution. We don't have to give up important pleasures, or spend huge amounts of money to save our starry skies. On the contrary, we'll actually save money – enormous sums – as well as massive amounts of energy by tackling light pollution. It's a win-win situation.'

7 sun phobia

Popular British weatherman Michael Fish used to warn viewers regularly against spending too long in the sun. But when he appeared on TV one August evening sporting his own holiday tan, he was roundly ticked off by the UK Skin Cancer Prevention Working Party. Fish should stay in the shade himself, they commented. And wouldn't it be nice if more high-profile figures – actors, models, TV personalities – set a good example by staying winter-pale?

The 'harmfulness' of the sun's ultraviolet (UV) rays has now become the accepted wisdom of the medical establishment, with few dissenting voices, and a vast chorus of agreement from the cosmetic and sunglasses industries. The American Medical Association has suggested to women that they should apply a waterproof and sweatproof suncream 30 minutes before leaving home. It's hard to buy a moisturizer today in anything but the cheapest skin-care ranges (or the 'natural' ranges), that doesn't come with built-in sun-protection factor (SPF). This may soon be true of more and more holiday clothes, too. An American manufacturer already offers a whole range of beachwear – from wide-brimmed sunhats to long-sleeved shirts, T-shirts, skirts and trousers – guaranteed to block out 97% of 'harmful' UV rays. One British product manufacturer has actually suggested that sun-care products should be regulated as preventive medicine.

As for the sunglasses industry, sun phobia as much as fashion has meant rocketing sales: now you can not only look like Tom Cruise or Nicole Kidman in your designer shades, you can also save your eyes from cataracts at the same time: didn't you know that sunshine gives you cataracts? Most sunglasses today offer 100% UV protection and you can order contact lenses that offer protection, too. Tragically, even children are being targeted by the sunglasses industry, and the sight of toddlers in pushchairs sporting flower-trimmed or lollipop-hued sunglasses in sunshine resorts is increasingly common.

In the view of sunphobes, of course, children are obviously specially vulnerable. A 1998 leaflet issued by the Health Education Board for Scotland warned that babies should be kept out of the sun. Taking this advice seriously, the manufacturers of a new anti-pollution baby buggy have equipped it with a protective canopy to shield its occupant from UV and infrared radiation.

It has been seriously suggested that schools should plant trees in their playgrounds to protect children from exposure. And the UK Health Education Authority now offers a range of trendy Lycra tops and pants for children to wear in and out of the sea, that offer maximum protection from sunshine.

In a scientific journal, I have even seen the sun described in passing as 'an environmental carcinogen'.

In the British Medical Association's *Family Doctor Guide to Skin and Sunlight*, its authors concede that 'very small amounts of UV radiation' promote the synthesis of vitamin D in our skins. But they go on to point out that dietary vitamin D from fish oils, eggs and dairy products 'provide all that we need in normal circumstances'. And they come to the amazing conclusion that 'Over all, it therefore seems that the UV radiation part of the spectrum may not be of any value to us at all, but is just responsible for most of the harmful effects associated with sun exposure, such as sunburn, photo-ageing and skin cancer.'

For more than three million years human beings have lived their lives happily in the sun, simply taking sensible precautions to protect themselves from its rays when these were at their hottest and strongest. Now, at the beginning of the twenty-first century, sunshine has suddenly become the most dangerous stuff on the planet. For a start, it's responsible for today's epidemic of skin cancers. Isn't it?

8 medical sunblock

In the hedonistic 1960s, a deep rich tan was the jetsetter's trademark. You couldn't be too rich, too thin or too tanned, and at least the tan was within reach of anyone who could raise the price of a Club Med holiday. Once you got to your beach, suntan oil was a mandatory accessory, to help promote that desirable deep tan.

As it slowly became apparent that crocodile skin was the long-term price tag on all that sensuous sun-worshipping, sun-oil makers frantically repositioned their brand image. Suntan oils were reborn as sunscreens. The new thinking was that you could still enjoy that sun-soaking session on the beach – as long as you wore your sunscreen.

Then alarm about skin cancers began to mount, and as evidence piled up of sun-damage to skin, sunscreen makers faced a dilemma. They needed their customers to believe that too much hot Mediterranean sun spelled ruin to the skin – and maybe skin cancer, too. But they also wanted to encourage them to stay in the sun – lavishly anointed with their product.

Sun Protection Factors (SPFs) became the no. 1 selling-point – the higher the better and the more expensive – and the total sunblock was born.

Fortunately for the sunscreen makers, an army of dermatologists has been labouring to promote their wares for well over a quarter of a century now, and the warnings grow more shrill and alarming every year. Darrell Rigel, President of the American Academy of Dermatologists, outlined his ten commandments for safe sunning in 1999. People should stay out of the sun between 10am and 4pm. They should cover up with long sleeves, long pants and wide-brimmed hats. But if they are exposed to the midday sun they should use SPF15 or higher in generous amounts – about a shot glass full for a person in a bathing suit. 'People apply 20–50% of the amount they should,' he said, 'which amounts to 20–50% of the SPF.'

Sunscreens aren't just for the beach, either. The beauty editors of glossy magazines constantly remind their readers that their complexion is at risk if it's not protected by sunscreen every single time they go out: even on cloudy days, even in winter. So sunscreens are built into virtually every day-care skin cream, too.

What exactly do sunscreens do? They protect our skins by screening out two types of ultraviolet radiation: UV-A, otherwise known as near-UV, and UV-B, or mid-UV. Far-UV or UV-C has the shortest wavelength and is an excellent bactericide, but by the same token it is bad news for both plants and human beings. Fortunately, it is mostly filtered out by the ozone layer. UV-B are the rays chiefly responsible for sunburn, skin wrinkling and general skin damage. UV-A rays were once thought of as the 'tanning rays' and tanning beds usually supply only UV-A: these rays penetrate further into the skin and they can weaken the whole structure of the skin.

When UV radiation strikes the skin, it generates a storm of Reactive Oxygen Species (ROS), potentially lethal molecules that can trigger a chain reaction of damage throughout our bodies and locally in our skin, where they can attack proteins, lipids, carbohydrates, DNA itself – and the elastin and collagen that keep our skin soft, supple and elastic. Too much sun and you could develop one of two types of skin cancer on exposed parts of your body. The most common – around 75% of all skin cancers – is basal cell carcinoma, a rodent ulcer that starts out like a shiny pink bump before it starts to bleed, ulcerate or develop a scab. It's most common in people who work indoors and have intermittent sun exposure. The second most common – around 20% – is squamous cell carcinoma, which can turn nasty if not caught in time: it starts out as a red scaly patch, often on the lip, ear or nose and usually affects those in their fifties who work outdoors.

There is a third type of skin cancer – the real killer: malignant melanoma, which in around 50% of cases starts out as a mole: it is often linked with episodes of sunburn and too much strong sunshine. But as we shall see, the jury is still out.

Some sunscreens only filter out the UV-B radiation, others only UV-A. Most of the expensive ranges claim to be broad spectrum, filtering out both. They protect skin either chemically or physically. The chemicals act by soaking up and reflecting away the sun's rays, and there have been scares about a couple of chemicals used in the past: one is PABA, which was found to cause allergic reactions as well as staining clothes; the second was psoralen, which was believed to be associated with a higher risk of skin cancer. Sunscreens which protect you physically use either zinc oxide or titanium dioxide, which work by scattering the light. Cricketers don't mind slathering white zinc oxide ointment all over their noses, but women do, so titanium dioxide is the number one choice of eco-friendly skincare companies.

The confusing SPF is a relative measure of how long you can stay in the sun without turning red and starting to burn. If you would normally burn after 10 minutes, an SPF 2 sunscreen will allow you to stay 20 minutes, and so on. Over SPF30, sunscreens become 'sunblocks' but even SPF 40 won't absorb 100% of UV-B radiation.

In 1999 the US Food and Drug Administration (FDA), in an effort to clear up some of the confusion and hype generated by the SPF system, announced new labelling rules, to apply to UV-B sunscreens. From May 2001 there will be only three categories: SPF 2–11 labelled 'minimum'; 12–29 labelled 'moderate'; and anything over 30 to be labelled 'high', with 30+ the highest claim allowed.

Dermatologists aren't happy with the new rules. The American Academy of Dermatology recommends an SPF of 15 or higher – not guaranteed for every product in the new 'moderate' bracket.

But a growing body of evidence suggests that sun exposure is not actually the major factor in the development of malignant melanoma, that sunscreens do not actually offer protection against it, and that indeed sunscreen use may be a risk factor in itself.

The melanoma–sunshine connection seemed obvious. The melanoma figures started to rise in the mid-1950s, at the rate of 3–7% a year until the early 1980s. From then onwards, studies showed much steeper rises, of up to 43% a year. The disease is especially common in Europe, Australia and North America, where more and more people head off to a beach for their annual break. And the figures are highest of all for Australia – where a high percentage of the population is fair skinned (another supposed risk factor) and of north-European origin.

But when medical statisticians took a closer look at the figures in 1982, they found that they had uncovered a surprising result.

The highest incidence of melanoma was among office workers who spent their days under fluorescent lighting, rather than those whose jobs kept them out in the sun.

Two more studies confirmed this finding: even when every other factor was taken into account, including skin colour, tendency to sunburn and frequency of exposure to sun, they showed that those who worked regularly under fluorescent lights were more likely to develop melanoma.

A study carried out over eight years among US Navy personnel produced equally surprising results: personnel who worked indoors had the highest rates of melanoma; those who worked outside as well as indoors actually had rates lower than the US national average.

There are other question marks. Skin cancers other than melanoma almost invariably appear on areas of skin often exposed to the sun, but melanoma can develop on the trunk or feet. It is becoming more common in Japan – a country with no tradition of sunbathing. Figures are rocketing in Norway – up 350% for men, 440% for women over the period 1957 to 1984. And in 1994 the US *Journal of the National Cancer Institute* carried a report of a study in which groups of mice were treated with three different kinds of sunscreen, with one untreated as a control, and then injected with melanoma cancer cells, before being blasted with UV-B. Sunburn and skin damage were much less apparent in the treated mice, which was good news for sunscreen-makers: but the sunscreens offered no protection against the artificially induced melanoma.

There is worse news for the sunscreen industry. In February 1998, at a conference in Philadelphia, USA, Dr Marianne Berwick, an epidemiologist from Memorial Sloan-Kettering Cancer Center in New York, dropped a bombshell. 'It's not safe to rely on sunscreen,' she told her audience. Of ten careful studies that had looked at the question, two suggested that sunscreens might prevent melanoma. Three of them, including her own, found no association between sunscreen use and diminished risk of melanoma. And five others found that the risk actually increased among sunscreen users, though this was perhaps because the people who used them most were more at risk – being fair-skinned – anyway.

In the same year, *The Journal of the National Cancer Institute* reported directly from the beach-head. A team of researchers had counted nevi – the small pigmented moles that are considered a risk factor for melanoma – on 631 six to seven-year-olds at the seaside and they quizzed their parents about sunscreen use. After adjusting for latitude and skin type, they found that those who had had the most sunscreen applied had the most moles, while those who had used the least sunscreen and worn protective clothing had the fewest.

There is one final and overwhelming question mark over the sunshine–melanoma hypothesis. If melanoma were indeed caused by continuous exposure to the sun in hot climates, particularly in fair-skinned people from the north of Europe, the British and Dutch navies could never have dispatched ships on voyages lasting years, often involving months in tropical waters. And life on the sides of mountains, with their higher levels of UV radiation, would have been a killer.

Much of medical opinion is now beginning to back off from the joyless damnation of sunbathing and heavy promotion of sunscreens.

'There is evidence,' said a July 1999 report in the *British Medical Journal*, 'that the potential benefits of exposure to sunlight may outweigh the widely publicized adverse effects on the incidence of skin cancer. For many people the small absolute increase in risk of melanoma could easily be outweighed by the effect of reduced sunlight on mood.'

A couple of dermatologists based at Newcastle in the north of England, actually accused the multi-million-pound skin protection industry of hyping the risks to increase sales. Professor Sam Shuster was quoted as saying, 'The melanoma story is largely made up. The evidence of ultraviolet light as the main cause is not there.'

So if unprotected sunbathing isn't causing today's epidemic of melanoma, what is? The most likely candidate appears to be – sunscreens, and there could be two explanations.

'Sunscreens could be passive carcinogens,' explains Professor John Knowland, Biochemistry lecturer at Oxford University in the UK who has made a special study of sunscreens. 'In other words, they encourage people to spend much longer in the sun than they would otherwise, in the mistaken belief that they are protected. When sunscreens are tested in the USA to establish their SPF, they are applied at the rate of 2mg per square centimetre. This is a lot of sunscreen. I'm quite tall, so there's a lot of skin to cover, so I'd need about 40g – and not just once a day, but two to three times a day, almost your average bottle of sunscreen. Most people lying on a beach, and giving themselves a few swipes with a little sunscreen, aren't nearly as protected as they think they are.'

The sunscreens themselves might be the problem. 'Sunscreens work by absorbing sunlight energy,' explains Knowland. 'But you cannot destroy energy – it has to go somewhere. And lots of chemical sunscreens penetrate the skin. This means that once you've had a swim and washed off the protective layer of sunscreen on top of your skin, the sunscreen which has been absorbed into your skin will get maximum illumination. In the case of one chemical which turns up in a lot of sunscreens – padimate-O – some studies suggest that when it's inside your skin, and it absorbs photons from UV light, it might cause strand breaks in DNA. What such DMA damage might lead to is uncertain, but some work indicates that the kind of genetic damage associated with melanoma might be triggered by strand breaks... This means that there could be two competing effects from sunscreens: protection from the layer on the surface of the skin, and damage from that which diffuses into the skin.'

The ideal sunscreen, in Knowland's view, would absorb UV-A and UV-B, but would not penetrate the skin. 'I'd avoid any that contained padimate-O', he says, 'but it's a chemical with a lot of different names, so it's not easy to be certain that you are avoiding it unless you know all the synonyms. I'm not a great one for lying in the sun myself, but if I did – I'd go for one containing titanium dioxide, which seems less likely to penetrate the skin.'

The jury is likely to be out on this question for some time. What is not in doubt, however, is that sunscreens block the formation of vitamin D3 in the skin and that Vitamin D has known anti-cancer powers, as the Garland research show (see also page 229).

It's often forgotten, too, that our skins have a double natural protection against over-exposure to the sun.

The first is the tan itself, which – as we shall see in chapter 9 – early practitioners of the therapy always insisted should be built up very slowly indeed. If, like other mammals, we had year-round exposure to the sun, this is, of course, exactly what would happen as winter changed to spring and then summer.

Natural tan is produced by the action of the sun triggering the synthesis of a pigment named melanin in our skin: as levels rise, our skin slowly turns a deeper colour. Since melanin is a powerful antioxidant it mops up the free radicals generated by UV radiation in our skins, converts some of the radiation into heat, scatters some and filters the rest, allowing just enough into the cells to stimulate key activities such as the synthesis of vitamin D. Melanin is found in the eyes, too, where it absorbs and filters light across the whole spectral range, particularly at the UV wavelengths which can damage the retina. Dermatologists have taught us to believe that any degree of tan is a sign of skin damage, but a moderate tan slowly and carefully built up over weeks and months rather than hours signals a protected, rather than a damaged, skin, although melanin levels decline with advancing years – which means that hours of sunshine will be much more damaging to the complexion at age 50 than at 20.

Our skin's second line of defence is the antioxidants in our diet. The rainbow colours of fruits and vegetables do more than stimulate our eye and our palate. These pigments are vital antioxidants, acting as powerful sunscreens for plants exposed to a daily blaze of sunshine. Without this protection, leaves would wither and fruits would shrivel and dry out even before they could ripen. When we feast on these colourful foods, we are helping ourselves, too, to large doses of antioxidants. So for maximum natural protection from sun-damage, we should eat fruits and salads in plenty all summer.

Beta-carotene in supplement form is just one of these antioxidant pigments: on the farms where it is produced in Australia, Israel and Hawaii, writes Caroline Wheater in her book *Beta-Carotene*, '...acres of bright orange algae are stretched out, soaking up the sun. The more the sun shines the more orange the algae turns, frantically producing beta-carotene to stop damage to their cells.'

Antioxidant supplements like vitamins C and E, and plant pigments like carotenoids and flavonoids, can be strongly protective against sun-damage, whether swallowed or applied directly to the skin, and their efficacy has been demonstrated in rigorous trials. In one study published in 2000 in the *Proceedings of the Society of Experimental Biology and Medicine*, 22 men and women took a mixed carotenoid supplement over 24 weeks, with the daily dose increasing at eight-week intervals from 30mg to 90mg. As the weeks went by, the skins of the volunteers became less and less vulnerable to reddening – the first indication of trouble – and levels of lipid peroxidation – a measure of free radical damage – declined.

When vitamin E was added in another study, the protective effect was greatly increased. When vitamin E was applied directly to the skin, it not only increased levels of important antioxidants – including vitamin C – in the skin itself, but also protected them from depletion after UV exposure.

You might lose friends if you started smoothing plenty of fish oil into your skin at the beach. But oily fish contain compounds which work to counter inflammation and suppress free radical activity, so what better or more delicious choice for a beach lunch than sardines or anchovies just hauled out of the sea and grilled to perfection, with a little olive oil and lemon juice?

The sunscreens of the future – and indeed, a number already on sale – will be crammed with these natural antioxidants rather than the chemicals that manufacturers have relied on up to now. If they are allowed to do so, most cosmetic houses will market high-antioxidant supplements to be taken internally, as well as topical skin care. Enterprising sunscreen makers in the USA are already putting melanin into their oils and creams.

They might consider extra-virgin olive oil, too, for after-sun preparations: Japanese scientists gave hairless mice a three-minute-a-week dose of UV light, then five minutes after the dose painted their skins with either olive oil or extra-virgin olive oil, leaving other mice unpainted as controls. The control mice started to develop tumours after 18 weeks, the olive-oil painted mice didn't do much better, but for those treated with extra-virgin olive oil it was another six weeks before any sign of cancer appeared – and then the tumours were smaller, and there was less DNA damage.

There are signs, too, that the skin-care industry is beginning to have second thoughts about the need for old-fashioned sunblocks. In the summer of 2000, the Yves St Laurent beauty company sent out a press release announcing an extraordinary volte-face in its perception of the sun–skin relationship. It announced the launch of a day-care cream christened 'Grand Jour' or 'Broad Daylight', which would protect against all environmental aggressions including UV rays without the use of sunscreens. 'With GRAND JOUR sunlight is transformed into a daily cure of radiance and vitality for your face... Light means life!'

If the holes in the ozone layer extend much further in the future, over densely occupied territory, the whole question of sun-protection will have to be urgently re-thought. Until then, let us enjoy sunshine for its marvellous healing, protective and energizing qualities.

the healing power of light

9 the sunshine cure

In 1815, a French medical journal published a paper about a revolutionary new therapy. Entitled *Important Opinions Regarding Insolation in Various Disorders*, by a Dr Loebel, it set out a list of conditions for which sun treatment might be favourable, and others in which it was inadvisable. 'Insolation' was excellent, in Loebel's view, for cases of general weakness, debility and sluggishness of the lymphatic system, for chronic dropsy, gout, rheumatism and chronic diarrhoea. It was not to be considered for cases where acute inflammation or congestion was involved, or for gastric problems.

Among those who followed in Loebel's footsteps was the surgeon Bonnet, who worked at the Hotel Dieu Hospital in Lyons. Surgery often failed miserably in tuberculous infections of the joints, which ate away at skin, muscle and bone. Bonnet found that when he exposed these patients to strong sunshine on the hospital balcony, infections often cleared up miraculously. At the Lyons hospital, heliotherapy became the treatment of choice for such cases.

By the mid-nineteenth century, heliotherapy was being investigated for much more general application: one doctor went so far as to suggest that regular sunbathing might be an answer to the 'malady' of old age. And at clinics on the Adriatic and in the Alps two nature-cure pioneers, Rikli and Lahmann, treated with air- and sun-baths thousands of patients who came complaining of fatigue, debility, 'nerves', depression and other disorders. Many of their wealthy patients had seldom been exposed to so much sun in the whole of their lives.

Nature-cure practitioners of the nineteenth century were indeed far ahead of their time in their appreciation of our need for the sun.

American Hygienists were stressing the importance of sunlight for growth and development, for bone formation, in the treatment of rickets and for tuberculosis (TB), while conventional doctors were still strapping rickety children into corsets to straighten their twisted spines.

One of the great pioneers was the Danish Niels Finsen, who won the Nobel prize in 1903 for his innovative treatment of the skin disease *Lupus vulgaris* with a specially developed ultraviolet lamp. Lupus is a form of TB that mainly affects the face: at that time, when no successful treatment except surgery was available, patients often became so hideously disfigured that they chose to become veiled social outcasts.

Finsen had been fascinated by the healing powers of the sun for years when he opened his Light Institute in Copenhagen, and as Richard Hobday has pointed out in *The Healing Sun* (see also page 232) he actually preferred to use direct sunlight in the treatment of his patients whenever possible, encouraging them to walk about naked. As far as possible, too, in so northerly a latitude, he investigated the effects of sunshine on other forms of TB, of the bones and joints.

In the year that Finsen was awarded his Nobel Prize, another doctor, Auguste Rollier, opened the first medical clinic exclusively for the sunshine treatment. Cases of the surgical TB which Bonnet had treated with sunshine filled hospital wards at this time, and they were the mainstay of the private clinic in Bern where Rollier had studied for four years under a brilliant surgeon, Professor Kocher. For all his marvels of technique and sepsis, however, Rollier observed that Kocher's patients almost always relapsed, while mutilation and loss of joint function were common even when the infection was arrested.

Sufferers from pulmonary TB were already being treated in a growing number of sanatoria sited high in the mountains with their pure air, and obviously benefiting, but few people were doing anything of the kind for patients of the dreadful surgical form of the disease. It was for them that Rollier opened his clinic at Leysin, high in the Swiss Alps. Like Rikli, he had come to the conclusion that 'The essential factors are the air of high altitudes and the sun-bath applied to the whole surface of the body: the bracing effect of the combination is of the greatest therapeutic value.'

At first, only victims of TB of the bone and joint were treated at Leysin. Soon Rollier was also dealing with gunshot wounds which had failed to heal in victims of the First World War, fractures, varicose or dreadful syphilitic ulcers, osteomyelitis – a stubborn infection of the bone – and the post-infection exhaustion and debility suffered by many who survived the great 'flu pandemic of 1918. Lupus was also successfully treated at Leysin, as were cases of anaemia and rickets.

Patients arriving at Leysin were immediately put to bed and for the first few days left to become acclimatized to the pure cold mountain air. Only when Rollier was satisfied that they were ready for it did treatment begin with just a few minutes of sunshine, on the feet alone. Gradually, more and more of the body was exposed, for longer periods of time until, when his patients had developed a glorious golden tan, they were allowed to spend hours a day, wearing only sun-hats and loin-cloths, on the verandahs of the hospital.

The diet was that of a modern health farm: no alcohol, no heavy red meat, a little chicken or fish – usually cold, plenty of cereals, vegetables – 'never to be omitted', and fruit – 'absolutely indispensable, at breakfast as well as supper'.

The results were extraordinary: they can be studied in Rollier's book *Ma Cure de Soleil*, published in 1913. Photographed before treatment are thin and pallid children with grossly distorted limbs, frightful open sores, and sunken faces marked by pain and apathy. The same children,after months of treatment, are cheerful, sturdy, straight of back and limb, with only well-healed scars to show they had ever been sick.

'Nowhere on earth have I seen, or heard all, of anything so beautiful, so significant, so hopeful... the whole, healed, happy flesh of hundreds,' wrote one English visitor to Leysin, a Dr Caleb Williams Saleeby. Early in his medical career he had seen the blackened lungs of a TB patient at autopsy, and had sworn never again to buy a single piece of coal for his own use. TB and rickets were for him the 'diseases of darkness' that flourished in the reeking, sunless slums of the UK's cities.

He became one of a few doctors campaigning actively in England for the introduction and study of heliotherapy. Another advocate, Sir Henry Gauvain, had been treating patients with the sun cure for some time at seaside clinics at Alton in Hampshire and Hayling Island. Together they talked the British Medical Research Council into setting up a committee to investigate the biological properties of light. The 'new' therapy – re-christened actinotherapy – was an artificial form of the sunshine therapy and rapidly established itself in both medical and public favour. Rollier's book was translated into English and enjoyed huge success. A growing volume of research identified ultraviolet (UV) as the active waveband of the spectrum and studied its activity on the skin.

In experiments at the National Institute of Medical Research, Sir Leonard Hill took blood from a normal healthy male and added pathogenic organisms – important players of the then little-understood immune system. In the course of time, phagocytic activity in the blood diminished or destroyed them. The same subject was then given doses of UV light, more blood was taken and the experiment repeated. This time the pathogens were cleared at startling speed. But after further doses, the bactericidal effect dwindled – to prove the need for exact prescription of sunshine.

Other studies showed that leucocytes and phagocytes both increased in the presence of sunshine; that key minerals like iodine, calcium and iron were better absorbed; that levels of haemoglobin and phosphorus in the blood rose in sunshine and that rickets could be cleared by UV treatment alone.

Soon artificial lamps were being developed to substitute for the real thing, hospitals began to appoint 'actinotherapists' to their consulting staff, and local authorities throughout the UK began setting up Light Clinics for the treatment of anaemic and rickety babies or children. And when a distinguished Harley Street physician, Dr Percy Hall (actinotherapist for Mount Vernon and Northwood), published in

1924 a careful scientific study of the subject called *Ultra-Violet Rays in the Treatment and Cure of Disease*, the book was an instant best-seller, reaching its fourth edition by 1929.

A chapter in this book describes Dr Hall's work with the pioneer municipal Light Clinic, set up in Hull in 1923. Hall was a member of the Child Welfare and Health and Maternity Committees for the city, and he was appalled by the numbers of cases of rickets and other deficiency diseases among the city's poorest. At his instigation, a small clinic equipped with a single tungsten UV lamp was set up.

The results exceeded all expectations. In the first two years over 300 cases were treated, including numbers of small children deformed by rickets. As long as the children were brought in regularly for their treatment, startling improvements were noted in the carefully kept records. The mothers were delighted by '...the disappearance of apathy and fretfulness... increased 'peacefulness' and desire for sleep after treatment', in place of the previous irritability and sleeplessness.

But by the early 1930s heliotherapy was doomed in medical eyes by its association with charlatans and quacks. Numbers of self-styled actinotherapists who had never read a line of Rollier's work began treating patients with reckless abandon. Saleeby wrote in 1922 of TB sufferers having their chests exposed to strong midday sun for an hour or so and then dying from the subsequent fever and spitting of blood. One 'specialist' actually advocated the severe reddening and blistering produced by over-exposure for certain cases.

UV lamps for home use were rushed onto the market without proper instructions for their safe use, and a crop of well-publicized accidents resulted. Sunshine and fresh-air therapy were coming to be closely associated, too, with the new practitioners of Nature Cure, for which quackery official medicine had nothing but contempt. And in 1935 the first of the sulphonamide drugs, Prontosil, was launched worldwide, ushering in the age of modern drug therapy.

Natural medicines such as sunshine and fresh air faded overnight from the curriculum of the medical student.

10 photomedicine

Premature babies are often born jaundiced. Their bodies turn yellow as the bile pigment bilirubin accumulates in skin and tissue, slowly poisoning them, instead of being broken down by the liver. Untreated, the condition can cause brain damage or even death, and the treatment until the mid-twentieth century was a traumatic total transfusion of the baby's blood.

Then in the mid-1950s an observant nurse noticed that jaundiced babies who had been wheeled out into a sunny courtyard were recovering without being given any transfusion: in fact, the yellow pigment is harmlessly degraded by sunshine. Sunlight became an experimental treatment, well publicized when three of a famous set of quintuplets, the Kienasts, were born jaundiced. Cured by full-spectrum lighting, they went home to nurseries fitted with the same bright natural lights.

But sunshine is in short supply in big modern hospitals, so researchers went to work on those sunbeams. It was the blue wavelength, they found, that worked the miracle, and tiny jaundiced babies are today treated by being bathed in blue light: one form of light therapy that is widely accepted. Here and there, other wavelengths or types of lighting are being pressed into the service of orthodox western medicine.

A lighting expert, the father of one such jaundiced baby, was appalled by his tiny son's screams of pain as nurses jabbed his heel almost daily to monitor blood bilirubin levels. He developed a scanner which shines a full spectrum of light on a baby's skin, and computer software analyses absorption patterns to determine if bilirubin deposits remain. His device is now in use in hundreds of hospitals.

Despite its long association with skin cancers, light is today being used to treat a wide range of skin problems.

In my acne-ridden early twenties, the only treatment which actually worked for me was a weekly appointment in a clinic with an ultraviolet (UV) lamp. Gradually, instead of tactfully averting their gaze, my friends began to tell me how well I was looking and asking where I'd been on holiday. And when I did go on holiday, my skin always magically cleared up.

As paranoia about UV light mounted among dermatologists, the UV treatment for acne fell out of favour, but researchers at London's Hammersmith Hospital have recently found that the red and blue wavelengths in light seem almost as effective. In a trial reported in the *British Journal of Dermatology*, 100 patients who had had initial treatment with oral antibiotics were given a lightbox emitting the red and blue wavelengths to take home. They were instructed to expose their be-goggled faces to it for 15 minutes a day. After 12 weeks there was a 76% decrease in the number of visible spots – a result that would have thousands of traumatized teenagers dancing in the streets. Dermatologist Dr Toby Chu, who developed the treatment, believes that the blue light kills the bacteria in the skin that cause acne, while the red wavelength speeds healing.

Urticaria, in which large itching wheals develop on the skin, and the disfiguring condition known as morphoea, characterized by hard flat white or reddish patches on the skin, have both responded well to UV treatment, as have some forms of eczema. In psoriasis, extensive areas of the skin – occasionally the head and the whole trunk – may become reddened and covered with thick silvery scales, a condition as devastating socially as it can be uncomfortable physically. Those who can afford to do so jet off to the Dead Sea in Israel, where the combination of strong sunshine and the salty waters works wonders. UV treatment works almost as well for many cases, however.

Sunshine is considered a high-risk factor for another disfiguring disease, *Lupus erythematosus*, in which a red blotchy rash often forms a butterfly pattern across the face. To the surprise of skin specialists, treatment with UV-A is proving successful in some cases.

'When I rise my breakfast is solitary, the black dog waits to share it', wrote Dr Samuel Johnson – the literary lion of eighteenth-century England who was cruelly subject to 'melancholy' – 'from breakfast to dinner he continues barking'. The victims of 'black dog' – depression – in western industrialized countries are numbered in millions, with medical costs running as high as $44 billion in the USA alone.

Depression is characterized as 'black' and its symptoms include feelings of sadness and hopelessness, low esteem, low energy, suicidal thoughts, diminished sex drive and flagging mental drive. But there's a subset of depression known as Seasonal Affective Disorder (SAD), which kicks in when the days begin to shorten in autumn, reaching its peak in midwinter, and declining in early spring as the days begin to lengthen again. For SAD victims, the need for sunshine becomes an overwhelming physiological need. They crave carbohydrates, and may put on up to 13.5kg in the winter months, to shed it again come summer. Unlike typical depressives, too, they can and do sleep for hours on end, up to 14 hours at a time, a heavy sleep from which they wake unrefreshed. (One psychiatrist in Oslo, Norway, told of a patient who used to go to bed in October every year and sleep through till spring.) It is estimated that nearly 25 million people in the USA suffer from SAD and, as you might expect, incidence is particularly high in Scandinavia, where sunless days last for months, and the winter suicide rate is one of the highest in the world.

It was two American psychiatrists, Dr Alfred Lewy and Dr Thomas Wehr, who first discovered in 1980 that bright light suppresses the secretion of melatonin, the 'darkness hormone'. After Dr Norman Rosenthal first identified the condition and named it SAD, Drs Lewy and Wehr suggested that treating patients with hours of bright light might trick their bodies and brains into thinking it was already spring, and the bright light treatment was born. The media took up the story, a brisk market in lightboxes sprang into being and eventually the bright light therapy became mainstream.

The treatment calls for lights of at least 2500 lux power (standard domestic indoor lighting is around 100 lux) and psychiatrists were impressed by the speed with which it worked. Patients usually started to feel better within three to four days, and were in total remission within a fortnight, as long as they continued the treatment. Conventional antidepressive drugs can take up to three weeks to kick in.

There have been changes to the therapy over the years. Initially patients needed to sit in front of their lightboxes for up to two hours a day. Now if they are office workers they can have a 10,000 lux light fitted at their work-station at eye level. Or they can start the day – mornings are the optimum time for therapy – wearing light visors fitted with bright lights under the brim, as they get breakfast or pack their children off to school. Or they can use a dawn simulator – a great way to start a winter day for any of us, actually – which works just like an alarm clock, except that half an hour before the alarm goes off, its great globe starts to glow, gradually filling your bedroom with light, until the alarm goes off and you wake into what looks like dawn.

Early in October every year, just as winter gets into its stride, the fashionable café Engel in Helsinki in Finland invites guests to a celebration breakfast, with pancakes and orange juice, to mark the switch-on of its 14 high-intensity full-spectrum sunlamps. The lamps at each of the windows will stay on from 7am to midnight every day, until the sun reappears in March. Hardly surprisingly, the café is packed all winter with people who come to bask in its marvellous light.

If bright light works for SAD, might it also work for classic, non-seasonal depression?

Psychiatrist Dr Daniel Kripke has been treating his depressive patients with bright light for a number of years now, with excellent results (see also page 229). Clinical trials have found the treatment as helpful in some cases as medication, and Kripke believes that patients should be started on light therapy at the same time as they begin a course of antidepressive drugs – which could produce both faster results and lower costs.

SAD is not the only seasonal disorder. How will light work with menstrual problems? George Brainard (see also page 227) reckons this will be a particularly hot topic over the next few years. If they can afford it, Dr Damien Downing (see also pages 224–5 and 232) advises women patients with irregular periods to take off for a sunshine holiday: '...once they've put in some sensible sunbathing and acquired a moderate tan,' he says, 'they'll usually see an improvement almost immediately – though the effect may wear off after a few months.'

At Hammersmith Hospital in London, Dr David Noton gave 17 women with severe premenstrual syndrome (PMS) an electronic eye-mask he had devised himself and christened the Light Mask. It was designed to be worn with the eyes closed and red lights flickered onto the closed eyes from inside the mask. The women were asked to wear it for 15 minutes a day through four complete menstrual cycles. At the end of that time, a report in the *Journal of Obstetrics and Gynaecology* revealed that 12 of the 17 no longer had PMS. Of the remaining 5, 1 had dropped out because her depression caused by the PMS got worse, 1 reported no change, and 3 showed some improvement.

Shift work and jet lag are other problems which light is being called upon to fix.

Astronauts suffer from both shift work and jet lag. 'Space is an extremely hostile environment', comments George Brainard, who responded to an SOS from the US National Aeronautics and Space Administration (NASA). 'Most of the astronauts are dreadfully sick most of the time they are there, and on top of that, every spacecraft is a shift facility so they're half-on, half-off duty: it's the most disordered circadian system a body could possibly have to contend with.'

The strategy devised by Brainard and his colleagues involved alternating doses of bright light and melatonin to create a 24-hour rhythm for the astronauts. On this night-and-day system, the astronauts were doing so well that the ground crews at the NASA base, who worked the same shifts, demanded the bright light treatment, too.

The success of the NASA strategy had obvious military implications. Soldiers often need to stay not just awake but alert as well for far longer than 24 hours, and strong coffee and amphetamines – yesterday's techniques – are a highly unsatisfactory fix. 'Sunshine spectacles', as a report in the *Sunday Times* of 10 October 1999 christened them, might be the answer: they were tried out by American pilots flying 36-hour sorties to bomb Kosovo during the war in the former Yugoslavia. The spectacles have tiny optical fibres imbedded in them, programmed to direct pulses of bright light around the eyes, creating a light 'tunnel' through which wearers can see normally.

Such spectacles could be a very simple way to help sufferers from shift work or jet lag reset their body clocks. In some hotels in the Hilton chain, jet lagged travellers can check into 'Sleep-Tight' rooms, equipped with both lightboxes and a dawn-simulating alarm clock.

Light is also being used in the battle against other diseases common in the modern world. Paramacia are minute, single-celled water-borne micro-organisms at the bottom of the aquatic food chain. A century ago, a researcher was studying the effects of lights and dyes on these tiny beings. He found that although light, darkness or dyes didn't affect them, if he first treated them with a dye and then exposed them to bright sunshine, they died. In 1924 researchers took up this theme and discovered that some tumours gave off a red-orange fluorescence when UV light was directed at them, perhaps because of dye-like substances within the human body. Similar dyes were injected into rats with tumours, who were then exposed to white light and the tumours were destroyed.

The pioneer of what is now called Photodynamic Therapy (PDT) is Dr Thomas Dougherty of Roswell Park Cancer Institute in Buffalo, New York State, where thousands of cancer patients with advanced as well as early tumours have been treated, with highly promising results. A photosensitive porphyrin-based chemical called Photofrin, developed by Dougherty, was approved by the FDA in 1995 and is now used in PDT treatment.

But just how does light become lethal to cancer cells? When the dye is injected into the patient, it accumulates in cells throughout the body. While normal cells are mostly dye-free within a few days – timing this interval is critical – the dye persists in cancer cells, and the second stage of the therapy can go ahead. In the interval, patients have to remain indoors and wear thick protective clothing if they go anywhere near daylight. Then the cancer cell site is exposed to a blast of red laser light, which reacts with the dye to create lethal free radicals called singlet oxygen, which destroy the tumour cells.

Initially PDT was limited to the treatment of cancers on or near the skin surface, but the invention of fibre optics made it possible to deliver light selectively to cancers deep in the body on the surface of organs such as the lungs, oesophagus or bladder. Research funded by the US

National Cancer Institute and other bodies is now exploring ways to take PDT deep inside organs such as the liver and pancreas.

Unlike surgery, which can be both painful and ineffective, the effects of PDT are seldom severe – depending on the area treated, they may include trouble swallowing, coughing or painful breathing – and are usually fairly short-lived. Both skin and eyes become highly light sensitive, so patients are advised to avoid bright light, particularly sunshine, for at least six weeks and to wear protective clothing and sunglasses if they have to go outdoors.

Skin cancers are an increasingly common problem, with over 50,000 new patients being diagnosed every year in the UK. 'Conventional treatment is usually fairly successful but the side-effects can be gruesome, since almost all of them damage the skin as well as seeing off the cancer,' explains scientist Dr Colin Whitehurst, who has been working at the Paterson Institute for Cancer Research in Manchester, in the UK, since 1991. 'There's cryotherapy which virtually gives you a controlled case of frostbite. It can be painful, it depigments the skin and you'll need repeated treatments. Surgery is excellent for very small cancers, but again leaves scars. Radiotherapy is highly effective – but it leaves you with an open wound which you'll spend the rest of your life going to the nearest hospital to have dealt with. And local chemotherapy needs to be applied every other day, over six weeks, so few patients last the course.'

'But photodynamic therapy is amazing. A natural chemical in the form of a cream is first applied to the skin. It knocks out the cancer and because the skin heals by regeneration not by scarring, it looks beautiful afterwards: you'd never know it had been there. The patients get their natural skin colour back – even freckles.'

But the Achilles heel of the treatment is that only a handful of hospitals can afford the lasers. So Dr Whitehurst developed a cheaper version, the 'Paterson lamp': a much smaller hand-held lamp which emits a laser beam. On the medical conference circuit, there is huge enthusiasm for the treatment now that it is more affordable. 'And it isn't just skin cancers,' points out Dr. Whitehurst. 'Gynaecological lesions, oral cancers – anywhere you can get to with the cream and the light is treatable.'

For decades from the 1890s onwards, polio was one of the most dreaded of all diseases, and epidemics regularly swept Europe and the USA, leaving their victims – mostly children – dead, crippled or imprisoned for life in an iron lung which breathed for them. By the 1930s, there were three leading options for future treatment.

One was the development of a vaccine, an idea being actively pursued by drug companies, who were finally successful with the Salk vaccine in the 1950s. One was a treatment developed in Australia by a nurse, Elizabeth Kenny, which emphasized the importance of exercise, hot and cold packs and constant physiotherapy.

The Knott Technique – the third option – will probably not be found in a medical dictionary, yet in his day Dr Emmitt Knott of Seattle, Washington State, was a highly reputed physician and his research papers were published in perfectly respectable journals. The Knott Technique was a refinement of a revolutionary treatment which had been developed in the 1930s and 1940s at the Hahnemann Medical College in Philadelphia, Pennsylvania. Patients with severe bacterial or viral infections were hooked up to a machine, a needle was inserted into one arm, and blood was extracted to run through a machine before being returned to their veins. In the machine, the blood was exposed to a carefully dosed pulse of UV light. The results were extraordinary. Patients who had been at death's door with polio or pneumonia recovered against all the odds, toxins were cleared from the blood and patients appeared not just cured but invigorated by the treatment.

Over three decades of use by doctors, a huge body of clinical knowledge was built up. There are published reports on its use in bacterial diseases, including septicaemias, pneumonias, polio, encephalitis, mumps, measles, mononucleosis and herpes, as well as in thrombophlebitis, diabetic ulcers and rheumatoid arthritis. Following the introduction of the Salk vaccine around 1950 and the general rise of antibiotics, Ultraviolet Blood Irradiation (UBI) then fell into disuse.

But it was not forgotten. The Foundation for Blood Irradiation, set up in the 1940s by Dr Knott and others, somehow survived, and today it is flowering into new and enthusiastic activity, under the direction of Dr Carl Schleicher, who is happy to laud its benefits. 'UBI,' he says, 'raises the resistance of the host, and is therefore able to control many disease processes. A fundamental effect is to "energize" the biochemical and physiological defences of the body by the introduction of ultraviolet energy into the bloodstream. The efficacy of this method is attested to by the remarkable and consistent recovery of patients with a wide variety of diseases. In addition, it may be stated that UBI has never caused any adverse side-effects, nor have there been any complications related to IBIT during long-term follow-up.'

One form of UBI, photophoresis, has been developed by a team at Yale University, and is now undergoing clinical trials around the country for the treatment of such major medical problems as multiple sclerosis, rheumatoid arthritis and systemic *Lupus erythematosus.*

In the cash-strapped Russian medical profession, there's barely enough money to cover basic equipment and salaries; there certainly aren't funds to cover the costs of properly controlled double-blind clinical trials. But in the case of light therapy it seems that they are carrying out exciting and ground breaking medical research.

Peggy Dobbin, a nurse running a laser clinic in Torquay in Devon, has been sending patients for some years to Russia for UBI treatment at a clinic in St. Petersburg. 'Its extraordinary to see the transformation,' she says. 'I've sent boys who've been on their backs for months with glandular fever – some for up to two years – and they come back normal strapping lads again. I've visited a number of Russian hospitals now and they are like something out of Dickens... . But they treat patients both before and after surgery with UBI – and they never have post-operative infections, the way we do here.'

At the Light Conference organized by Jacob Liberman – a pioneer of modern light and colour therapy – at Reading in Berkshire in 1999, Professor Kira Samoilova, Head of Photobiology at the St. Petersburg Academy of Sciences, talked for an hour about Russian use of UBI to a stunned audience. They use it, she explains, for cancer patients, after chemotherapy and radiotherapy, to restore lost immunity. They use it for viral pneumonias, for stomach ulcers, for detoxing addicts and alcoholics. 'You smoke? We cure you in half an hour.'

The effect can be instantaneous, Samoilova told journalists. 'We take 2% of blood from an ill patient, irradiate it, put it back, and the whole of the patient's blood is instantly changed. The quickest we can take a new blood sample is two minutes afterwards, but by then it's all done!'

11 colour me healthy

Advertising and marketing specialists have long known the hidden power of colours to influence our moods, our appetites, the choices we make, even our ability to work or relax. Would you pick a new breakfast cereal if it came packaged in grey and turquoise? Would you eat in a restaurant with a violet décor? Would you find it easy to sleep in a bright red and orange bedroom? Could you fancy a plateful of bright blue pasta? Can you imagine working all day in a black room?

These are simple examples of what colour can do to us, but for thousands of years, healers have been exploiting the singular powers of colour to affect our health and well-being at a profound level.

In the 19th century, with new scientific knowledge and techniques at their disposal, a number of researchers began investigating the therapeutic effects of specific wavelengths of the rainbow spectrum. Jacob Liberman (see also page 264) has explored the history of this work in his ground-breaking book *Light: Medicine of the Future.*

In 1877, a US physician called Dr Seth Pancoast published a book called *Blue and Red Lights*, in which he described the effect of sunlight filtered through coloured glass to rebalance the nervous system: red, he found, stimulated it, while blue relaxed it. Just a year later another physician, Dr Edwin Babbitt, published *The Principles of Light and Colour*, in which he detailed treatments of various ailments with his Chromo Disk, which could be fitted with filters of many different colours and directed at specific areas of the body.

The work of Pancoast and Babbitt inspired two later pioneers. One was Dr Harry Spitler, who, over 17 years of research, developed a treatment aimed at rebalancing the nervous system by shining specific intensities or frequencies of coloured light directly into the eyes. He called his system Syntonics, from the word syntony – to 'bring into balance'. Spitler, says Liberman, 'recognised that light therapy by way of the eyes could augment the major control centres in the brain that regulate all body functions.' Many studies have since confirmed the validity of Spitler's approach. In 1958, for instance, Robert Berard published a study showing that the autonomic nervous system and visual cortex were significantly less aroused when stimulated with blue or white light than with red. 'We can now conclusively state,' sums up Liberman, 'that light plays a major role in regulating our physiological and emotional balance, while stimulation with different colours (wavelengths) of light has distinctly different physiological and emotional effects.'

Another pioneer was Dinshah P. Ghadiali, born in 1873, who encountered the exciting findings of Pancoast and Babbitt in his early twenties, and spent the next 23 years developing a scientific basis for a new healing system based on colour. In 1920 he opened his Spectro-Chrome Institute where he trained both doctors and lay people, and in 1933 he published the massive *Spectro-Chrome Metry Encyclopedia*.

Practitioners following the Spectro-Chrome system used a set of 12 colour filters – red, orange, yellow, lemon, green, turquoise, blue, indigo, violet, purple, magenta and scarlet – to direct beams of the appropriate colour at specific areas of the human body, precisely indicated on the chart. Over years of clinical practice Ghadiali made general observations. Green was the great balancer, to be included in almost all treatments. Purple and scarlet or magenta were colours of choice for all conditions involving the heart or circulatory system.

Ghadiali's system was used by many doctors. One of the most enthusiastic was a Philadelphia surgeon named Dr Kate Baldwin. 'After nearly thirty-seven years of active hospital and private practice in medicine and surgery,' she told a meeting of the Pennsylvania Medical Society, 'I can produce quicker and more accurate results with colours than with any or all other methods combined – and with less strain on the patient.' Surgery, she told them, was more effective if colour was used before and afterwards, and among the many conditions to respond were sprains, bruises, traumata, septic conditions, asthma, pneumonia and eye diseases such as glaucoma and cataracts.

These pioneers were true scientists and dedicated medical practitioners. If their work had been developed, we might have had today a highly advanced system of medicine, the most effective in known history, operating at low cost and able to cope with the whole spectrum of human ills – emotional, mental and psychological as well as physical. Instead, colour and light therapy was denounced as quackery and consigned to the garbage heap by proponents of an increasingly narrow and drug-dominated 'modern' medicine.

In the 1950s US researchers proved that red light could raise blood pressure and blue lower it.

In the early 1980s, blue light was shown to help relieve joint pain. More recently, dermatologists at London's Hammersmith Hospital, for instance, have been successfully treating acne patients with red and blue lights. But on the whole colour therapy, with all its exciting possibilities, has been advanced almost entirely by lay practitioners, working without the financial and scientific resources or the hospital facilities available in mainstream medicine.

A bewildering array of therapies and a whole catalogue of colour-therapy gadgets are on offer today. You might try, for instance, Colour Breathing, Visible Incoherent Polarized Light Therapy or Colourpuncture. You could have a Total Health Colour Analysis, or undergo Light Wave Stimulation or Brief Strobic Photostimulation. You might consider the Ocular Light Therapy of Dr John Downing or the system of Colourpuncture developed by German naturopath Peter Mandel and used by practitioners – many of them doctors – in Europe, the USA and Australia today.

Dr Downing's Ocular Light Therapy, developed in the USA over 27 years of study, was based on Spitler's work. He uses different colours and wavelengths of light projected into the eyes to improve a wide range of conditions including epilepsy, panic attacks, depression, anxiety, fatigue, headaches, hormonal imbalance, hyperactivity, bad memory and learning problems: problems rampant at the start of the twenty-first century.

Peter Mandel is an extraordinarily gifted German naturopath whose Colourpuncture is based on the premise, now virtually established by science, that light is actually the medium by which the cells of the body communicate and transmit information. Colourpuncture therapists work with the acupuncture points mapped out in traditional

Chinese five element acupuncture. But instead of needles, the points are stimulated with glass rods which emit different colours of light through a focused tip, to transmit light energy along the acupuncture meridians deep into the body, targeting specific organs. As the light is absorbed by the skin and transmitted along these meridians, it stimulates intracellular communication to speed healing.

But Colourpuncture isn't just about rebalancing and healing the body. Like many intuitive colour therapists, Mandel has explored the ways in which coloured lights affect human subtle-energy systems. We are in the realm of energy medicine, or what one of its most brilliant exponents, Dr Richard Gerber, has christened Vibrational Medicine, based in part on atomic physics, and in part on ancient insights developed in eastern religion and philosophy. 'Whereas the existing world of medicine sees the body as a great clockwork machine of biological gears and parts,' explains Gerber, 'the new world-view of healing sees the body as a complex energy system.' Colourpuncture acts on these energies, and the first diagnosis for new patients is made by using Kirlian photographs of their hands and feet, in which corona-like emissions ray out like an aura from fingers and toes, and which show gaps or blockages in the energy field. Mandel calls this Energy Emission Analysis (EEA). Using this and other complex diagnostic systems, Colourpuncture has also proved successful at identifying and releasing buried traumas, which can stunt emotional growth and blight personal development for so many people.

Talk of auras and energies and chakras may seem way-out. But more and more, the findings of colour-therapists like Mandel, Liberman and Downing is being confirmed in the realms of physics and cellular biology. Biophysicist Dr Fritz Albert Popp has presented evidence that living cells pass on biological information through photons, the 'words' of the language of light, and that these photons can initiate or arrest cascade-like reactions in the cells. Moreover, even genetic cellular damage can be repaired within hours, by faint beams of light.

'We are still on the threshold of fully understanding the complex relationship between light and life,' says Dr Popp, 'but we can now say, emphatically, that the function of our entire metabolism is dependent on light.'

light

solar power

13

tapping into the sun's energy

In the remote village of Suddheswor in west Nepal, Pramila Thapa runs an evening class for local women in the windowless mud hut that is her home. Her pupils learn to knit and to weave, simple skills which will earn them a little badly needed money. But until March 1999, the women worked by the light of a kerosene lamp, and by the time class ended, they had dry throats and reddened eyes from the kerosene fumes. Now Pramila's hut has an astonishing luxury: bright electric light from a solar system. It was installed by volunteers from the Solar Sisters Programme of the Himalayan Light Foundation, whose work was reported in the magazine *Renewable Energy World* in May 1999.

Around two billion people in the world have homes too scattered or too inaccessible to make connection to the national electricity grid either feasible or economic. In some countries, only a tiny minority of rural communities are connected. Out of Senegal's 13,000 villages, for instance, only 260 were grid-connected by the mid-1990s. So for cooking and heating, Third World villages usually rely on locally gathered wood, while lighting is supplied by candles or kerosene lamps, and radios and other items are powered by batteries. As local woods and forests are laid low in the quest for fuel, families have to trudge further and further each day for their wood supplies, and batteries, candles and kerosene eat up as much as 30% of a family's income.

Meanwhile, the sun pours tantalizing amounts of radiant energies down on them daily: it has been calculated that sunshine provides 10 MW of power every 24 hours for every single person on the planet. Even in the extravagant West, 2kW a day is a good average consumption. But how can this inexhaustible supply be tapped?

The original breakthrough came in the 1950s, when a group of scientists working at the Bell Laboratories in New Jersey, USA, discovered that a silicon device they were testing produced electricity when exposed to sunlight. They went on to develop experimental cells that could convert up to 14% of the energy they received into electricity.

At this time fossil fuel supplies still appeared inexhaustible, pollution was a word only a few cranks were uttering, and global warming a concept far in the future. But the silicon sun-converters – or photo-voltaic cells (PVs) as they became known – had one immediate application: they could be the power that sustained man in space. Unlike batteries, the silicon wafers weighed very little, and they could go on producing power indefinitely. The US space agency (NASA) installed silicon PVs on its second space satellite Vanguard 1 to power a radio transmitter, and they worked beautifully.

So it was the space race that gave the initial big push to the development of PV technology. The second came with the oil crisis of the early 1970s, when governments in western Europe suddenly woke up to the fact that a handful of small Middle Eastern sheikdoms had them literally over a barrel. The most recent incentive for the development of clean and renewable energy has built up over the last decade, as even sceptics now concede that global warming is for real, and that drastic cuts must be made in carbon dioxide emission from conventional power stations burning fossil fuels (see Air, chapter 8).

By the early 1990s, millions of dollars were being invested in the research and development of renewable energy. BP set up BP Solar in 1981, and when the 1998 merge with Amoco brought with it a 50% share in the leading US PV makers, Solarex, BP bought the other 50% for $45 million to set up BP Solarex, today the world's leader in solar business with a 20% share of the global market.

In mid-2000, BP spent millions on a corporate re-branding with a new green and yellow sunflower-shaped logo, a promise to invest heavily in solar and a new take on the letters BP: Beyond Petroleum. The campaign was denounced as a cynical public relations ploy by some environmentalists, timed to distract attention from BPs plans to turn the Arctic wilderness into a huge new oilfield, but it sent out important and encouraging signals to the whole solar industry.

The global market is already expanding rapidly. Apart from the huge potential of those two billion customers in developing countries, solar is already attractive even to western customer applications sited many kilometres from the nearest grid, where the alternative is a high-maintenance diesel generator: solar energy today is powering light-houses, monitoring remote pipelines for leaks, and pumping water for cattle troughs, highway signals and purification systems.

Advances in technology have made solar power much more attractive, while giving it greater appeal for architects and designers.

It's possible now to integrate PV directly into roof shingles, tiles or even glass, and new 'thin-film' solar cells no longer need to be encased in box-like panels, but can be applied in big flexible sheets.

With big players like Shell and BP in the business, the race is on to make solar power cheap enough to compete with grid power. 'The big push now is to reduce costs,' says Ian Gregory of Shell Solar. 'It's not the big breakthrough that will do it, it's a number of smaller breakthroughs. Material is the most expensive part of a solar panel so if you use less it costs less. For 20–25 years everybody's been using silicon and it's quite expensive to process. The next step might be less of it – or other materials. The new crystalline silicons are very efficient, converting from 14 to 18% of energy. If you can make them as cheaply, that might be the way forward. One really exciting area is organic solar cells modelled quite closely on photosynthesis and using titanium dioxide. There are so many options that we're focusing on just three or four. The ultimate dream: you could just coat the glass of a large building and that would make electricity as well as produce light. How far ahead? It's an open guess. Five years maybe.'

'The Holy Grail in PV technology is probably going to be a thin-film technique,' according to BP. 'PVs need to be cheaper to make, install and maintain, as well as visually attractive. It needs to be 25% of the cost today: in the UK solar is up to five times more expensive than grid. It's only 30% more expensive in Japan. We believe solar power can be competitive in ten years' time.' Currently prices have fallen by 60%, but they need to come down by another 30% for PVs to be economically viable.

'Costs will scale down as production rises,' forecasts Dan Davies of Solar Century, a company set up with a mission – to accelerate the solar revolution. 'Like mobile phones and computers, the faster you can turn the handle on the assembly line, the cheaper the end-product becomes.' And for Harry Shimp of Solarex, the analogy is spot-on: 'We're going to be the cellphone/personal computer business of the next decade – and that means that our growth rates will jump from a very respectable 20% to 50% or 60%.' Even cautious estimates suggest that the market will move from today's $1 billion annually to $10 billion by 2010.

Governments around the world are already investing heavily in solar, and see such investment as vital.

The USA has plans to fund the installation of solar roofs on over a million homes. Germany has over 100,000 in the pipeline, Spain and Italy are each funding 10,000, and Japan aims for 70,000. Recently, Germany announced a spectacular double-break for its solar industry, giving massive impetus for the expansion of its manufacturing base: it's now possible to get a government loan for PV installation at a mere 1% interest, and the owners of solar installations will be able to sell surplus power back to the grid at a guaranteed price.

By contrast, the UK Department of Trade and Industry plans for a trial funding of a mere 100 solar roofs has been criticized within the industry as 'staggeringly unambitious'. The £50 million it was prepared to shell out as a bribe to the Japanese company Nissan to keep jobs in the UK has been compared bitterly with the meagre £3–4 million it recently offered in subsidies for three or four flagship PV installations on major corporate buildings: 'And we're talking of an industry that could mean anything up to 200,000 new jobs.'

And even if it costs more, growing numbers of homeowners are willing to pay over the odds for solar, either from personal eco-conviction, or because they want to be 'seen to be green'. At Sacramento in California, the local Municipal Utility District launched a PV Pioneers Program in 1993. Each year the Utility buys about 100 solar systems and installs them on area homes to feed power into the electric grid. Householders pay $4 monthly for the moral satisfaction of hosting this clean energy source. So successful was the scheme that in 1998 the Utility launched phase two – in which a homeowner can buy and install a grid-connected system from the Utility, and have the value of his roof-top harvest deducted from his bill, which may be up to 80% lower.

The European Commission (EC) – until recently lukewarm on the subject of renewable energy – has been galvanized by its parliament into the drafting of a new initiative. DG17, issued by the EC Directorate of Energy in April 1999, is a call to action. It was showcased at the Amsterdam World Renewable Energy Fair, Sustain '99, as the Campaign for Take-off. And it calls for current EC use of renewable energy (mainly from hydropower) to double from its present level of 6% to at least 12%, from a full spectrum of renewable sources, by 2010 – and then keep on rising. Between them, member states will invest 6 billion in renewable energy: the Commission will contribute 600,000 million for research and development.

On the United Nations Education, Scientific and Cultural Organization (UNESCO's) initiative, with the support of many heads of state and governments, the World Solar Commission was set up in March 1995 to encourage wider use of renewable energy. The World Solar Programme 1996–2005 was approved by the UN General Assembly in October 1998: it has given strong moral leadership to the renewable race.

Almost all our planet's available energy comes from the sun, either directly for harvesting through PVs and solar collectors, or in the form of wind or tidal power, both produced when the sun heats different layers of our atmosphere, or stored in plants to be used in biomass techniques. But unlike fossil fuel energy, largely produced in the world's richest countries, the sun beats down on rich and poor alike and the wind whistles through remote passes in the Andes as readily as it sets the turbines of wealthy Germany spinning. Thus, as well as its appeal on environmental grounds, renewable energy offers a bright and hopeful future for Third World countries.

At the World Solar Summit in Zimbabwe in September 1996, Unesco's World Solar Programme was formally adopted by Director-General Federico Mayor. In a thoughtful preface to Madanjeet Singh's book *The Timeless Energy of the Sun*, Mayor pointed out not only the obvious benefits for the Third World in terms of improved amenities for isolated rural communities and better health and education facilities, but some less tangible advantages. 'Small and dispersed solar energy projects in rural areas... have a cardinal role to play in halting the increasing rush to the cities by peasants living in the poorest regions. Such projects, by virtue of their local and participatory nature, are also more 'democratic', tending to create new cooperative structures that resist the concentration of power in a few authoritarian hands. By promoting sustainable development based on partnership with nature they protect the environment and favour the emergence of a culture of peace...

'Sustainable energy, with its peaceful, participatory and environmentally friendly associations, seems poised to repair the long-standing divorce between science and culture, through the traditional use of heliotechnology, the principal energy of the future.'

light

the natural light action plan

1. Tune in to your circadian rhythms. Sunrise is a good time to get up, and, if you want to enjoy a good night's sleep, 10.30pm or even earlier is a great time to go to bed.

2. If you have to finish off a demanding piece of work, don't sit up late or you'll find it really hard to get to sleep: go to bed early, set your alarm clock and do it before breakfast.

3. In winter our energy levels are generally lower, and long nights signal our need for more sleep. In summer we're at our most energetic: make the most of the long days.

4. Fight jet lag by adopting the rhythm of your destination immediately. If you arrive at breakfast time, get into the strongest light you can find to wake you up, stay up all day if possible, in the brightest light you can find, eat meals at the local times and go to bed as early as your schedule allows, making your bedroom as pitch black as possible.

5. Year-round, spend as much time as you can out of doors in natural light – especially if you work under fluorescent lighting.

6. If you work in an office, take at least some of your lunch break out of doors during the short days of winter. At weekends, make the most of daylight.

7. If you work at home, equip your workplace with full-spectrum lighting (see Resources).

8. If you wear prescription glasses or contact lenses, ask your optician to use ultraviolet-light-transmitting glass or plastic. If your spectacles are made of ordinary glass – which doesn't transmit UV light, wear them as little as possible when you're out of doors.

9. Wear a big-brimmed shady hat to protect your face and eyes from sunshine. Keep sunglasses for times when you really need them – to protect your eyes from glare – and choose a neutral grey colour, which cuts down light evenly across the spectrum. Trendy pinks, blues and greens are highly unnatural and could damage your health.

10. On holiday, avoid exposure to strong midday sunshine, especially in latitudes nearer the Equator than you normally live. No sunscreen ever invented will protect your skin from damage in such high-intensity light, particularly when its UV content is at maximum. The classic rule is: stay out of the sun if your shadow is shorter than you are. At least take refuge under a beach umbrella – but remember that even then UV light is bouncing back on you from sand.

11. A tan should be built up gradually round the year, starting in spring. Or even in winter: 'The secret to this,' says Dr Kime (see also pages 223–4), 'is getting completely out of the wind with no air movement over your body... The sun's rays will feel hot on your skin if you are out of the wind. But lie on a warm blanket – and cover up the minute the sun goes in.'

12. If you're cramming a year's sunshine into two weeks in the Mediterranean, you'd be well advised to use a high-factor sunscreen. Look for one as 'green' as possible, with a minimum of chemicals in it, preferably no fragrance and preferably a physical sunscreen, such as titanium dioxide. If you're tanning prudently, you may only need a sunscreen in the early days, as long as you avoid middle-of-the-day sunshine. Use a good moisturizer afterwards: aloe vera is terrific.

13. Eat plenty of colourful fruits and vegetables, especially at the beach when your skin needs antioxidant protection against potentially damaging free-radical activity generated by intense UV light. The oils in popular Mediterranean fish like sardines and anchovies are protective for the skin, too. And remember that alcohol and smoking generate free radicals. So by all means enjoy that merry beach lunch – but spare a thought for your poor skin and cover up.

14. For extra protection for your skin, take a good vitamin E supplement and mixed antioxidants daily for several weeks before you go on holiday and while you're there.

resources

Throughout this book I've referred to a number of things like ionizers, full spectrum lighting and non-polluting household cleaners. There are numerous places you can get hold of these objects, and many other aids to making your home and life more healthy and environmentally friendly, but of course I don't have space to list them all here, so I have selected some of the best for you. The more general information has been broken down into objects and aids under the headings of Garden, Home, Food and Babies and Sanitaryware. Therapies and specific information on current environmentally friendly practices and research is listed underneath the relevant part heading of Earth, Air, Water or Light. Finally, there is a list of organizations to join or to contact for more information. Good luck!

Garden

Organic gardening is rapidly catching hold around the UK and has long been established in the USA. The two organic gardening bibles are Geoff Hamilton's book (Hamilton was an English gardener who brought pleasure to thousands with his down-to-earth guidance), and *Rodale's Encyclopaedia of Organic Gardening*, which was updated in the USA during the last few decades and is overflowing with helpful information. Both of these books are listed in Further Reading, along with further information.

For organic gardening products, the first-stop shop in the UK has to be **Chase**, in partnership with the famous **Henry Doubleday Research Association**. **Chase** offer a mail-order service through the **Organic Gardening Catalogue** (Riverdene Estate, Molesey Road, Hersham, Surrey KT12 4RG. Tel: 01932 253 666) and sell just about everything you could possibly need – plants, sprays and organic fertilizers included.

Original Organics (Unit 9, Langlands Business Park, Plymtree, Devon EX15 3DA. Tel: 01884 841 515) also supply a good selection of products designed for the organic gardener, including wormeries, compost bins and organic activators, organic pest control and water butts.

You might also want to contact **Blackwall Products** (Seacroft Estate, Coal Road, Leeds, West Yorks, LS14 2AQ. Tel: 0113 276 1646), who supply compost bins and rainwater butts to councils around the country. In the UK these products are often locally subsidized and you may find that they are cheaper than you thought.

Finally, **Wiggly Wigglers** (Lower Blakemere Farm, Blakemere, Herefordshire HR2 9PX. Tel: 01981 500 391 or 0800 216 990 for mail order) are specialists in wormeries. They are positively evangelical on the subject and front their catalogue with a quote from Charles Darwin about earthworms: 'It may be doubted whether there are many other animals which have played so important a role in the history of the world as these lowly organised creatures.'

Home

If you're building or renovating your home you can make your house a more healthy place by using organic or natural products. For these healthy building blocks there are several options within the UK.

Construction Resources (16 Great Guildford Street, London SE1. Tel: 020 7450 2211; www.ecoconstruct.com) stock a large range of building materials, which include organic paints, solar panel systems, natural wood flooring and organic wool carpets.

Ecomerchant (Tel: 01795 530 130; www.ecomerchants.demon.co.uk) specializes in green building products including paints, lime and clay products (think breathable walls), insulation and flooring. They also offer locally sourced brick and tiles, as promoting local goods is very important to them.

Natural Building Technologies (Tel: 01491 638 911; www.naturalbuilding.co.uk) were set up fairly recently because of the difficulty of finding green materials: they do their own range of paints and waxes, and also offer plaster and natural insulation. They're also developing contacts with green builders and consultants, so they can offer advice or put you in touch with their contacts so that you can choose the best products and designs for your requirements.

Natural Wood Flooring Company (20 Smugglers Way, London, SW18. Tel: 020 8871 9771) will supply you with over 120 types of timber, which is either reclaimed or sourced from sustainably managed forests.

The Swedish Window Company (Millbank, Earls Colne Industrial Park, The Airfield, Earls Colne, Colchester, CO6 2NS. Tel: 01787 223 931; swc@millbank.co.uk) sell windows and doors made of sustainably sourced Scandinavian wood.

Organizations to talk to during the process of constructing your house should include the **Centre for Alternative Technology** (Machynlleth, Powys, SY20 9AZ. Tel: 01654 700 402; www.cat.org.uk), who can advise on energy saving techniques like insulation etc. They also do weekend courses in all sorts of fascinating subjects, including the art of composting and solar electrical systems – you can even learn how to build your own house! Make a visit to the centre before you buy or make any of their technology, as it will give you real inspiration and show you just how successful environmentally friendly systems can be.

You may also want to approach the **Association for Environment Conscious Building** (Tel: 01559 370 908; www.aecb.net) who are the authority in this field in the UK. They are an information source for the public and a way that green architects and builders can keep up to date with news. If you're looking for an organic paint that won't set off your allergies, you can ring them for information, or, if you're looking for an architect or builder to work on your extension, send them a stamped addressed envelope to the value of 92p, and they'll send you two of their information packs, which list all their members with contact details.

If you're thinking about alternative energy sources, the people above will often be able to help you. There are also two main trade organizations in Britain for solar power: the **British Photovoltaic Association** (The Warren, Bramshill Road, Eversley, Nr Reading, Berks, RG27 0PR. Tel: 0118 932 4418), which only deals with photovoltaics; and the smaller **Solar Trade Association** (Pengillan, Lerryn, Lostwithiel, Cornwall, PL22 0QE. Tel: 01208 873518), which deals with photovoltaics and solar water heating systems. Contact either for membership lists and advice.

When it comes to products for use in the inside of your house, there are a couple of excellent UK sources.

The Healthy House (Cold Harbour, Ruscombe, Stroud, Glos GL8 6DA. Tel: 01453 752 216; www.healthy-house.co.uk) specializes in products for people who suffer from dust allergies, asthma, hay fever, chemical sensitivity, eczema, electrical sensitivity and Seasonal Affective Disorder (SAD). They offer organic cotton duvets, dust-mite barrier mattresses, air purifiers, car filters, ionizers, humidifiers and dehumidifiers, water purifiers, eco balls, Greenline carpets – which require no detergents or chemicals and save water – and the range of Ecos paints. Ecos are solvent free, and designed specifically to protect the health of the user: they come in a wide range of colours and finishes, and prices start at £13.95 for a litre of eggshell white.

The Green Shop is another very useful address (Tel: 01452 770 629, jane@greenshop.co.uk; www.greenshop.co.uk.) for household goodies such as environmentally friendly cleaners, recycling products, water saving devices, paints, finishes, insulation, environmentally friendly doors and windows. They also supply books and their stock contains some of the most useful available (many of those in Further Reading can be obtained through **The Green Shop**).

For household cleaning products look for the Ecover range, which includes many of the products you'll want and is available from most grocery stores and supermarkets. **Green People** (www.greenpeople.co.uk) also do a chemical-free Homecare range, as well as their famous skin-care and dental products.

For ionizers, the Rolls-Royce is the **Elanra** developed by Joshua Shaw and mentioned in the text, which consistently produces the small therapeutic negative ions. There's also a portable Elanra ionizer, about the size of a paperback, which should be in every jetsetter's pack. These are available from **Bionic Products** (www.negativeions.com). In the UK and Ireland contact **Aircare products** (PO Box 46, Greenford, Middlesex, UB6 7SU; Freephone 0800 074 5668). Other excellent ionizers are produced by Honeywell and Topair.

For advice on air purification generally, consult the excellent **Air Improvement Centre** (23 Denbigh St. London SW1V 2HF. Tel: 020 7834 2834).

Food

The Organic revolution in the UK has forced many supermarkets to supply good quality organic foods. For most people this is the first place that they'll come across these foods and most supermarkets will stock a selection of organic produce, although the size of the range may vary. But for those who choose to take it a bit further a local box scheme may be the perfect solution. These can be found through the nearest health food store or by having a quick search on the internet. With a box scheme you get a weekly or bi-weekly delivery of a selection of organic fruit and vegetables. Most box schemes are local, so you'll have to hunt around to find what suits you.

Organics Direct (Tel: 020 7729 2828; www.organicsdirect.co.uk) is my favourite national organic food supplier – they offer a very good box scheme that is excellent value for money and well handled.

You may also be interested in checking out your nearby **Farmer's Market**: these have been around for years in the USA, but they are a relatively new phenomenon in the UK. They are weekly markets where the farmers sell directly to the public, giving both a chance to interact and learn a little more about the sources of our food. The produce is fresh and because it comes from your local area it will not require either environmentally damaging transport from producer to shop or non-biodegradable packaging. In the UK you can find out more about these markets by contacting the **National Association of Farmer's Markets** (Tel: 01225 787 914) or – if you live in London – by contacting **Wheatland Farmers Markets Ltd** (Tel: 020 7704 9569; www.londonfarmersmarket.com).

In the USA there are over ninety organic certifying bodies, and in the UK there are six. Although there is a set of national legal standards in the UK set by the **United Kingdom Register of Organic Food Standards** (UK ROFS), the **Soil Association** (www.soilassociation.org), which represents over 80% of organic farmers in Britain, regards them as being far too lenient, particularly in terms of issues like animal welfare. Meanwhile in the USA, the government is working on a proposal to implement a national guideline in order to make things simpler, while in Europe a set of European guidelines came into force in August 2000.

Babies and sanitaryware

One of the big sources of waste, internationally, are disposable nappies and sanitaryware. In the UK alone, we use 3 billion towels and tampons, never mind the mountains of nappies we get through every day. There are more environmentally friendly alternatives available, however. You should really consider using washable nappies, which are cheaper and less problematic for the environment. You can find out more about these by contacting **Naturally for Baby** (Tel: 0141 400 6456), **Eco-babes** (Tel: 01353 664 941) and **The Organic Baby Company** (Tel: 01323 411 515), among many other mail-order companies who supply washable nappies.

Most of the companies listed above can also offer help and information on the different types of washable nappies available, but one of the best organizations for advice on nappies is the **Real Nappy Association** (Tel: 020 8299 4519).

If you do choose washables, you will probably want a nappy-washing service: the **National Association of Nappy Services** (Tel: 0121 693 4949) can tell you where your nearest service is. And if you still really can't face it, **Weenies** (Tel: 01582 484899) sell a disposable nappy that biodegrades much faster than traditional disposables (taking only 150 days rather than the 500 years taken by disposable nappies).

As for Sanitaryware, there are numerous alternatives available. Washable organic cotton sanitary towels are available in the UK from **Nature's Alternatives** (Tel: 01772 467 546), or (non-organic) from **Ecofemme** (Tel: 0117 904 9726). Or perhaps consider organic cotton tampons (less pesticide use and no bleaches) from **Natracare** (Tel: 0117 946 6649; www.natural-woman.com).

Earth

These addresses are useful for all those wanting to find out more about the therapies, research and products mentioned specifically within the Earth section.

For more information on soil and agricultural practices contact **The Soil Association** (Tel: 01179 290661; www.soilassociation.org.uk).

If you want to use a wormery, which I would highly recommend, **Wiggly wigglers** (www.wigglywigglers.co.uk), who are mentioned in the text, are one of the best companies to contact in the UK. Wormeries make all kinds of sense and offer fantastic compost – at no cost – that will be richer than any you'll be able to buy in garden centres.

Wastebusters (Tel: 020 7207 3434), mentioned in Earth, chapter 8, The Throwaway World, work with companies to make offices more efficient. Their mission is to educate about resource conservation and recycling and they have published the *Green Office Manual*, which is available through Earthscan.

The **Biodynamic Agriculture Assocation** (Painswick Inn Project, Gloucester St., Stroud, Glos GL5 1QG. Tel: 01453 759501; www.anth.org.uk/biodynamic) is working to promote sustainability and offers both advice and visits.

If you would like more information on biodiversity and why it is so necessary for the earth longterm, contact **The Environment Council** (212 High Holborn, London, WC1V 7VW. Tel: 020 7836 2626; fax: 020 7242 1186; www.the-environment-council.org.uk).

For more about Permaculture and its practices, contact the **Permaculture Association** (BCM Permaculture Association, London, WC1N 3XX. Tel: 07041 390170; www.permaculture.org.uk). **Permaculture Magazine** (www.permaculture.co.uk) offers advice and information plus new research on achieving the sustainable ideal.

Contact **Sunny Clay** (Tel: 020 7586 3412 for mail order) for all kinds of clay supplies – for both internal and external treatments – including powder and a ready-mixed paste.

Air

For unbiased advice and information on potential dangers from electromagnetic radiation, and products designed to protect yourself from it, there are a number of organizations:

The Powerwatch Helpline (Tel: 0906 401237 – at a premium rate of £1.50 per minute – or www.powerwatch.org.uk).

For the quarterly news report **Electromagnetic Hazard & Therapy**, published by medical editor Simon Best with electrical engineer Alasdair Philips, send an sae for detail and back contents to POBox 2039, Shoreham, W.Sussex BN43 5JD. See also their website (www.em-hazard-therapy.com).

Another highly informative website is run by independent scientist Roger Coghill (**The Roger Coghill Research Laboratories**. Tel: 01495 752122; www.cogreslab.demon.co.uk), where you can also purchase a wide range of products offering protection from electro-magnetic hazards.

Two protective devices for mobile phones have been tested by independent experts and found to be effective. Both devices have comprehensive websites where you can review the studies: **Tecno Ao** (Tel: 01793 741080 to order; www.tecnoaouk.com); **Microshield** (Tel: 020 8363 3333 to order; www.microshield.co.uk).

For advice and information on air travel health problems visit the website of Farrol Khan, Director of the **Aviation Health Institute** (www.aviationow.com). You can also order masks for extra protection against airborne infection on longhaul flights through the website.

For advice on setting up a **Walking Bus** to take your children to school, as mentioned in the Clean Air Action Plan, send for a 'Walk to School' information pack from **The Pedestrians Association** (31–33 Broadway, Vauxhall, London SW8 1SJ. Tel: 020 7820 1010). It really is worth taking the time to organize this properly with other parents, as the air at the school gates in the morning and afternoon is highly polluted – not what you want your children to be exposed to day after day.

For information and courses of the Buteyko treatment in the UK, contact **Breath Connection** (35 Chartley Avenue, Stanmore, Middlesex HA7 3RB. Freephone: 0800 018 7879; email: info@breathconnection.com; www.breathconnection.com).

For other alternative therapies, contact **The Hale Clinic** (1 Park Crescent, London W1N 3HE. Tel: 020 7631 0156; email: admin@haleclinic.com; www.haleclinic.com).

If you are going to be using essential oils for massage or any of the treatments in the book it is essential that you use pure oils. There are a number of excellent suppliers, all of whom offer mail order, but I can't list them all – so here are some of my favourites:

Natural by Nature Oils (The Aromatherapy Centre, 9 Vivian Avenue, Hendon Central, London NW4 3UT. Tel: 01582 840848 for mail order; www.naturalbynature.co.uk). Nature by Nature offer an excellent range of pure essential oils, cold-pressed vegetable oils, massage and bath oils.

Neal's Yard Remedies (15 Neals' Yard, London WC2. Tel: 01618 317875 for mail order). Neal's Yard is a well-known mail-order range, which includes essential oils and herbs both in tincture form and dried (many organic), bath oils, skincare products and soaps. Ask for their catalogue.

Water

For more about the flowforms, as discussed in Water, chapter 3,The Weirdness of Water, visit the flowforms website (www.flowforms.com).

For information on the work of the **Centre for Implosion Research**, and details of their products discussed in Water, chapter 4, The Energy of Water, contact the Centre (PO Box 38, Plymouth PL7 5YX. Tel: +44 1752 345552; e-mail: enquiries@implosionResearch.com; www.implosionResearch.com). You could also try their Personal Harmonizer.

Light

For more information on full-spectrum lighting contact these companies, who will be able to give you advice on installing this form of lighting in your home or office: Allan Wilson at **Spectra-Light** (York House, Lower Harlestone, Northampton NN7 4EW. Tel: 01604 821902), or **Full Spectrum Lighting Ltd** (Tel: 01494 527005).

For bright-light-boxes and Light Visors used in the treatment of Seasonal Affective Disorder, the Jet Lag Kit and the Natural Alarm Clock Dawn Simulator – which mimics a natural sunrise from the first faint glimmer of dawn, gradually getting brighter to light up your bedroom as you wake – contact Steve Hayes at **Outside In** (Cambridge) Ltd (Unit 21 Scotland Road Estate, Dry Drayton, Cambridge CB3 8AT. Tel 01954 211955; www.outsidein.co.uk). Items can be supplied for a 21-day home trial.

For Solar Energy, contact **Solar Century** (91–94 Lower Marsh, London SE1 7AB. Tel: 0870 735 8100; www.solarcentury.co.uk). This is a company set up with a mission: to accelerate the uptake of PV (photovoltaics) by working with potential users to help them integrate PV into their homes, offices and appliances.

There are a number of useful contacts for finding out about colour therapy. For more about Jacob Liberman's **Spectral Receptivity System** used in colour therapy, visit his website (www.ulight.com).

For more information about colour therapy and its uses contact **The International Association for Colour Therapy** (73 Elmbank Gardens, London SW13 ONX).

You could also contact Theo Gimble at **The Hygeia College of Colour Therapy** (Brook House, Avening, Tetbury, Gloucestershire GL8 8NS. Tel: 01453 832150).

Also, you could try **The Colour Therapy Association** (PO Box 306, Camberley, Surrey GU15 2LE; www.coloursofthesoul.co.uk).

For some idea of the dazzling range of resources for colour therapy, visit the website of the world's largest one-stop shopping centre for alternative therapies in the USA (www.toolsforexploration.com) and order their catalogue.

Campaigning organizations

UK

ActionAid
Hamlyn House
Macdonald Road, Archway
London N19 SPG
www.actionaid.org
Actionaid fights the corner of small farmers in the developing world against the many threats to their livelihood and way of life of global capitalism.

Campaign for Dark Skies
www.cfds.co.uk

International Campaign for Dark Skies
www.ida.com

Friends of the Earth
26-28 Underwood St
London N1 7JQ
020 7490 1555
www.foe.co.uk

Greenpeace UK
Canonbury Villas
London N1 2PN
020 7865 8100.
www.greenpeace.org

National Pure Water Association (NPWA)
12 Dennington Lane
Crigglestone
Wakefield WF4 3ET
Tel: 01924 254433
www.npwa.freeserve.co.uk

Pesticide Action Network (PAN)
The Eurolink Centre
49 Effra Road
London SW2 1BZ,
www.pan-uk.org

WWF (The World Wildlife Fund UK)
Panda House
Wayside Park
Godalming
Surrey GU7 1XR
Tel: 01483 426444
www.wwf-uk.org.uk

Australia

Australian Conservation Foundation
33 George St
Sydney
NSW 2000
Tel: (02) 9247 4285

Australian Conservation Foundation Inc.
340 Gore St
Fitzroy
VIC 3065
Tel: (03) 9416 1455

Australian Trust for Conservation Volunteers
15 Lydiard St
Ballarat North
VIC 3350
Tel: (03) 5333 1483

Friends of the Earth
17 Lord St
Newtown
NSW 2042
Tel: (02) 9517 3900
or
312 Smith St
Collingwood
VIC 3066
Tel: (03) 9419 8700

Greenpeace Australia Ltd
Freephone: 1 800 815 151

New Zealand

Department of Conservation
Government Buildings
15 Lambton Qy
Wellington
0-4-472 7356
www.govt.doc.nz

Friends of the Earth NZ
PO Box 5599
Wellesley
Auckland
0-9-303 4319

Greenpeace NZ Inc
Private Bag 92507
Wellesley St
Auckland
0-9-630 6317
www.greenpeace.org.nz

World Wide Fund for Nature
PO Box 6237, The Tree House
Wellington Botanical Gardens
Glenmore St
Wellington
Tel: (04) 499 2930
info@wwf.org.nz
www.panda.org

Other New Zealand organizations can be found on these websites:
www.converge.org.nz/eco/
www.nzes.org.nz

further reading

My chief sources for much of this book were the work of excellent scientific journalists – many of whom are named in the text – and a number of journals – outstanding among which is the incomparable New Scientist. The chief book sources are listed below, for the benefit of anyone wanting to read further into the wide range of subjects covered here, together with some useful reference works.

General

Fortey, Richard *Life: An Unauthorised Biography* (Flamingo, 1998)
Gribbin, John *Almost Everyone's Guide to Science* (Weidenfeld and Nicholson, 1998)
Gribbin, John *In the Beginning* (Viking, 1993)
Gould, Stephen Jay *Wonderful Life* (Penguin Books, 1989)
Grayson, Anna *Equinox: the Earth* (Channel 4 Books, 2000)
Lamb, Simon and Sington, David *Earth Story* (BBC Books, 1998)
Leakey, Richard, and Lewin, Roger *The Sixth Extinction* (Weidenfeld and Nicholson, 1996)
Lovelock, James *The Ages of Gaia* (Oxford University Press, 1995)
Margulis, Lynn *The Symbiotic Planet* (Phoenix, 1999)
Philip's Nature Encyclopedia (Philips, 1998)
Shelton, Herbert *The Hygienic System: Vols I–IV: The Nature Doctors*

Earth

Abehsera, Michel *The Healing Clay* (Citadel Press, edw York, 1994)
Appelhof, Mary *Worms, Eat my Garbage* (Flower Press, 1982)
Balfour, Eve *The Living Soil* (Faber & Faber, 1940)
Barrett, Thomas J. *Harnessing the Earthworm* (Faber & Faber, 1949)
Brown, Michael H. *Laying Waste: The Poisoning of America by Toxic Chemicals* (Pantheon Books, New York, 1980)
Carson, Rachel *Silent Spring* (Penguin, 1965)
Clark, Grahame *World Prehistory* (Cambridge University Press, 1977)
Confold, Philip ed. *The Organic Tradition* (Green Books, Bideford, Devond, 1988)

Darwin, Charles *The Formation of Vegetable Mould, through the Action of Worms* (John Murray, 1897)

Dextreit, Raymond *L'Argile quie Guerit*

Donadieu, Dr Yves *L'Argile* (Librairie Maloine, 1980)

Fussell, G.E. *The Story of Farming* (Pergamon Press, London, 1965)

ibid. Farming Techniques from Prehistoric to Modern Times (Pergamon Press, London, 1965)

Gaston, Kevin J., and Spicer, John I. *Biodiversity, an Introduction* (Blackwell, 1998)

Graham Jr, Frank *Since Silent Spring* (Pan / Ballantine, 1970)

Griggs, Barbara *The Food Factor* (Viking, 1986)

Hamilton, Geoff *Successful Organic Gardening* (Dorling Kindersley, 1987)

Hopkins, Donald P. *Chemicals, Humus, and the Soil* (Faber and Faber, 1945)

Howard, Sir Albert *Farming and Gardening for Health and Disease* (Faber and Faber, 1945)

Jenkins, J.C. *The Humanure Handbook* (Jenkins, 1994)

Lang, Dr Tim and Clutterbuck, Dr Charlie *P is for Pesticides* (Ebury Press, 1991)

McHughen, Alan *A Consumer's Guide to GM Food* (Oxford University Press, 2000)

Marco, Gino J. and Hollingworth, Robert M. ed. *Silent Spring revisited* (American Chemical Society, Washington DC, 1987)

Maxted-Frost, Tanyia *The Organic Baby Book* (Green Books, 1999)

Mellanby Kenneth *Pesticides and Pollution* (Collins, 1969)

Nottingham, Stephen *Eat Your Genes* (Zed Books, 1998)

Pfeiffer, E. *Soil Fertility, Renewal and Preservation* (Lanthorn Press, 1983)

Rodale's All-New Encyclopaedia of Organic Gardening (Rodale Press, 1997)

Russell, Sir E. John *The World of the Soil* (Collins, 1957)

Ryssell, W.M.S. *Man, Nature and History* (Aldus Books, London, 1967)

Schilthuis, Willy *Biodynamic Agriculture* (Floris Books, 1994)

Schopf, J. William *The Cradle of Life* (Princeton University Press, 1999)

Semlyen, Anna *Cutting your Car Use* (Green Books, 2000)

Shiva, Vandana *Biopiracy* (Green Books, 1998)

Teitel, Martin and Wilson, Kimberley A. *Changing the Nature of Nature* (Vision Paperbacks, 2000)

Tompkins, Peter and Bird, Christopher *Secrets of the Soil* (Arkana, 1992)

Van den Bosch, Robert *The Pesticide Conspiracy* (Prism Press, 1980)

Wargo, John *Our Children's Toxic Legacy* (Yale University Press, 1996)

Whitefield, Patrick *Permaculture in a Nutshell* (Permanent Productions, 1993)
Willis, Dr Harold *The Rest of the Story about Agriculture Today* (A-R Editions, 1983)
Wrench, G.T. *Reconstruction by Way of the Soil* (Faber & Faber, London, 1946)

Air

Ashton, John and Laura, Ron *The Perils of Progress* (Zed Books, 1998)
Becker, Robert O. and Selden, Gary *The Body Electric* (Quill, 1985)
Bradley, Dinah *Hyperventilation Syndrome* (Kyle Cathie, London, 1998)
Coghill, Roger W. *Something in the Air* (Coghill Research Laboratories, 1997)
Davis, Patricia *Aromatherapy, An A-Z* (C.W.Daniel, 1988)
Emsley, John *The Consumer's Good Chemical Guide* (Corgi Books, 1994)
Hale, Teresa *Breathing Free* (Hodder & Stoughton, London, 1999)
Halvorson, Christine and Sheldon, Kenneth M *Clean and Simple* (Time Life Books, 1999)
Hill, Leonard *Sunshine and Open Air* (Edward Arnold & Co, 1924)
Kahn, Farrol S. *Why Flying Endangers your Health* (Aurora Press, 1990)
Levitt, B. Blake *Electromagnetic Fields* (Harcourt Brace and Company, 1995)
Motor Industry of Great Britain *World Automotive Statistics 2000* (Society of Motor Manufacturer's and Traders)
Smith, Cyril W. and Best, Simon *Electromagnetic Man* (J.M.Dent & Sons, 1989)
Soyka, Fred, with Edmonds, Alan *The Ion Effect* (Bantam Books, 1981)
Stalmatski, Alexander *Freedom from Asthma* (Kyle Cathie, London, 1997)
Tisserand, Robert *The Art of Aromatherapy* (C.W.Daniel, 1979)
Valnet, Dr Jean *The Practice of Aromatherapy* (C.W.Daniel, 1980)
Watson, Franzesca Aromatherapy Blends and Remedies (Thorsons, 1995)
Weller, Stella *The Breath Book* (Thorsons, 1999)
Wolverton, Bill *How to Grow Fresh Air* (Penguin, London, 1977)

Water

Alexandersson, Olof *Living Water* (Gateway, 1976)
Ball, Philip *H20, A Biography of Water* (Wiedenfeld and Nicolson, 1999)
Batmanghelidj, F. *Your Body's Many Cries for Water* (Global Health Solutions inc, 1997)

Buchman, Dian Dincin *The Complete Book of Water Therapy*
Leon Chaitow *Water Therapy* (Thorsons, London 1994)
Carson, Rachel *The Sea Around Us* (Oxford University Press, 1961)
Chaitow, Leon *Water Therapy* (Thorsons, London, 1994)
Coats, Callum *Living Energies* (Gateway, 1996)
Coats, Callum, ed. *The Water Wizard* (Gateway, 1998)
Colborn, Theo, Dumanoski, Dianna, and Myers, John Peterson *Our Stolen Future* (Plume, 1997)
Emsley, John *The Shocking History of Phosphorus* (Macmillan, 2000)
Kavounas, Alice *Water, Pure Therapy* (Kyle Cathie, 2000)
John Harvey Kellogg *Rational Hydrotherapy: A Manual of the Physiological and Therapeutic Effects of Hydriatic Procedure, and the Technique of Their Application in the Treatment of Disease* (Philadelphia, 1901)
Kronberger, Hans and Lattacher, Siegbert *On the Track of Water's Secret* (Uranus, 1995)
Kunzig, Robert *The Restless Sea* (Norton, 1999)
McCully, Patrick *Silenced Rivers* (Zed Books, 1996)
Moolenburgh, Dr Hans *Flouride, The Freedom Fight* (Mainstream Publishing, 1987)
Pielou, E.C. *Fresh Water* (The University of Chicago Press, 1998)
Ryrie, Charlie *The Healing Energies of Water* (Gaia Books, 1998)
Schauberger, Viktor *Nature as Teacher* (Gateway, 1998)
Schiff, Michel *The Memory of Water* (Thorsons, 1995)
Schwenk, Theodor *Sensitive Chaos* (Rudolf Steiner Press, 1965)
Thomson, William A.R. *Spas that Heal* (Adam and Charles Black, 1978)
Weiss, Harry B., and Kemble, Howard R. *The Great American Water-Cure Craze* (The Past Times Press, New Jersey, 1967)

Light

Allanach, Jack *Colour me Healing* (Element, 1997)
Downing, Dr Damien *Daylight Robbery* (Arrow Books, 1988)
Gerber, Richard *Vibrational Medicine for the Twenty-First Century* (Piatkus, 2000)
Gimbel, Theo *Healing with Colour* (Gaia Books, 1994)
ibid. Healing through Colour (C.W.Daniel, 1980)

Hall, Percy *Ultra-Violet Rays in the Treatment and Cure of Disease* (William Heinemann (Medical Books) Ltd, London, 1929)
Hobday, Richard *The Healing Sun* (Findhorn Press, 1999)
Kime, Zane R. *Sunlight* (World Health Publications, 1980)
Liberman, Jacob *Light Medicine of the Future* (Bear and Company, 1991)
Ott, John N. *Health and Light* (Pocket Books, New York, 1973)
ibid. Light, Radiation, and You (Devin-Adair, 1982)
Rollier, Auguste *MD Heliotherapy* (Oxford University Press, 1927)
Singh, Madanjeet *The Timeless Energy of the Sun* (Thames & Hudson 1998)
Walker, David *Energy, Plants and Man* (Oxygraphics, 1992)
Wall, Vicky *The Miracle of Colour Healing* (Thorsons, 1995)
Wills, Pauline *Colour Therapy* (Element, 1993)

Magazines

Green Futures (published by Forum for the Future, B1 25N. Tel: 01233 354643)
Living Earth (the journal of the Soil Association)
New Scientist
Positive Living
Resurgence
The Ecologist (www.theecologist.org)

index

Acknowledgements

This book owes its being to the enthusiasm and persistence of Jane O'Shea, Editorial Director of Quadrille, with whom it has been a delight and a privilege to work, and whose unflagging encouragement, patience and understanding kept me going over many long months. My first thank yous are to her, and to Nicki Marshall, Project Editor at Quadrille, whose sensitive editing skills I appreciated as much as her unflappable calm while deadlines came and went.

A legion of experts in the many fields over which this book ranges were extraordinarily generous with their time and their knowledge, and tolerant of an ignorance that was often nearly total. A special thank you to my friend Anna Grayson, geologist and broadcaster, who read through and made suggestions for some of the key chapters, correcting many howlers; and to my daughter, author and journalist Bibi van der Zee, whose skilled research and assistance was invaluable for several chapters of the book, especially in the Water section.

Special thank yous to Simon Best, editor and publisher of the quarterly news report Electromagnetic Hazard & Therapy; for much-needed help with the chapter Our Wired World; to science journalist Toby Murcott who did his best to steer me through the heavily mined field of GM technology; and to Joshua Shaw, director of Bionic Products, who enlightened my extreme ignorance about negative and positive ions.

Special thanks, too, to the delightful, helpful and incredibly well-informed staff of the Centre for Alternative Technology, who responded instantly to innumerable calls for help or suggestions.

I should also like to acknowledge help and information given to me by Nicholas Abson, Director of Zetek Power; Dr. Elizabeth Alvarez, Associate Director of the International Dark-Skies Association; Dr. George Brainard, Professor of Neurology at Thomas Jefferson University, Philadelphia; Dr. Chris Busby of Green Audit; Dr. Daniel Davies of Solar Century; Heather Cholerton, Manager of the Water Management Information Bureau; Dr. James Clark, Professor of Industrial Chemistry at the University of York; John Creasey, Librarian and Information Officer at the Rural History Centre of Reading University; Dr. Damien Downing; Robert Duxbury of Sainsbury; Simon Fraser, Director of Fibropower; Patricia Farchy; Andry Goldring of the Permaculture Association; Teresa Hale; Innovative Design of Raleigh, North Carolina; Dr. Hugh Jones, lecturer in zoology at the

University of Manchester; Jane Jones, Campaign Director of the National Pure Water Association; Farrol Kahn,Director of the Aviation Health Institute; Professor John Knowland, lecturer in biochemistry at Oxford University; David Langston, Business Development Manager of Wavegen; Dr. Jacob Liberman; Sir Thomas Lucas; Lesley Millett of Wastebusters; Bob Mizon, Coordinator, British Astronomical Association Campaign for Dark Skies; Dr. James Merryweather, soil ecologist of the University of York; science journalist Toby Murcott; Alasdair Philips, Director of Powerwatch; Richard Scott, plant ecologist and Manager of the research programme on Soil Biodiversity of the UK National Environmental Research Council; Joshua Shaw, director of Bionic Products; Jonathan Stromberg and Dolly Knight of the Centre for Implosion Research; Valerie Taplin, Managing Director of the Air Improvement Centre, London; Liizzie Vann, Director of Organix; Marijke Vogel; Alex Wijeratna of Action Aid; John Wilkes and many others. If, despite this panoply of learning and experience, errors have crept into the book, they are mine alone.

Some parts of the text are based on articles which were originally written for the health pages of *Country Living* magazine.

Thank you to the friendly, helpful librarians at the Linnean Society, the London Library and the British Naturopathic and Osteopathic Association.

Thank you to my admirable agent, Fiona Lindsay of Limelight Management.

And a big thank you, finally, to my husband Henri van der Zee, for his warm encouragement, for useful textual suggestions or criticisms and for putting up for long months with a fairly absent and completely distracted wife.

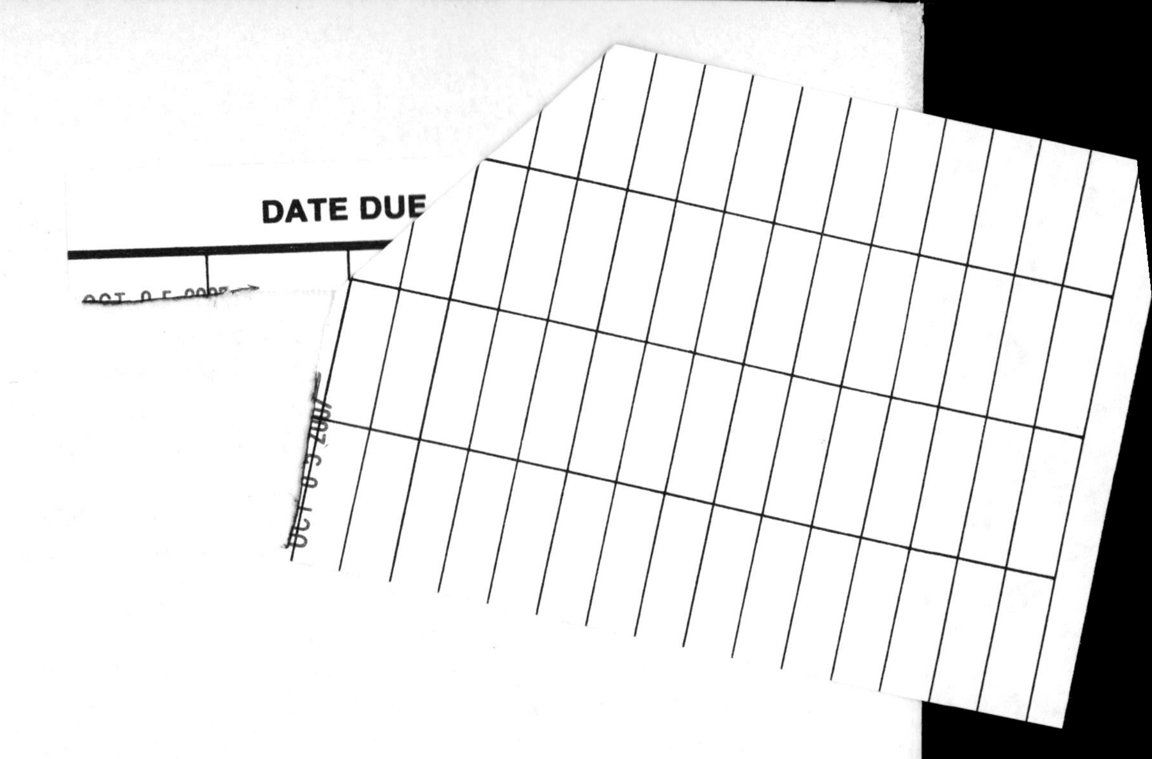